A COURSE IN MATHEMATICAL ANALYSIS

FUNCTIONS OF
A COMPLEX VARIABLE

BEING PART I OF VOLUME II

BY

ÉDOUARD GOURSAT
PROFESSOR OF MATHEMATICS, THE UNIVERSITY OF PARIS

TRANSLATED BY

EARLE RAYMOND HEDRICK
PROFESSOR OF MATHEMATICS, THE UNIVERSITY OF MISSOURI

AND

OTTO DUNKEL
INSTRUCTOR IN MATHEMATICS, THE UNIVERSITY OF MISSOURI

GINN AND COMPANY
BOSTON · NEW YORK · CHICAGO · LONDON
ATLANTA · DALLAS · COLUMBUS · SAN FRANCISCO

The Athenæum Press

GINN AND COMPANY · PRO-
PRIETORS · BOSTON · U.S.A.

AUTHOR'S PREFACE — SECOND FRENCH EDITION

The first part of this volume has undergone only slight changes, while the rather important modifications that have been made appear only in the last chapters.

In the first edition I was able to devote but a few pages to partial differential equations of the second order and to the calculus of variations. In order to present in a less summary manner such broad subjects, I have concluded to defer them to a third volume, which will contain also a sketch of the recent theory of integral equations. The suppression of the last chapter has enabled me to make some additions, of which the most important relate to linear differential equations and to partial differential equations of the first order.

E. GOURSAT

TRANSLATORS' PREFACE

As the title indicates, the present volume is a translation of the first half of the second volume of Goursat's "Cours d'Analyse." The decision to publish the translation in two parts is due to the evident adaptation of these two portions to the introductory courses in American colleges and universities in the theory of functions and in differential equations, respectively.

After the cordial reception given to the translation of Goursat's first volume, the continuation was assured. That it has been delayed so long was due, in the first instance, to our desire to await the appearance of the second edition of the second volume in French. The advantage in doing so will be obvious to those who have observed the radical changes made in the second (French) edition of the second volume. Volume I was not altered so radically, so that the present English translation of that volume may be used conveniently as a companion to this; but references are given here to both editions of the first volume, to avoid any possible difficulty in this connection.

Our thanks are due to Professor Goursat, who has kindly given us his permission to make this translation, and has approved of the plan of publication in two parts. He has also seen all proofs in English and has approved a few minor alterations made in translation as well as the translators' notes. The responsibility for the latter rests, however, with the translators.

E. R. HEDRICK
OTTO DUNKEL

CONTENTS

A COURSE IN
MATHEMATICAL ANALYSIS

VOLUME II. PART I

THEORY OF FUNCTIONS OF A COMPLEX VARIABLE

CHAPTER I

ELEMENTS OF THE THEORY

I. GENERAL PRINCIPLES. ANALYTIC FUNCTIONS

1. Definitions. An *imaginary quantity*, or *complex quantity*, is any expression of the form $a + bi$ where a and b are any two real numbers whatever and i is a special symbol which has been introduced in order to generalize algebra. Essentially a complex quantity is nothing but a system of two real numbers arranged in a certain order. Although such expressions as $a + bi$ have in themselves no concrete meaning whatever, we agree to apply to them the ordinary rules of algebra, with the additional convention that i^2 shall be replaced throughout by -1.

Two complex quantities $a + bi$ and $a' + b'i$ are said to be equal if $a = a'$ and $b = b'$. The sum of two complex quantities $a + bi$ and $c + di$ is a symbol of the same form $a + c + (b + d)i$; the difference $a + bi - (c + di)$ is equal to $a - c + (b - d)i$. To find the product of $a + bi$ and $c + di$ we carry out the multiplication according to the usual rules for algebraic multiplication, replacing i^2 by -1, obtaining thus

$$(a + bi)(c + di) = ac - bd + (ad + bc)i.$$

The quotient obtained by the division of $a + bi$ by $c + di$ is defined to be a third imaginary symbol $x + yi$, such that when it is multiplied by $c + di$, the product is $a + bi$. The equality

$$a + bi = (c + di)(x + yi)$$

is equivalent, according to the rules of multiplication, to the two relations

$$cx - dy = a, \qquad dx + cy = b,$$

whence we obtain

$$x = \frac{ac + bd}{c^2 + d^2}, \qquad y = \frac{bc - ad}{c^2 + d^2}.$$

The quotient obtained by the division of $a + bi$ by $c + di$ is represented by the usual notation for fractions in algebra, thus,

$$x + yi = \frac{a + bi}{c + di}.$$

A convenient way of calculating x and y is to multiply numerator and denominator of the fraction by $c - di$ and to develop the indicated products.

All the properties of the fundamental operations of algebra can be shown to apply to the operations carried out on these imaginary symbols. Thus, if A, B, C, $\cdots$ denote complex numbers, we shall have

$$A \cdot B = B \cdot A, \quad A \cdot B \cdot C = A \cdot (B \cdot C), \quad A(B + C) = AB + AC, \quad \cdots$$

and so on. The two complex quantities $a + bi$ and $a - bi$ are said to be *conjugate imaginaries*. The two complex quantities $a + bi$ and $-a - bi$, whose sum is zero, are said to be *negatives* of each other or *symmetric* to each other.

Given the usual system of rectangular axes in a plane, the complex quantity $a + bi$ is represented by the point M of the plane xOy, whose coördinates are $x = a$ and $y = b$. In this way a concrete representation is given to these purely symbolic expressions, and to every proposition established for complex quantities there is a corresponding theorem of plane geometry. But the greatest advantages resulting from this representation will appear later. Real numbers correspond to points on the x-axis, which for this reason is also called the *axis of reals*. Two conjugate imaginaries $a + bi$ and $a - bi$ correspond to two points symmetrically situated with respect to the x-axis. Two quantities $a + bi$ and $-a - bi$ are represented by a pair of points symmetric with respect to the origin O. The quantity $a + bi$, which corresponds to the point M with the coördinates (a, b), is sometimes called its *affix*.* When there is no danger of ambiguity, we shall denote by the same letter a complex quantity and the point which represents it.

Let us join the origin to the point M with coördinates (a, b) by a segment of a straight line. The distance OM is called the *absolute value* of $a + bi$, and the angle through which a ray must be turned from Ox to bring it in coincidence with OM (the angle being measured, as in trigonometry, from Ox toward Oy) is called the *angle* of $a + bi$.

---

* This term is not much used in English, but the French frequently use the corresponding word *affixe*. — TRANS.

Let ρ and ω denote, respectively, the absolute value and the angle of $a + bi$; between the real quantities a, b, ρ, ω there exist the two relations $a = \rho \cos \omega$, $b = \rho \sin \omega$, whence we have

$$\rho = \sqrt{a^2 + b^2}, \qquad \cos \omega = \frac{a}{\sqrt{a^2 + b^2}}, \qquad \sin \omega = \frac{b}{\sqrt{a^2 + b^2}}.$$

The absolute value ρ, which is an essentially positive number, is determined without ambiguity; whereas the angle, being given only by means of its trigonometric functions, is determined except for an additive multiple of $2\,\pi$, which was evident from the definition itself. Hence every complex quantity may have an infinite number of angles, forming an arithmetic progression in which the successive terms differ by $2\,\pi$. In order that two complex quantities be equal, their absolute values must be equal, and moreover their angles must differ only by a multiple of $2\,\pi$, and these conditions are sufficient. The absolute value of a complex quantity z is represented by the same symbol $|z|$ which is used for the absolute value of a real quantity.

Let $z = a + bi$, $z' = a' + b'i$ be two complex numbers and m, m' the corresponding points; the sum $z + z'$ is then represented by the point m'', the vertex of the parallelogram constructed upon Om, Om'. The three sides of the triangle $Om\ m''$ (Fig. 1) are equal respectively to the absolute values of the quantities z, z', $z + z'$. From this we conclude that *the absolute value of the sum of two quantities is less than or at most equal to the sum of the absolute values of the two quantities, and greater than or at least equal to their difference.* Since two quantities that are negatives of each other have the same absolute value, the theorem is also true for the absolute value of a difference. Finally, we see in the same way that the absolute value of the sum of any number of complex quantities is at most equal to the sum of their absolute values, the equality holding only when all the points representing the different quantities are on the same ray starting from the origin.

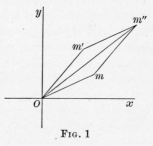

FIG. 1

If through the point m we draw the two straight lines mx' and my' parallel to Ox and to Oy, the coördinates of the point m' in this system of axes will be $a' - a$ and $b' - b$ (Fig. 2). The point m' then represents $z' - z$ in the new system; the absolute value of

$z' - z$ is equal to the length mm', and the angle of $z' - z$ is equal to the angle θ which the direction mm' makes with mx'. Draw through

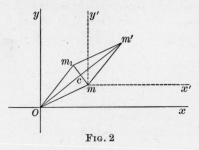

FIG. 2

O a segment Om_1 equal and parallel to mm'; the extremity m_1 of this segment represents $z' - z$ in the system of axes Ox, Oy. But the figure $Om'm_1$ is a parallelogram; the point m_1 is therefore the symmetric point to m with respect to c, the middle point of Om'.

Finally, let us obtain the formula which gives the absolute value and angle of the product of any number of factors. Let

$$z_k = \rho_k (\cos \omega_k + i \sin \omega_k), \qquad (k = 1, 2, \cdots, n),$$

be the factors; the rules for multiplication, together with the addition formulæ of trigonometry, give for the product

$$z_1 z_2 \cdots z_n = \rho_1 \rho_2 \cdots \rho_n [\cos (\omega_1 + \omega_2 + \cdots + \omega_n) + i \sin (\omega_1 + \omega_2 + \cdots + \omega_n)],$$

which shows that *the absolute value of a product is equal to the product of the absolute values, and the angle of a product is equal to the sum of the angles of the factors*. From this follows very easily the well-known formula of De Moivre:

$$\cos m\omega + i \sin m\omega = (\cos \omega + i \sin \omega)^m,$$

which contains in a very condensed form all the trigonometric formulæ for the multiplication of angles.

The introduction of imaginary symbols has given complete generality and symmetry to the theory of algebraic equations. It was in the treatment of equations of only the second degree that such expressions appeared for the first time. Complex quantities are equally important in analysis, and we shall now state precisely what meaning is to be attached to the expression *a function of a complex variable*.

2. Continuous functions of a complex variable. A complex quantity $z = x + yi$, where x and y are two real and independent variables, is a complex variable. If we give to the word *function* its most general meaning, it would be natural to say that every other complex quantity u whose value depends upon that of z is a *function of z.*

Certain familiar definitions can be extended directly to these functions. Thus, we shall say that a function $u = f(z)$ is continuous if the absolute value of the difference $f(z + h) - f(z)$ approaches zero when the absolute value of h approaches zero, that is, if to every positive number ϵ we can assign another positive number η such that

$$|f(z + h) - f(z)| < \epsilon,$$

provided that $|h|$ be less than η.

A series,
$$u_0(z) + u_1(z) + \cdots + u_n(z) + \cdots,$$

whose terms are functions of the complex variable z is *uniformly convergent* in a region A of the plane if to every positive number ϵ we can assign a positive integer N such that

$$|R_n| = |u_{n+1}(z) + u_{n+2}(z) + \cdots| < \epsilon$$

for all the values of z in the region A, provided that $n \geqq N$. It can be shown as before (Vol. I, § 31, 2d ed.; § 173, 1st ed.) that if a series is uniformly convergent in a region A, and if each of its terms is a continuous function of z in that region, its sum is itself a continuous function of the variable z in the same region.

Again, a series is uniformly convergent if, for all the values of z considered, the absolute value of each term $|u_n|$ is less than the corresponding term v_n of a convergent series of real positive constants. The series is then both absolutely and uniformly convergent.

Every continuous function of the complex variable z is of the form $u = P(x, y) + Q(x, y)i$, where P and Q are real continuous functions of the two real variables x, y. If we were to impose no other restrictions, the study of functions of a complex variable would amount simply to a study of a pair of functions of two real variables, and the use of the symbol i would introduce only illusory simplifications. In order to make the theory of functions of a complex variable present some analogy with the theory of functions of a real variable, we shall adopt the methods of Cauchy to find the conditions which the functions P and Q must satisfy in order that the expression $P + Qi$ shall possess the fundamental properties of functions of a real variable to which the processes of the calculus apply.

3. Analytic functions. If $f(x)$ is a function of a real variable x which has a derivative, the quotient

$$\frac{f(x + h) - f(x)}{h}$$

approaches $f'(x)$ when h approaches zero. Let us determine in the same way under what conditions the quotient

$$\frac{\Delta u}{\Delta z} = \frac{\Delta P + i\Delta Q}{\Delta x + i\Delta y}$$

will approach a definite limit when the absolute value of Δz approaches zero, that is, when Δx and Δy approach zero independently. It is easy to see that this will not be the case if the functions $P(x, y)$ and $Q(x, y)$ are any functions whatever, for the limit of the quotient $\Delta u/\Delta z$ depends in general on the ratio $\Delta y/\Delta x$, that is, on the way in which the point representing the value of $z + h$ approaches the point representing the value of z.

Let us first suppose y constant, and let us give to x a value $x + \Delta x$ differing but slightly from x; then

$$\frac{\Delta u}{\Delta z} = \frac{P(x + \Delta x, y) - P(x, y)}{\Delta x} + i\,\frac{Q(x + \Delta x, y) - Q(x, y)}{\Delta x}.$$

In order that this quotient have a limit, it is necessary that the functions P and Q possess partial derivatives with respect to x, and in that case

$$\lim \frac{\Delta u}{\Delta z} = \frac{\partial P}{\partial x} + i\,\frac{\partial Q}{\partial x}.$$

Next suppose x constant, and let us give to y the value $y + \Delta y$; we have

$$\frac{\Delta u}{\Delta z} = \frac{P(x, y + \Delta y) - P(x, y)}{i\Delta y} + \frac{Q(x, y + \Delta y) - Q(x, y)}{\Delta y},$$

and in this case the quotient will have for its limit

$$\frac{\partial Q}{\partial y} - i\,\frac{\partial P}{\partial y}.$$

if the functions P and Q possess partial derivatives with respect to y. In order that the limit of the quotient be the same in the two cases, it is necessary that

(1) $$\frac{\partial P}{\partial x} = \frac{\partial Q}{\partial y}, \qquad \frac{\partial P}{\partial y} = -\frac{\partial Q}{\partial x}.$$

Suppose that the functions P and Q satisfy these conditions, and that the partial derivatives $\partial P/\partial x$, $\partial P/\partial y$, $\partial Q/\partial x$, $\partial Q/\partial y$ are continuous functions. If we give to x and y any increments whatever, Δx, Δy, we can write

$$\begin{aligned}\Delta P &= P(x + \Delta x, y + \Delta y) - P(x + \Delta x, y) + P(x + \Delta x, y) - P(x, y)\\ &= \Delta y P'_y(x + \Delta x, y + \theta\Delta y) + \Delta x P'_x(x + \theta'\Delta x, y)\\ &= \Delta x[P'_x(x, y) + \epsilon] + \Delta y[P'_y(x, y) + \epsilon_1],\end{aligned}$$

where θ and θ' are positive numbers less than unity; and in the same way

$$\Delta Q = \Delta x [Q'_x(x, y) + \epsilon'] + \Delta y [Q'_y(x, y) + \epsilon'_1],$$

where ϵ, ϵ', ϵ_1, ϵ'_1 approach zero with Δx and Δy. The difference $\Delta u = \Delta P + i \Delta Q$ can be written by means of the conditions (1) in the form,

$$\Delta u = \Delta x \Big(\frac{\partial P}{\partial x} + i \frac{\partial Q}{\partial x} \Big) + \Delta y \Big(-\frac{\partial Q}{\partial x} + i \frac{\partial P}{\partial x} \Big) + \eta \Delta x + \eta' \Delta y$$

$$= (\Delta x + i \Delta y) \Big(\frac{\partial P}{\partial x} + i \frac{\partial Q}{\partial x} \Big) + \eta \Delta x + \eta' \Delta y,$$

where η and η' are infinitesimals. We have, then,

$$\frac{\Delta u}{\Delta z} = \frac{\partial P}{\partial x} + i \frac{\partial Q}{\partial x} + \frac{\eta \Delta x + \eta' \Delta y}{\Delta x + i \Delta y}.$$

If $|\eta|$ and $|\eta'|$ are smaller than a number α, the absolute value of the complementary term is less than 2α. This term will therefore approach zero when Δx and Δy approach zero, and we shall have

$$\lim \frac{\Delta u}{\Delta z} = \frac{\partial P}{\partial x} + i \frac{\partial Q}{\partial x}.$$

The conditions (1) are then necessary and sufficient in order that the quotient $\Delta u / \Delta z$ have a unique limit for each value of z, provided that the partial derivatives of the functions P and Q be continuous. The function u is then said to be an *analytic* function * of the variable z, and if we represent it by $f(z)$, the derivative $f'(z)$ is equal to any one of the following equivalent expressions :

$$(2) \quad f'(z) = \frac{\partial P}{\partial x} + i \frac{\partial Q}{\partial x} = \frac{\partial Q}{\partial y} - i \frac{\partial P}{\partial y} = \frac{\partial P}{\partial x} - i \frac{\partial P}{\partial y} = \frac{\partial Q}{\partial y} + i \frac{\partial Q}{\partial x}.$$

It is important to notice that neither of the pair of functions $P(x, y)$, $Q(x, y)$ can be taken arbitrarily. In fact, if P and Q have derivatives of the second order, and if we differentiate the first of the relations (1) with respect to x, and the second with respect to y, we have, adding the two resulting equations,

$$\Delta P = \frac{\partial^2 P}{\partial x^2} + \frac{\partial^2 P}{\partial y^2} = 0.$$

---

* Cauchy made frequent use of the term *monogène*, the equivalent of which, *monogenic*, is sometimes used in English. The term *synectique* is also sometimes used in French. We shall use by preference the term *analytic*, and it will be shown later that this definition agrees with the one which has already been given (I, § 197, 2d ed.; § 191, 1st ed.)

We can show in the same way that $\Delta Q = 0$. The two functions $P(x, y)$, $Q(x, y)$ must therefore be a pair of solutions of Laplace's equation.

Conversely, any solution of Laplace's equation may be taken for one of the functions P or Q. For example, let $P(x, y)$ be a solution of that equation; the two equations (1), where Q is regarded as an unknown function, are compatible, and the expression

$$u = P(x, y) + i\left[\int_{(x_0,\, y_0)}^{(x,\, y)}\left(\frac{\partial P}{\partial x}\, dy - \frac{\partial P}{\partial y}\, dx\right) + C\right],$$

which is determined except for an arbitrary constant C, is an analytic function whose real part is $P(x, y)$.

It follows that the study of analytic functions of a complex variable z amounts essentially to the study of a pair of functions $P(x, y)$, $Q(x, y)$ of two real variables x and y that satisfy the relations (1). It would be possible to develop the whole theory without making use of the symbol i.*

We shall continue, however, to employ the notation of Cauchy, but it should be noticed that there is no essential difference between the two methods. Every theorem established for an analytic function $f(z)$ can be expressed immediately as an equivalent theorem relating to the pair of functions P and Q, and conversely.

Examples. The function $u = x^2 - y^2 + 2xyi$ is an analytic function, for it satisfies the equations (1), and its derivative is $2x + 2yi = 2z$; in fact, the function is simply $(x + yi)^2 = z^2$. On the other hand, the expression $v = x - yi$ is not an analytic function, for we have

$$\frac{\Delta v}{\Delta z} = \frac{\Delta x - i\Delta y}{\Delta x + i\Delta y} = \frac{1 - i\dfrac{\Delta y}{\Delta x}}{1 + i\dfrac{\Delta y}{\Delta x}},$$

and it is obvious that the limit of the quotient $\Delta v/\Delta z$ depends upon the limit of the quotient $\Delta y/\Delta x$.

If we put $x = \rho \cos \omega$, $y = \rho \sin \omega$, and apply the formulæ for the change of independent variables (I, § 63, 2d ed.; § 38, 1st ed., Ex. II), the relations (1) become

(3) $$\frac{\partial P}{\partial \omega} = -\rho\frac{\partial Q}{\partial \rho}, \qquad \frac{\partial Q}{\partial \omega} = \rho\frac{\partial P}{\partial \rho},$$

and the derivative takes the form

$$f'(z) = \left(\frac{\partial P}{\partial \rho} + i\frac{\partial Q}{\partial \rho}\right)(\cos \omega - i \sin \omega).$$

---

* This is the point of view taken by the German mathematicians who follow Riemann.

It is easily seen on applying these formulæ that the function

$$z^m = \rho^m (\cos m\omega + i \sin m\omega)$$

is an analytic function of z whose derivative is equal to

$$m\rho^{m-1}(\cos m\omega + i \sin m\omega)(\cos \omega - i \sin \omega) = mz^{m-1}.$$

4. Functions analytic throughout a region. The preceding general statements are still somewhat vague, for so far nothing has been said about the limits between which z may vary.

A portion A of the plane is said to be *connected*, or to *consist of a single piece*, when it is possible to join any two points whatever of that portion by a continuous path which lies entirely in that portion of the plane. A connected portion situated entirely at a finite distance can be bounded by one or several closed curves, among which there is always one closed curve which forms the exterior boundary. A portion of the plane extending to infinity may be composed of all the points exterior to one or more closed curves; it may also be limited by curves having infinite branches. We shall employ the term *region* to denote a connected portion of the plane.

A function $f(z)$ of the complex variable z is said to be analytic * in a connected region A of the plane if it satisfies the following conditions :

1) To every point z of A corresponds a definite value of $f(z)$;

2) $f(z)$ is a continuous function of z when the point z varies in A, that is, when the absolute value of $f(z + h) - f(z)$ approaches zero with the absolute value of h ;

3) At every point z of A, $f(z)$ has a uniquely determined derivative $f'(z)$; that is, to every point z corresponds a complex number $f'(z)$ such that the absolute value of the difference

$$\frac{f(z + h) - f(z)}{h} - f'(z)$$

approaches zero when $|h|$ approaches zero. Given any positive number ϵ, another positive number η can be found such that

$$(4) \qquad |f(z + h) - f(z) - hf'(z)| \leqq \epsilon |h|$$

if $|h|$ is less than η.

For the moment we shall not make any hypothesis as to the values of $f(z)$ on the curves which limit A. When we say that a function is analytic in the interior of a region A bounded by a closed curve Γ

---

* The adjective *holomorphic* is also often used. — TRANS.

and *on the boundary curve itself*, we shall mean by this that $f(z)$ is analytic in a region A containing the boundary curve Γ and the region A.

A function $f(z)$ need not necessarily be analytic throughout its region of existence. It may have, in general, singular points, which may be of very varied types. It would be out of place at this point to make a classification of these singular points, the very nature of which will appear as we proceed with the study of functions which we are now commencing.

5. Rational functions. Since the rules which give the derivative of a sum, of a product, and of a quotient are logical consequences of the definition of a derivative, they apply also to functions of a complex variable. The same is true of the rule for the derivative of a function of a function. Let $u = f(Z)$ be an analytic function of the complex variable Z; if we substitute for Z another analytic function $\phi(z)$ of another complex variable z, u is still an analytic function of the variable z. We have, in fact,

$$\frac{\Delta u}{\Delta z} = \frac{\Delta u}{\Delta Z} \times \frac{\Delta Z}{\Delta z};$$

when $|\Delta z|$ approaches zero, $|\Delta Z|$ approaches zero, and each of the quotients $\Delta u / \Delta Z$, $\Delta Z / \Delta z$ approaches a definite limit. Therefore the quotient $\Delta u / \Delta z$ itself approaches a limit:

$$\lim \frac{\Delta u}{\Delta z} = f'(Z)\phi'(z).$$

We have already seen (§ 3) that the function

$$z^m = (x + yi)^m$$

is an analytic function of z, and that its derivative is mz^{m-1}. This can be shown directly as in the case of real variables. In fact, the binomial formula, which results simply from the properties of multiplication, obviously can be extended in the same way to complex quantities. Therefore we can write

$$(z + h)^m = z^m + \frac{m}{1} z^{m-1} h + \frac{m(m-1)}{1.2} z^{m-2} h^2 + \cdots,$$

where m is a positive integer; and from this follows

$$\frac{(z + h)^m - z^m}{h} = mz^{m-1} + h \left[\frac{m(m-1)}{1.2} z^{m-2} + \cdots + h^{m-2} \right].$$

It is clear that the right-hand side has mz^{m-1} for its limit when the absolute value of h approaches zero.

It follows that any polynomial with constant coefficients is an analytic function throughout the whole plane. A rational function (that is, the quotient of two polynomials $P(z)$, $Q(z)$, which we may as well suppose prime to each other) is also in general an analytic function, but it has a certain number of singular points, the roots of the equation $Q(z) = 0$. It is analytic in every region of the plane which does not include any of these points.

6. Certain irrational functions. When a point z describes a continuous curve, the coördinates x and y, as well as the absolute value ρ, vary in a continuous manner, and the same is also true of the angle,

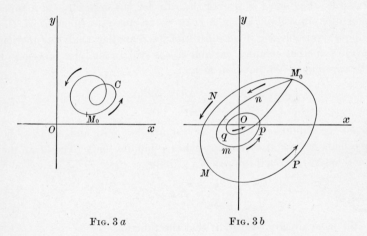

Fig. 3 a   Fig. 3 b

provided the curve described does not pass through the origin. If the point z describes a closed curve, x, y, and ρ return to their original values, but for the angle ω this is not always the case. If the origin is outside the region inclosed by the closed curve (Fig. 3 a), it is evident that the angle will return to its original value; but this is no longer the case if the point z describes a curve such as M_0NPM_0 or M_0npqM_0 (Fig. 3 b). In the first case the angle takes on its original value increased by 2π, and in the second case it takes on its original value increased by 4π. It is clear that z can be made to describe closed curves such that, if we follow the continuous variation of the angle along any one of them, the final value assumed by ω will differ from the initial value by $2n\pi$, where n is an arbitrary integer, positive or negative. In general, when z describes a closed curve, the angle of $z - a$ returns to its initial value if the point a lies outside of the region bounded by that closed curve, but the curve described by z can always be chosen so that the final value assumed by the angle of $z - a$ will be equal to the initial value increased by $2n\pi$.

Let us now consider the equation

(5) $$u^m = z,$$

where m is a positive integer. To every value of z, except $z = 0$, there are m distinct values of u which satisfy this equation and therefore correspond to the given value of z. In fact, if we put

$$z = \rho(\cos\omega + i\sin\omega), \qquad u = r(\cos\phi + i\sin\phi),$$

the relation (5) becomes equivalent to the following pair:

$$r^m = \rho, \qquad m\phi = \omega + 2k\pi.$$

From the first we have $r = \rho^{1/m}$, which means that r is the mth arithmetic root of the positive number ρ; from the second we have

$$\phi = (\omega + 2k\pi)/m.$$

To obtain all the distinct values of u we have only to give to the arbitrary integer k the m consecutive integral values $0, 1, 2, \cdots, m-1$; in this way we obtain expressions for the m roots of the equation (5)

(6) $$u_k = \rho^{\frac{1}{m}}\left[\cos\left(\frac{\omega + 2k\pi}{m}\right) + i\sin\left(\frac{\omega + 2k\pi}{m}\right)\right],$$
$$(k = 0, 1, 2, \cdots, m - 1).$$

It is usual to represent by $z^{1/m}$ any one of these roots.

When the variable z describes a continuous curve, each of these roots itself varies in a continuous manner. If z describes a closed curve to which the origin is exterior, the angle ω comes back to its original value, and each of the roots $u_0, u_1, \cdots, u_{m-1}$ describes a closed curve (Fig. 4 a). But if the point z describes the curve M_0NPM_0 (Fig. 3 b), ω changes to $\omega + 2\pi$, and the final value of the root u_i is equal to the initial value of the root u_{i+1}. Hence the arcs described by the different roots form a single closed curve (Fig. 4 b).

These m roots therefore undergo a cyclic permutation when the variable z describes in the positive direction any closed curve without double points that incloses the origin. It is clear that by making z describe a suitable closed path, any one of the roots, starting from the initial value u_0, for example, can be made to take on for its final value the value of any of the other roots. If we wish to maintain continuity, we must then consider these m roots of the equation (5) not as so many distinct functions of z, but as m distinct *branches* of the same function. The point $z = 0$, about which the permutation of the m values of u takes place, is called a *critical point* or a *branch point*.

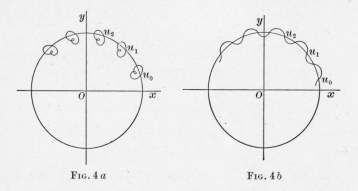

FIG. 4 a FIG. 4 b

In order to consider the m values of u as distinct functions of z, it will be necessary to disrupt the continuity of these roots along a line proceeding from the origin to infinity. We can represent this break in the continuity very concretely as follows: imagine that in the plane of z, which we may regard as a thin sheet, a cut is made along a ray extending from the origin to infinity, for example, along the ray OL (Fig. 5), and that then the two edges of the cut are slightly separated so that there is no path along which the variable z can move directly from one edge to the other. Under these circumstances no closed path whatever can inclose the origin; hence to each value of z corresponds a completely determined value u_i of the m roots, which we can obtain by taking for the angle ω the value included between α and $\alpha - 2\pi$. But it must be noticed that the values of u_i at two points m, m' on opposite sides of the cut do not approach the same limit as the points approach the same point of the cut. The limit of the value of u_i at the point m' is equal to the limit of the value of u_i at the point m, multiplied by $[\cos(2\pi/m) + i\sin(2\pi/m)]$.

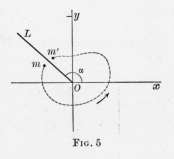

FIG. 5

Each of the roots of the equation (5) is an analytic function. Let u_0 be one of the roots corresponding to a given value z_0; to a value of z near z_0 corresponds a value of u near u_0. Instead of trying to find the limit of the quotient $(u - u_0)/(z - z_0)$, we can determine the limit of its reciprocal

$$\frac{z - z_0}{u - u_0} = \frac{u^m - u_0^m}{u - u_c},$$

and that limit is equal to $m u_0^{m-1}$. We have, then, for the derivative of u

$$u' = \frac{1}{m} \frac{1}{u^{m-1}} = \frac{1}{m} \frac{u}{z},$$

or, using negative exponents,

$$u' = \frac{1}{m} z^{\frac{1}{m} - 1}.$$

In order to be sure of having the value of the derivative which corresponds to the root considered, it is better to make use of the expression $(1/m)(u/z)$.

In the interior of a closed curve not containing the origin each of the determinations of $\sqrt[m]{z}$ is an analytic function. The equation $u^m = A(z - a)$ has also m roots, which permute themselves cyclically about the critical point $z = a$.

Let us consider now the equation

$$(7) \qquad u^2 = A(z - e_1)(z - e_2) \cdots (z - e_n),$$

where $e_1, e_2, \cdots, e_n$ are n distinct quantities. We shall denote by the same letters the points which represent these n quantities. Let us set

$$A = R(\cos \alpha + i \sin \alpha),$$

$$z - e_k = \rho_k(\cos \omega_k + i \sin \omega_k), \qquad (k = 1, 2, \cdots, n),$$

$$u = r(\cos \theta + i \sin \theta),$$

where ω_k represents the angle which the straight-line segment $e_k z$ makes with the direction Ox. From the equation (7) it follows that

$$r^2 = R \rho_1 \rho_2 \cdots \rho_n, \qquad 2\theta = \alpha + \omega_1 + \cdots + \omega_n + 2m\pi;$$

hence this equation has two roots that are the negatives of each other,

$$(8) \quad \begin{cases} u_1 = (R\rho_1\rho_2 \cdots \rho_n)^{\frac{1}{2}}\left[\cos\left(\frac{\alpha + \omega_1 + \cdots + \omega_n}{2}\right) \right. \\ \qquad\qquad \left. + i \sin\left(\frac{\alpha + \omega_1 + \cdots + \omega_n}{2}\right)\right], \\ u_2 = (R\rho_1\rho_2 \cdots \rho_n)^{\frac{1}{2}}\left[\cos\left(\frac{\alpha + \omega_1 + \cdots + \omega_n + 2\pi}{2}\right) \right. \\ \qquad\qquad \left. + i \sin\left(\frac{\alpha + \omega_1 + \cdots + \omega_n + 2\pi}{2}\right)\right]. \end{cases}$$

When the variable z describes a closed curve C containing within it p of the points $e_1, e_2, \cdots, e_n$, p of the angles $\omega_1, \omega_2, \cdots, \omega_n$ will increase by 2π; the angle of u_1 and that of u_2 will therefore increase by $p\pi$. If p is even, the two roots return to their initial values; but if p is odd, they are permuted. In particular, if the curve incloses a single point e_i, the two roots will be permuted. The n points e_i are branch points. In order that the two roots u_1 and u_2 shall be functions of z that are always uniquely determined, it will suffice to make a system of cuts such that any closed curve whatever will always contain an even number of critical points. We might, for example, make cuts along rays proceeding from each of the points e_i to infinity and not cutting each other. But there are many other possible arrangements. If, for example, there are four critical points e_1, e_2, e_3, e_4, a cut could be made along the segment of a straight line e_1e_2, and a second along the segment e_3e_4.

7. Single-valued and multiple-valued functions. The simple examples which we have just treated bring to light a very important fact. The value of a function $f(z)$ of the variable z does not always depend entirely upon the value of z alone, but it may also depend in a certain measure upon the succession of values assumed by the variable z in passing from the initial value to the actual value in question, or, in other words, upon the path followed by the variable z.

Let us return, for example, to the function $u = \sqrt[m]{z}$. If we pass from the point M_0 to the point M by the two paths M_0NM and M_0PM (Fig. 3 b), starting in each case with the same initial value for u, we shall not obtain at M the same value for u, for the two values obtained for the angle of z will differ by 2π. We are thus led to introduce a new distinction.

An analytic function $f(z)$ is said to be *single-valued* * in a region A when all the paths in A which go from a point z_0 to any other point whatever z lead to the same final value for $f(z)$. When, however, the final value of $f(z)$ is not the same for all possible paths in A, the function is said to be *multiple-valued*.† A function that is analytic at every point of a region A is necessarily single-valued in that region. In general, in order that a function $f(z)$ be single-valued in a given region, it is necessary and sufficient that the function return to its original value when the variable makes a circuit of

---

* In French the term *uniforme* or the term *monodrome* is used. — TRANS.

† In French the term *multiforme* is used. — TRANS.

any closed path whatever. If, in fact, in going from the point A to the point B by the two paths AMB (Fig. 6) and ANB, we arrive in the two cases at the point B with the same determination of $f(z)$, it is obvious that, when the variable is made to describe the closed

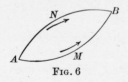

FIG. 6

curve $AMBNA$, we shall return to the point A with the initial value of $f(z)$.

Conversely, let us suppose that, the variable having described the path $AMBNA$, we return to the point of departure with the initial value u_0; and let u_1 be the value of the function at the point B after z has described the path AMB. When z describes the path BNA, the function starts with the value u_1 and arrives at the value u_0; then, conversely, the path ANB will lead from the value u_0 to the value u_1, that is, to the same value as the path AMB.

It should be noticed that a function which is not single-valued in a region may yet have no critical points in that region. Consider, for example, the portion of the plane included between two concentric circles C, C' having the origin for center. The function $u = z^{1/m}$ has no critical point in that region; still it is not single-valued in that region, for if z is made to describe a concentric circle between C and C', the function $z^{1/m}$ will be multiplied by $\cos(2\pi/m) + i\sin(2\pi/m)$.

II. POWER SERIES WITH COMPLEX TERMS. ELEMENTARY TRANSCENDENTAL FUNCTIONS

8. Circle of convergence. The reasoning employed in the study of power series (Vol. I, Chap. IX) will apply to power series with complex terms; we have only to replace in the reasoning the phrase "absolute value of a real quantity" by the corresponding one, "absolute value of a complex quantity." We shall recall briefly the theorems and results stated there. Let

$$(9) \qquad a_0 + a_1 z + a_2 z^2 + \cdots + a_n z^n + \cdots$$

be a power series in which the coefficients and the variable may have any imaginary values whatever. Let us also consider the series of absolute values,

$$(10) \qquad A_0 + A_1 r + A_2 r^2 + \cdots + A_n r^n + \cdots,$$

where $A_i = |a_i|$, $r = |z|$. We can prove (I, § 181, 2d ed.; § 177, 1st ed.) the existence of a positive number R such that the series

(10) is convergent for every value of $r < R$, and divergent for every value of $r > R$. The number R is equal to the reciprocal of the greatest limit of the terms of the sequence

$$A_1, \quad \sqrt[2]{A_2}, \quad \sqrt[3]{A_3}, \quad \cdots, \quad \sqrt[n]{A_n}, \quad \cdots,$$

and, as particular cases, it may be zero or infinite.

From these properties of the number R it follows at once that the series (9) is absolutely convergent when the absolute value of z is less than R. It cannot be convergent for a value z_0 of z whose absolute value is greater than R, for the series of absolute values (10) would then be convergent for values of r greater than R (I, § 181, 2d ed.; § 177, 1st ed.). If, with the origin as center, we describe in the plane of the variable z a circle C of radius R (Fig. 7), the power series (9) is absolutely convergent for every value of z inside the circle C, and divergent for every value of z outside; for this reason the circle is called the *circle of convergence*. In a point of the circle itself the series may be convergent or divergent, according to the particular series.*

In the interior of a circle C' concentric with the first, and with a radius R' less than R, the series (9) is uniformly convergent. For at every point within C' we have evidently

$$|a_{n+1}z^{n+1} + \cdots + a_{n+p}z^{n+p}| < A_{n+1}R'^{n+1} + \cdots + A_{n+p}R'^{n+p},$$

and it is possible to choose the integer n so large that the second member will be less than any given positive number ϵ, whatever p may be. From this we conclude that the sum of the series (9) is a continuous function $f(z)$ of the variable z at every point within the circle of convergence (§ 2).

By differentiating the series (9) repeatedly, we obtain an unlimited number of power series, $f_1(z), f_2(z), \cdots, f_n(z), \cdots$, which have the same circle of convergence as the first (I, § 183, 2d ed.; § 179, 1st ed.). We prove in the same way as in § 184, 2d ed., that $f_1(z)$ is the derivative of $f(z)$, and in general that $f_n(z)$ is the derivative

---

* Let $f(z) = \Sigma a_n z^n$ be a power series whose radius of convergence R is equal to 1. If the coefficients $a_0, a_1, a_2, \cdots$, are positive decreasing numbers such that a_n approaches zero when n increases indefinitely, the series is convergent in every point of the circle of convergence, except perhaps for $z = 1$. In fact, the series Σz^n, where $|z| = 1$, is *indeterminate* except for $z = 1$, for the absolute value of the sum of the first n terms is less than $2/|1 - z|$; it will suffice, then, to apply the reasoning of § 166, Vol. I, based on the generalized lemma of Abel. In the same way the series $a_0 - a_1 z + a_2 z^2 - \cdots$, which is obtained from the preceding by replacing z by $-z$, is convergent at all the points of the circle $|z| = 1$, except perhaps for $z = -1$. (Cf. I, § 166.)

of $f_{n-1}(z)$. *Every power series represents therefore an analytic func-tion in the interior of its circle of convergence.* There is an infinite

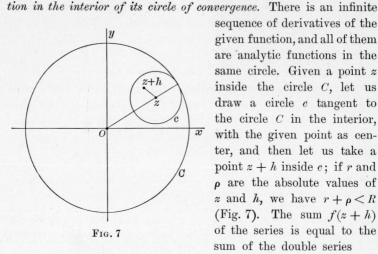

FIG. 7

sequence of derivatives of the given function, and all of them are analytic functions in the same circle. Given a point z inside the circle C, let us draw a circle c tangent to the circle C in the interior, with the given point as cen-ter, and then let us take a point $z + h$ inside c; if r and ρ are the absolute values of z and h, we have $r + \rho < R$ (Fig. 7). The sum $f(z + h)$ of the series is equal to the sum of the double series

(11)
$$\begin{cases} a_0 + a_1 z + a_2 z^2 \ + \cdots + a_n z^n + \cdots \\ \quad + a_1 h + 2\,a_2 zh + \cdots + na_n z^{n-1} h + \cdots \\ \qquad + a_2 h^2 \ + \cdots + \dfrac{n(n-1)}{1 \cdot 2}\,a_n z^{n-2} h^2 + \cdots \\ \qquad + \cdots\cdots\cdots\cdots\cdots\cdots\cdots\cdots \end{cases}$$

when we sum by columns. But this series is absolutely convergent, for if we replace each term by its absolute value, we shall have a double series of positive terms whose sum is

$$A_0 + A_1(r + \rho) + \cdots + A_n(r + \rho)^n + \cdots.$$

We can therefore sum the double series (11) by rows, and we have then, for every point $z + h$ inside the circle c, the relation

(12) $\quad f(z + h) = f(z) + hf_1(z) + \dfrac{h^2}{2!}f_2(z) + \cdots + \dfrac{h^n}{n!}f_n(z) + \cdots.$

The series of the second member is surely convergent so long as the absolute value of h is less than $R - r$, but it may be convergent in a larger circle. Since the functions $f_1(z), f_2(z), \cdots, f_n(z), \cdots$ are equal to the successive derivatives of $f(z)$, the formula (12) is identical with the Taylor development.

If the series (9) is convergent at a point Z of the circle of con-vergence, the sum $f(Z)$ of the series is the limit approached by the sum $f(z)$ when the point z approaches the point Z along a radius which terminates in that point. We prove this just as in Volume I (§ 182, 2d ed.; § 178, 1st ed.), by putting $z = \theta Z$ and letting θ increase from 0 to 1. The theorem is still true when z, remaining inside the circle, approaches Z along a curve which is not tangent at Z to the circle of convergence.*

When the radius R is infinite, the circle of convergence includes the whole plane, and the function $f(z)$ is analytic for every value of z. We say that this is an *integral function;* the study of transcendental functions of this kind is one of the most important objects of Analysis.† We shall study in the following paragraphs the classic elementary transcendental functions.

9. Double series. Given a power series (9) with any coefficients whatever, we shall say again that a second power series $\Sigma \alpha_n z^n$, whose coefficients are all real and positive, *dominates* the first series if for every value of n we have $|a_n| \leqq \alpha_n$. All the consequences deduced by means of dominant functions (I, §§ 186–189, 2d ed.; §§ 181–184, 1st ed.) follow without modification in the case of complex variables. We shall now give another application of this theory.

Let

(13) $$f_0(z) + f_1(z) + f_2(z) + \cdots + f_n(z) + \cdots$$

be a series of which each term is itself the sum of a power series that converges in a circle of radius equal to or greater than the number $R > 0$,

$$f_i(z) = a_{i0} + a_{i1}z + \cdots + a_{in}z^n + \cdots .$$

Suppose each term of the series (13) replaced by its development according to powers of z; we obtain thus a double series in which each column is formed by the development of a function $f_i(z)$. When that series is absolutely convergent for a value of z of absolute value ρ, that is, when the double series

$$\sum_i \sum_n |a_{in}| \rho^n$$

is convergent, we can sum the first double series by rows for every value of z whose absolute value does not exceed ρ. We obtain thus the development of the sum $F(z)$ of the series (13) in powers of z,

$$F(z) = b_0 + b_1 z + \cdots + b_n z^n + \cdots,$$
$$b_n = a_{0n} + a_{1n} + \cdots + a_{in} + \cdots, \qquad (n = 0, 1, 2, \cdots).$$

This proof is essentially the same as that for the development of $f(z + h)$ in powers of h.

Suppose, for example, that the series $f_i(z)$ has a dominant function of the form $M_i r/(r - z)$, and that the series ΣM_i is itself convergent. In the double

---

* See PICARD, *Traité d'Analyse,* Vol. II, p. 73.

† The class of *integral functions* includes polynomials as a special case. If there are an infinite number of terms in the development, we shall use the expression *integral transcendental function.* — TRANS.

series the absolute value of the general term is less than $M_i|z|^n/r^n$. If $|z| < r$, the series is absolutely convergent, for the series of the absolute values is convergent and its sum is less than $r\Sigma M_i/(r - |z|)$.

10. Development of an infinite product in power series. Let

$$F(z) = (1 + u_0)(1 + u_1) \cdots (1 + u_n) \cdots$$

be an infinite product where each of the functions u_i is a continuous function of the complex variable z in the region D. If the series ΣU_i, where $U_i = |u_i|$, is uniformly convergent in the region, $F(z)$ is equal to the sum of a series that is uniformly convergent in D, and therefore represents a continuous function (I, §§ 175, 176, 2d ed.). When the functions u_i are analytic functions of z, it follows, from a general theorem which will be demonstrated later (§ 39), that the same is true of $F(z)$.

For example, the infinite product

$$F(z) = z(1 - z^2)\left(1 - \frac{z^2}{4}\right) \cdots \left(1 - \frac{z^2}{n^2}\right) \cdots$$

represents a function of z analytic throughout the entire plane, for the series $\Sigma |z|^2/n^2$ is uniformly convergent within any closed curve whatever. This product is zero for $z = 0, \pm 1, \pm 2, \cdots$ and for these values only.

We can prove directly that the product $F(z)$ can be developed in a power series when each of the functions u_i can be developed in a power series

$$u_i(z) = a_{i0} + a_{i1}z + \cdots + a_{in}z^n + \cdots, \qquad (i = 0, 1, 2, \cdots),$$

such that the double series

$$\sum_i \sum_n |a_{in}| r^n$$

is convergent for a suitably chosen positive value of r.

Let us set, as in Volume I (§ 174, 2d ed.),

$$v_0 = 1 + u_0, \qquad v_n = (1 + u_0)(1 + u_1) \cdots (1 + u_{n-1}) u_n.$$

It is sufficient to show that the sum of the series

(14) $$v_0 + v_1 + \cdots + v_n + \cdots,$$

which is equal to the infinite product $F(z)$, can be developed in a power series. Now, if we set

$$u_i' = |a_{i0}| + |a_{i1}|z + \cdots + |a_{in}|z^n + \cdots,$$

it is clear that the product

$$v_n' = (1 + u_0')(1 + u_1') \cdots (1 + u_{n-1}') u_n'$$

is a dominant function for v_n. It is therefore possible to arrange the series (14) according to powers of z if the following auxiliary series

(15) $$v_0' + v_1' + \cdots + v_n' + \cdots$$

can be so arranged.

If we develop each term of this last series in power series, we obtain a double series with positive coefficients, and it is sufficient for our purpose to prove that the double series converges when z is replaced by r. Indicating by U_n' and V_n' the values of the functions u_n' and v_n' for $z = r$, we have

$$V_n' = (1 + U_0')(1 + U_1') \cdots (1 + U_{n-1}')\, U_n',$$

and therefore

$$V_0' + V_1' + \cdots + V_n' = (1 + U_0') \cdots (1 + U_n'),$$

or, again,

$$V_0' + V_1' + \cdots + V_n' < e^{U_0' + \cdots + U_n'}.$$

When n increases indefinitely, the sum $U_0' + \cdots + U_n'$ approaches a limit, since the series $\Sigma U_n'$ is supposed to be convergent. The double series (15) is then absolutely convergent if $|z| \leqq r$; the double series obtained by the development of each term v_n of the series (14) is then a fortiori absolutely convergent within the circle C of radius r, and we can arrange it according to integral powers of z.

The coefficient b_p of z^p in the development of $F(z)$ is equal, from the above, to the limit, as n becomes infinite, of the coefficient b_{pn} of z^p in the sum $v_0 + v_1 + \cdots + v_n$, or, what amounts to the same thing, in the development of the product

$$P_n = (1 + u_0)(1 + u_1) \cdots (1 + u_n).$$

Hence this coefficient can be obtained by applying to infinite products the ordinary rule which gives the coefficient of a power of z in the product of a finite number of polynomials. For example, the infinite product

$$F(z) = (1 + z)(1 + z^2)(1 + z^4) \cdots (1 + z^{2^n}) \cdots$$

can be developed according to powers of z if $|z| < 1$. Any power of z whatever, say z^N, will appear in the development with the coefficient unity, for any positive integer N can be written in one and only one way in the form of a sum of powers of 2. We have, then, if $|z| < 1$,

$$(16) \qquad F(z) = 1 + z + z^2 + \cdots + z^n + \cdots = \frac{1}{1 - z},$$

which can also be very easily obtained by means of the identity

$$\frac{1 - z^{2^n}}{1 - z} = (1 + z)(1 + z^2)(1 + z^4) \cdots (1 + z^{2^{n-1}}).$$

11. The exponential function. The arithmetic definition of the exponential function evidently has no meaning when the exponent is a complex number. In order to generalize the definition, it will be necessary to start with some property which is adapted to an extension to the case of the complex variable. We shall start with the property expressed by the functional relation

$$a^x \times a^{x'} = a^{x + x'}.$$

Let us consider the question of determining a power series $f(z)$, convergent in a circle of radius R, such that

$$(17) \qquad f(z + z') = f(z) f(z')$$

when the absolute values of z, z', $z + z'$ are less than R, which will surely be the case if $|z|$ and $|z'|$ are less than $R/2$. If we put $z' = 0$ in the above equation, it becomes

$$f(z) = f(z) f(0).$$

Hence we must have $f(0) = 1$, and we shall write the desired series

$$f(z) = 1 + \frac{a_1}{1} z + \frac{a_2}{2!} z^2 + \cdots + \frac{a_n}{n!} z^n + \cdots.$$

Let us replace successively in that series z by λt, then by $\lambda' t$, where λ and λ' are two constants and t an auxiliary variable; and let us then multiply the resulting series. This gives

$$f(\lambda t) f(\lambda' t) = 1 + \frac{a_1}{1} (\lambda + \lambda') t + \cdots$$
$$+ \frac{t^n}{n!} \left(a_n \lambda^n + \frac{n}{1} a_{n-1} a_1 \lambda^{n-1} \lambda' + \cdots + a_n \lambda'^n \right) + \cdots.$$

On the other hand, we have

$$f(\lambda t + \lambda' t) = 1 + \frac{a_1}{1} (\lambda + \lambda') t + \cdots + \frac{a_n}{n!} (\lambda + \lambda')^n t^n + \cdots.$$

The equality $f(\lambda t + \lambda' t) = f(\lambda t) f(\lambda' t)$ is to hold for all values of λ, λ', t such that $|\lambda| < 1, |\lambda'| < 1, |t| < R/2$. The two series must then be identical, that is, we must have

$$a_n (\lambda + \lambda')^n = a_n \lambda^n + \frac{n}{1} a_{n-1} a_1 \lambda^{n-1} \lambda'$$
$$+ \frac{n(n-1)}{1 \cdot 2} a_{n-2} a_2 \lambda^{n-2} \lambda'^2 + \cdots + a_n \lambda'^n,$$

and from this we can deduce the equations

$$a_n = a_{n-1} a_1, \qquad a_n = a_{n-2} a_2, \qquad \cdots,$$

all of which can be expressed in the single condition

(18)　　　　　　　　　　$a_{p+q} = a_p a_q,$

where p and q are any two positive integers whatever. In order to find the general solution, let us suppose $q = 1$, and let us put successively $p = 1, p = 2, p = 3, \cdots$; from this we find $a_2 = a_1^2$, then $a_3 = a_2 a_1 = a_1^3, \cdots$, and finally $a_n = a_1^n$. The expressions thus obtained satisfy the condition (18), and the series sought is of the form

$$f(z) = 1 + \frac{a_1 z}{1} + \frac{(a_1 z)^2}{2!} + \cdots + \frac{(a_1 z)^n}{n!} + \cdots.$$

This series is convergent in the whole plane, and the relation

$$f(z + z') = f(z) f(z')$$

is true for all values of z and z'.

The above series depends upon an arbitrary constant a_1. Taking $a_1 = 1$, we shall set

$$e^z = 1 + \frac{z}{1} + \frac{z^2}{2!} + \cdots + \frac{z^n}{n!} + \cdots,$$

so that the general solution of the given problem is $e^{a_1 z}$. The integral function e^z coincides with the exponential function e^x studied in algebra when z is real, and it always satisfies the relation

$$e^{z + z'} = e^z \times e^{z'},$$

whatever z and z' may be. The derivative of e^z is equal to the function itself. Since we may write by the addition formula

$$e^{x + yi} = e^x e^{yi},$$

in order to calculate e^z when z has an imaginary value $x + yi$, it is sufficient to know how to calculate e^{yi}. Now the development of e^{yi} can be written, grouping together terms of the same kind,

$$e^{yi} = 1 - \frac{y^2}{2!} + \frac{y^4}{4!} - \cdots + i\left(\frac{y}{1} - \frac{y^3}{3!} + \frac{y^5}{5!} - \cdots\right).$$

We recognize in the second member the developments of $\cos y$ and of $\sin y$, and consequently, if y *is real*,

$$e^{yi} = \cos y + i \sin y.$$

Replacing e^{yi} by this expression in the preceding formula, we have

$$(19) \qquad e^{x + yi} = e^x(\cos y + i \sin y);$$

the *function* $e^{x + yi}$ *has* e^x *for its absolute value and* y *for its angle.* This formula makes evident an important property of e^z; if z changes to $z + 2\pi i$, x is not changed while y is increased by 2π, but these changes do not alter the value of the second member of the formula (19). We have, then,

$$e^{z + 2\pi i} = e^z;$$

that is, *the exponential function* e^z *has the period* $2\pi i$.

Let us consider now the solution of the equation $e^z = A$, where A is any complex quantity whatever different from zero. Let ρ and ω be the absolute value and the angle of A; we have, then,

$$e^{x + yi} = e^x(\cos y + i \sin y) = \rho (\cos \omega + i \sin \omega),$$

from which it follows that

$$e^x = \rho, \qquad y = \omega + 2\,k\pi.$$

From the first relation we find $x = \log \rho$, where the abbreviation *log* shall always be used for the natural logarithm of a real positive number. On the other hand, y is determined except for a multiple of $2\,\pi$. If A is zero, the equation $e^x = 0$ leads to an impossibility. Hence *the equation $e^z = A$, where A is not zero, has an infinite number of roots given by the expression* $\log \rho + i(\omega + 2\,k\pi)$; *the equation $e^z = 0$ has no roots, real or imaginary.*

Note. We might also define e^z as the limit approached by the polynomial $(1 + z/m)^m$ when m becomes infinite. The method used in algebra to prove that the limit of this polynomial is the series e^z can be used even when z is complex.

12. Trigonometric functions. In order to define $\sin z$ and $\cos z$ when z is complex, we shall extend directly to complex values the series established for these functions when the variable is real. Thus we shall have

$$(20) \qquad \begin{cases} \sin z = \dfrac{z}{1} - \dfrac{z^3}{3!} + \dfrac{z^5}{5!} - \cdots, \\[2mm] \cos z = 1 - \dfrac{z^2}{2!} + \dfrac{z^4}{4!} - \cdots. \end{cases}$$

These are integral transcendental functions which have all the properties of the trigonometric functions. Thus we see from the formulæ (20) that the derivative of $\sin z$ is $\cos z$, that the derivative of $\cos z$ is $-\sin z$, and that $\sin z$ becomes $-\sin z$, while $\cos z$ does not change at all when z is changed to $-z$.

These new transcendental functions can be brought into very close relation with the exponential function. In fact, if we write the expansion of e^{zi}, collecting separately the terms with and without the factor i,

$$e^{zi} = 1 - \frac{z^2}{2!} + \frac{z^4}{4!} + \cdots + i\left(\frac{z}{1} - \frac{z^3}{3!} + \cdots\right),$$

we find that that equality can be written, by (20), in the form

$$e^{zi} = \cos z + i \sin z.$$

Changing z to $-z$, we have again

$$e^{-zi} = \cos z - i \sin z,$$

and from these two relations we derive

$$(21) \qquad \cos z = \frac{e^{zi} + e^{-zi}}{2}, \qquad \sin z = \frac{e^{zi} - e^{-zi}}{2\,i}.$$

These are the well-known formulæ of Euler which express the trigonometric functions in terms of the exponential function. They show plainly the periodicity of these functions, for the right-hand sides do not change when we replace z by $z + 2\,\pi$. Squaring and adding them, we have

$$\cos^2 z + \sin^2 z = 1.$$

Let us take again the addition formula $e^{(z + z')i} = e^{zi} e^{z'i}$, or

$$\cos(z + z') + i \sin(z + z')$$
$$= (\cos z + i \sin z)(\cos z' + i \sin z')$$
$$= \cos z \cos z' - \sin z \sin z' + i(\sin z \cos z' + \sin z' \cos z),$$

and let us change z to $-z$, z' to $-z'$. It then becomes

$$\cos(z + z') - i \sin(z + z')$$
$$= \cos z \cos z' - \sin z \sin z' - i(\sin z \cos z' + \sin z' \cos z),$$

and from these two formulæ we derive

$$\cos(z + z') = \cos z \cos z' - \sin z \sin z'$$
$$\sin(z + z') = \sin z \cos z' + \sin z \cos z'.$$

The addition formulæ and therefore all their consequences apply for complex values of the independent variables. Let us determine, for example, the real part and the coefficient of i in $\cos(x + yi)$ and $\sin(x + yi)$. We have first, by Euler's formulæ,

$$\cos yi = \frac{e^{-y} + e^{y}}{2} = \cosh y, \qquad \sin yi = \frac{e^{-y} - e^{y}}{2\,i} = i \sinh y;$$

whence, by the addition formulæ,

$$\cos(x + yi) = \cos x \cos yi - \sin x \sin yi = \cos x \cosh y - i \sin x \sinh y,$$
$$\sin(x + yi) = \sin x \cos yi + \cos x \sin yi = \sin x \cosh y + i \cos x \sinh y.$$

The other trigonometric functions can be expressed by means of the preceding. For example,

$$\tan z = \frac{\sin z}{\cos z} = \frac{1}{i} \frac{e^{zi} - e^{-zi}}{e^{zi} + e^{-zi}},$$

which may be written in the form

$$\tan z = \frac{1}{i} \frac{e^{2zi} - 1}{e^{2zi} + 1}.$$

The right-hand side is a rational function of e^{2zi}; the period of the tangent is therefore π.

13. Logarithms. Given a complex quantity z, different from zero, we have already seen (§ 11) that the equation $e^u = z$ has an infinite number of roots. Let $u = x + yi$, and let ρ and ω denote the absolute value and angle of z, respectively. Then we must have

$$e^x = \rho, \qquad y = \omega + 2\,k\pi.$$

Any one of these roots is called the *logarithm* of z and will be denoted by $\mathrm{Log}\,(z)$. We can write, then,

$$\mathrm{Log}\,(z) = \log\rho + i\,(\omega + 2\,k\pi),$$

the symbol *log* being reserved for the ordinary natural, or Napierian, logarithm of a real positive number.

Every quantity, real or complex, different from zero, has an infinite number of logarithms, which form an arithmetic progression whose consecutive terms differ by $2\,\pi i$. In particular, if z is a real positive number x, we have $\omega = 0$. Taking $k = 0$, we find again the ordinary logarithm; but there are also an infinite number of complex values for the logarithm, of the form $\log x + 2\,k\pi i$. If z is real and negative, we can take $\omega = \pi$; hence all the determinations of the logarithm are imaginary.

Let z' be another imaginary quantity with the absolute value ρ' and the angle ω'. We have

$$\mathrm{Log}\,(z') = \log\rho' + i\,(\omega' + 2\,k'\pi).$$

Adding the two logarithms, we obtain

$$\mathrm{Log}\,(z) + \mathrm{Log}\,(z') = \log\rho\rho' + i\,[\omega + \omega' + 2\,(k + k')\,\pi].$$

Since $\rho\rho'$ is equal to the absolute value of zz', and $\omega + \omega'$ is equal to its angle, this formula can be written in the form

$$\mathrm{Log}\,(z) + \mathrm{Log}\,(z') = \mathrm{Log}\,(zz'),$$

which shows that, when we add any one whatever of the values of $\mathrm{Log}\,(z)$ to any one whatever of the values of $\mathrm{Log}\,(z')$, the sum is one of the determinations of $\mathrm{Log}\,(zz')$.

Let us suppose now that the variable z describes in its plane any continuous curve whatever not passing through the origin; along this curve ρ and ω vary continuously, and the same thing is true of the different determinations of the logarithm. But two quite distinct cases may present themselves when the variable z traces a closed curve. When z starts from a point z_0 and returns to that point after having described a closed curve not containing the origin within it, the angle ω of z takes on again its original value ω_0, and the different determinations of the logarithm come back to their initial values. If we represent each value of the logarithm by a point, each of these points traces out a closed curve. On the contrary, if the variable z describes a closed curve such as the curve M_0NMP (Fig. 3 b), the angle increases by 2π, and each determination of the logarithm returns to its initial value increased by $2\pi i$. In general, when z describes any closed curve whatever, the final value of the logarithm is equal to its initial value increased by $2k\pi i$, where k denotes a positive or negative integer which gives the number of revolutions and the direction through which the radius vector joining the origin to the point z has turned. It is, then, impossible to consider the different determinations of $\mathrm{Log}\,(z)$ as so many distinct functions of z if we do not place any restriction on the variation of that variable, since we can pass continuously from one to the other. They are so many branches of the same function, which are permuted among themselves about the critical point $z = 0$.

In the interior of a region which is bounded by a single closed curve and which does not contain the origin, each of the determinations of $\mathrm{Log}\,(z)$ is a continuous single-valued function of z. To show that it is an analytic function it is sufficient to show that it possesses a unique derivative at each point. Let z and z_1 be two neighboring values of the variable, and $\mathrm{Log}\,(z)$, $\mathrm{Log}\,(z_1)$ the corresponding values of the chosen determination of the logarithm. When z_1 approaches z, the absolute value of $\mathrm{Log}\,(z_1) - \mathrm{Log}\,(z)$ approaches zero. Let us put $\mathrm{Log}\,(z) = u$, $\mathrm{Log}\,(z_1) = u_1$; then

$$\frac{\mathrm{Log}\,(z_1) - \mathrm{Log}\,(z)}{z_1 - z} = \frac{u_1 - u}{e^{u_1} - e^{u}}.$$

When u_1 approaches u, the quotient

$$\frac{e^{u_1} - e^{u}}{u_1 - u}$$

approaches as its limit the derivative of e^u; that is, e^u or z. Hence the logarithm has a uniquely determined derivative at each point, and that derivative is equal to $1/z$. In general, $\mathrm{Log}\,(z - a)$ has an infinite number of determinations which permute themselves about the critical point $z = a$, and its derivative is $1/(z - a)$.

The function z^m, where m is any number whatever, real or complex, is defined by means of the equality

$$z^m = e^{m\,\mathrm{Log}\,(z)}.$$

Unless m be a real rational number, this function possesses, just as does the logarithm, an infinite number of determinations, which permute themselves when the variable turns about the point $z = 0$. It is sufficient to make an infinite cut along a ray from the origin in order to make each branch an analytic function in the whole plane.

The derivative is given by the expression

$$\frac{m}{z}\, e^{m\,\text{Log}\,(z)} = m z^{m-1},$$

and it is clear that we ought to take the same value for the angle of z in the function and in its derivative.

14. Inverse functions: arc sin z, arc tan z. The inverse functions of $\sin z$, $\cos z$, $\tan z$ are defined in a similar way. Thus, the function $u = \text{arc sin } z$ is defined by the equation

$$z = \sin u.$$

In order to solve this equation for u, we write

$$z = \frac{e^{ui} - e^{-ui}}{2\,i} = \frac{e^{2\,ui} - 1}{2\,ie^{ui}},$$

and we are led to an equation of the second degree,

$$(22) \qquad\qquad U^2 - 2\,izU - 1 = 0,$$

to determine the auxiliary unknown quantity $U = e^{ui}$. We obtain from this equation

$$(23) \qquad\qquad U = iz \pm \sqrt{1 - z^2},$$

or

$$(24) \qquad\qquad u = \text{arc sin } z = \frac{1}{i}\,\text{Log}\big(iz \pm \sqrt{1 - z^2}\big).$$

The equation $z = \sin u$ has therefore two sequences of roots, which arise, on the one hand, from the two values of the radical $\sqrt{1 - z^2}$, and, on the other hand, from the infinite number of determinations of the logarithm. But if one of these determinations is known, all the others can easily be determined from it. Let $U' = \rho'e^{i\omega'}$ and $U'' = \rho''e^{i\omega''}$ be the two roots of the equation (22); between these two roots exists the relation $U'U'' = -1$, and therefore $\rho'\rho'' = 1$, $\omega' + \omega'' = (2\,n + 1)\,\pi$. It is clear that we may suppose $\omega'' = \pi - \omega'$, and we have then

$$\text{Log}\,(U') = \log\rho' + i(\omega' + 2\,k'\pi),$$
$$\text{Log}\,(U'') = -\log\rho' + i(\pi - \omega' + 2\,k''\pi).$$

Hence all the determinations of arc sin z are given by the two formulæ

$$\text{arc sin } z = \omega' + 2\,k'\pi - i \log \rho',$$

$$\text{arc sin } z = \pi + 2\,k''\pi - \omega' + i \log \rho',$$

and we may write

(A) $\qquad\qquad \text{arc sin } z = u' + 2\,k'\pi,$

(B) $\qquad\qquad \text{arc sin } z = (2\,k'' + 1)\,\pi - u',$

where $u' = \omega' - i \log \rho'$.

When the variable z describes a continuous curve, the various determinations of the logarithm in the formula (24) vary in general in a continuous manner. The only critical points that are possible are the points $z = \pm 1$, around which the two values of the radical $\sqrt{1 - z^2}$ are permuted; there cannot be a value of z that causes $iz \pm \sqrt{1 - z^2}$ to vanish, for, if there were, on squaring the two sides of the equation $iz = \pm \sqrt{1 - z^2}$ we should obtain $1 = 0$.

Let us suppose that two cuts are made along the axis of reals, one going from $-\infty$ to the point -1, the other from the point $+1$ to $+\infty$. If the path described by the variable is not allowed to cross these cuts, the different determinations of arc sin z are single-valued functions of z. In fact, when the variable z describes a closed curve not crossing any of these cuts, the two roots U', U'' of equation (22) also describe closed curves. None of these curves contains the origin in its interior. If, for example, the curve described by the root U' contained the origin in its interior, it would cut the axis Oy in a point above Ox at least once. Corresponding to a value of U of the form $i\alpha\,(\alpha > 0)$, the relation (22) determines a value $(1 + \alpha^2)/2\,\alpha$ for z, and this value is real and > 1. The curve described by the point z would therefore have to cross the cut which goes from $+1$ to $+\infty$.

The different determinations of arc sin z are, moreover, analytic functions of z.* For let u and u_1 be two neighboring values of

---

* If we choose in $U = iz + \sqrt{1 - z^2}$ the determination of the radical which reduces to 1 when $z = 0$, the real part of U remains positive when the variable z does not cross the cuts, and we can put $U = Re^{i\Phi}$, where Φ lies between $-\pi/2$ and $+\pi/2$. The corresponding value of $(1/i)\, \text{Log } U$, namely,

$$\text{arc sin } z = \frac{1}{i} \text{Log } U = \Phi - i \text{Log } R,$$

is sometimes called the *principal value* of arc sin z. It reduces to the ordinary determination when z is real and lies between -1 and $+1$.

arc sin z, corresponding to two neighboring values z and z_1 of the variable. We have

$$\frac{u_1 - u}{z_1 - z} = \frac{u_1 - u}{\sin u_1 - \sin u}.$$

When the absolute value of $u_1 - u$ approaches zero, the preceding quotient has for its limit

$$\frac{1}{\cos u} = \frac{\pm 1}{\sqrt{1 - z^2}}.$$

The two values of the derivative correspond to the two sequences of values (A) and (B) of arc sin z.

If we do not impose any restriction on the variation of z, we can pass from a given initial value of arc sin z to any one of the determinations whatever, by causing the variable z to describe a suitable closed curve. In fact, we see first that when z describes about the point $z = 1$ a closed curve to which the point $z = -1$ is exterior, the two values of the radical $\sqrt{1 - z^2}$ are permuted and so we pass from a determination of the sequence (A) to one of the sequence (B). Suppose next that we cause z to describe a circle of radius $R\,(R > 1)$ about the origin as center; then each of the two points U', U'' describes a closed curve. To the point $z = + R$ the equation (22) assigns two values of U, $U' = i\alpha$, $U'' = i\beta$, where α and β are positive; to the point $z = -R$ there correspond by means of the same equation the values $U' = -i\alpha'$, $U'' = -i\beta'$, where α' and β' are again positive. Hence the closed curves described by these two points U', U'' cut the axis Oy in two points, one above and the other below the point O; each of the logarithms Log (U'), Log (U'') increases or diminishes by $2\pi i$.

In the same way the function arc tan z is defined by means of the relation tan $u = z$, or

$$z = \frac{1}{i}\frac{e^{2ui} - 1}{e^{2ui} + 1};$$

whence we have

$$e^{2ui} = \frac{1 + iz}{1 - iz} = \frac{i - z}{i + z},$$

and consequently

$$\text{arc tan } z = \frac{1}{2i} \text{Log}\left(\frac{i - z}{i + z}\right).$$

This expression shows the two logarithmic critical points $\pm i$ of the function arc tan z. When the variable z passes around one of these points, Log $[(i - z)/(i + z)]$ increases or diminishes by $2\pi i$, and arc tan z increases or diminishes by π.

15. Application to the integral calculus. The derivatives of the functions which we have just defined have the same form as when the variable is real. Conversely, the rules for finding primitive functions apply also to the elementary functions of complex variables. Thus, denoting by $\int f(z)\,dz$ a function of the complex variable z whose derivative is $f'(z)$, we have

$$\int \frac{A\,dz}{(z-a)^m} = -\frac{A}{m-1}\frac{1}{(z-a)^{m-1}}, \qquad (m>1),$$

$$\int \frac{A\,dz}{z-a} = A \operatorname{Log}(z-a).$$

These two formulæ enable us to find a primitive function of any rational function whatever, with real or imaginary coefficients, provided the roots of the denominator are known. Consider as a special case a rational function of the real variable x with real coefficients. If the denominator has imaginary roots, they occur in conjugate pairs, and each root has the same multiplicity as its conjugate. Let $\alpha + \beta i$ and $\alpha - \beta i$ be two conjugate roots of multiplicity p. In the decomposition into simple fractions, if we proceed with the imaginary roots just as with the real roots, the root $\alpha + \beta i$ will furnish a sum of simple fractions

$$\frac{M_1 + N_1 i}{x - \alpha - \beta i} + \frac{M_2 + N_2 i}{(x - \alpha - \beta i)^2} + \cdots + \frac{M_p + N_p i}{(x - \alpha - \beta i)^p},$$

and the root $\alpha - \beta i$ will furnish a similar sum, but with numerators that are conjugates of the former ones. Combining in the primitive function the terms which come from the corresponding fractions, we shall have, if $p > 1$,

$$\int \frac{M_p + N_p i}{(x - \alpha - \beta i)^p}\,dx + \int \frac{M_p - N_p i}{(x - \alpha + \beta i)^p}\,dx$$

$$= -\frac{1}{p-1}\left[\frac{M_p + N_p i}{(x - \alpha - \beta i)^{p-1}} + \frac{M_p - N_p i}{(x - \alpha + \beta i)^{p-1}}\right]$$

$$= -\frac{1}{p-1}\frac{(M_p + N_p i)(x - \alpha + \beta i)^{p-1} + \cdots}{[(x-\alpha)^2 + \beta^2]^{p-1}},$$

and the numerator is evidently the sum of two conjugate imaginary polynomials. If $p = 1$, we have

$$\int \frac{M_1 + N_1 i}{x - \alpha - \beta i}\,dx + \int \frac{M_1 - N_1 i}{x - \alpha + \beta i}\,dx$$

$$= (M_1 + N_1 i)\operatorname{Log}[(x-\alpha) - \beta i] + (M_1 - N_1 i)\operatorname{Log}[(x-\alpha) + \beta i].$$

If we replace the logarithms by their developed expressions, there remains on the right-hand side

$$M_1 \log \left[(x - \alpha)^2 + \beta^2 \right] + 2 N_1 \arctan \frac{\beta}{x - \alpha}.$$

It suffices to replace

$$\arctan \frac{\beta}{x - \alpha} \quad \text{by} \quad \frac{\pi}{2} - \arctan \frac{x - \alpha}{\beta}$$

in order to express the result in the form in which it is obtained when imaginary symbols are not used.

Again, consider the indefinite integral

$$\int \frac{dx}{\sqrt{Ax^2 + 2Bx + C}},$$

which has two essentially different forms, according to the sign of A. The introduction of complex variables reduces the two forms to a single one. In fact, if in the formula

$$\int \frac{dx}{\sqrt{1 + x^2}} = \mathrm{Log}\left(x + \sqrt{1 + x^2}\right)$$

we change x to ix, there results

$$\int \frac{dx}{\sqrt{1 - x^2}} = \frac{1}{i} \mathrm{Log}\left(ix + \sqrt{1 - x^2}\right),$$

and the right-hand side represents precisely arc sin x.

The introduction of imaginary symbols in the integral calculus enables us, then, to reduce one formula to another even when the relationship between them might not be at all apparent if we were to remain always in the domain of real numbers.

We shall give another example of the simplification which comes from the use of imaginaries. If a and b are real, we have

$$\int e^{(a + bi)x} dx = \frac{e^{(a + bi)x}}{a + bi} = \frac{a - bi}{a^2 + b^2} e^{ax} (\cos bx + i \sin bx).$$

Equating the real parts and the coefficients of i, we have at one stroke two integrals already calculated (I, § 109, 2d ed.; § 119, 1st ed.):

$$\int e^{ax} \cos bx \, dx = \frac{e^{ax} (a \cos bx + b \sin bx)}{a^2 + b^2},$$

$$\int e^{ax} \sin bx \, dx = \frac{e^{ax} (a \sin bx - b \cos bx)}{a^2 + b^2}.$$

In the same way we may reduce the integrals

$$\int x^m e^{ax} \cos bx \, dx, \qquad \int x^m e^{ax} \sin bx \, dx$$

to the integral $\int x^m e^{(a+bi)x} dx$, which can be calculated by a succession of integrations by parts, where m is any integer.

16. Decomposition of a rational function of $\sin z$ and $\cos z$ into simple elements. Given a rational function of $\sin z$ and $\cos z$, $F(\sin z, \cos z)$, if in it we replace $\sin z$ and $\cos z$ by their expressions given by Euler's formula, it becomes a rational function $R(t)$ of $t = e^{zi}$. This function $R(t)$, decomposed into simple elements, will be made up of an integral part and a sum of fractions coming from the roots of the denominator of $R(t)$. If that denominator has the root $t = 0$, we shall combine with the integral part the fractions arising from that root, which will give a polynomial or a rational function $R_1(t) = \Sigma K_m t^m$, where the exponent m may have negative values.

Let $t = a$ be a root of the denominator different from zero. That root will give rise to a sum of simple fractions

$$f(t) = \frac{A_1}{t-a} + \frac{A_2}{(t-a)^2} + \cdots + \frac{A_n}{(t-a)^n}.$$

The root a not being zero, let α be a root of the equation $e^{\alpha i} = a$; then $1/(t-a)$ can be expressed very simply by means of $\operatorname{ctn}[(z-\alpha)/2]$. We have, in fact,

$$\operatorname{ctn} \frac{z-\alpha}{2} = i \frac{e^{zi} + e^{\alpha i}}{e^{zi} - e^{\alpha i}} = i \left(1 + \frac{2 e^{\alpha i}}{e^{zi} - e^{\alpha i}} \right);$$

whence it follows that

$$\frac{1}{t-a} = \frac{1}{e^{zi} - e^{\alpha i}} = -\frac{1}{2 e^{\alpha i}} \left(1 + i \operatorname{ctn} \frac{z-\alpha}{2} \right).$$

Hence the rational fraction $f(t)$ changes to a polynomial of degree n in $\operatorname{ctn}[(z-\alpha)/2]$,

$$A_0' + A_1' \operatorname{ctn} \frac{z-\alpha}{2} + A_2' \operatorname{ctn}^2 \left(\frac{z-\alpha}{2} \right) + \cdots + A_n' \operatorname{ctn}^n \left(\frac{z-\alpha}{2} \right).$$

The successive powers of the cotangent up to the nth can be expressed in turn in terms of its successive derivatives up to the $(n-1)$th; we have first

$$\frac{d \operatorname{ctn} z}{dz} = -\frac{1}{\sin^2 z} = -1 - \operatorname{ctn}^2 z,$$

which enables us to express $\operatorname{ctn}^2 z$ in terms of $d(\operatorname{ctn} z)/dz$, and it is easy to show, by mathematical induction, that if the law is true up to $\operatorname{ctn}^n z$, it will also be true for $\operatorname{ctn}^{n+1} z$. The preceding polynomial of degree n in $\operatorname{ctn}[(z-\alpha)/2]$ will change to a linear expression in $\operatorname{ctn}[(z-\alpha)/2]$ and its derivatives,

$$\mathcal{A}_0 + \mathcal{A}_1 \operatorname{ctn} \frac{z-\alpha}{2} + \mathcal{A}_2 \frac{d}{dz}\left(\operatorname{ctn}\frac{z-\alpha}{2}\right) + \cdots + \mathcal{A}_n \frac{d^{n-1}}{dz^{n-1}}\left(\operatorname{ctn}\frac{z-\alpha}{2}\right).$$

Let us proceed in the same way with all the roots b, c, $\cdots$, l of the denominator of $R(t)$ different from zero, and let us add the results obtained after having replaced t by e^{zi} in $R_1(t)$. The given rational function $F(\sin z,\ \cos z)$ will be composed of two parts,

$$(25) \qquad F(\sin z,\ \cos z) = \Phi(z) + \Psi(z).$$

The function $\Phi(z)$, which corresponds to the integral part of a rational function of the variable, is of the form

$$(26) \qquad \Phi(z) = C + \Sigma(\alpha_m \cos mz + \beta_m \sin mz),$$

where m is an integer not zero. On the other hand, $\Psi(z)$, which corresponds to the fractional part of a rational function, is an expression of the form

$$\Psi(z) = \mathcal{A}_1 \operatorname{ctn}\left(\frac{z-\alpha}{2}\right) + \mathcal{A}_2 \frac{d}{dz}\operatorname{ctn}\left(\frac{z-\alpha}{2}\right) + \cdots + \mathcal{A}_n \frac{d^{n-1}}{dz^{n-1}}\operatorname{ctn}\left(\frac{z-\alpha}{2}\right)$$

$$+ \mathcal{B}_1 \operatorname{ctn}\left(\frac{z-\beta}{2}\right) + \mathcal{B}_2 \frac{d}{dz}\operatorname{ctn}\left(\frac{z-\beta}{2}\right) + \cdots + \mathcal{B}_p \frac{d^{p-1}}{dz^{p-1}}\operatorname{ctn}\left(\frac{z-\beta}{2}\right)$$

$$+ \cdots\cdots\cdots\cdots\cdots\cdots\cdots\cdots\cdots\cdots\cdots\cdots\cdots\cdots\cdots\cdots$$

It is the function $\operatorname{ctn}[(z-\alpha)/2]$ which here plays the rôle of the simple element, just as the fraction $1/(z-\alpha)$ does for a rational function. The result of this decomposition of $F(\sin z,\ \cos z)$ is easily integrated; we have, in fact,

$$(27) \qquad \int \operatorname{ctn}\left(\frac{z-\alpha}{2}\right) dz = 2\operatorname{Log}\left[\sin\left(\frac{z-\alpha}{2}\right)\right],$$

and the other terms are integrable at once. In order that the primitive function may be periodic, it is necessary and sufficient that all the coefficients C, $\mathcal{A}_1$, $\mathcal{B}_1$, $\cdots$ be zero.

In practice it is not always necessary to go through all these successive transformations in order to put the function $F(\sin z,\ \cos z)$ into its final form (25). Let α be a value of z which makes the function F infinite. We can always calculate, by a simple division, the coefficients of $(z - \alpha)^{-1}$, $(z - \alpha)^{-2}$, $\cdots$, in the part that is infinite for $z = \alpha$ (I, § 188, 2d ed.; § 183, 1st ed.). On the other hand, we have

$$\operatorname{ctn}\left(\frac{z - \alpha}{2}\right) = \frac{2}{z - \alpha} + P(z - \alpha),$$

where $P(z - \alpha)$ is a power series; equating the coefficients of the successive powers of $(z - \alpha)^{-1}$ in the two sides of the equation (25), we shall then obtain easily $\mathcal{A}_1, \mathcal{A}_2, \cdots, \mathcal{A}_n$.

Consider, for example, the function $1/(\cos z - \cos \alpha)$. Setting $e^{zi} = t$, $e^{\alpha i} = a$, it takes the form

$$\frac{2\,at}{a(t^2 + 1) - t(a^2 + 1)}.$$

The denominator has the two simple roots $t = a$, $t = 1/a$, and the numerator is of lower degree than the denominator. We shall have, then, a decomposition of the form

$$\frac{1}{\cos z - \cos \alpha} = C + \mathcal{A} \operatorname{ctn} \frac{z - \alpha}{2} + \mathcal{B} \operatorname{ctn} \frac{z + \alpha}{2}.$$

In order to determine $\mathcal{A}$, let us multiply the two sides by $z - \alpha$, and let us then put $z = \alpha$. This gives $\mathcal{A} = -1/(2 \sin \alpha)$. In a similar manner, we find $\mathcal{B} = 1/(2 \sin \alpha)$. Replacing $\mathcal{A}$ and $\mathcal{B}$ by these values and setting $z = 0$, it is seen that $C = 0$, and the formula takes the form

$$\frac{1}{\cos z - \cos \alpha} = \frac{1}{2 \sin \alpha}\left(\operatorname{ctn} \frac{z + \alpha}{2} - \operatorname{ctn} \frac{z - \alpha}{2}\right).$$

Let us now apply the general method to the integral powers of $\sin z$ and of $\cos z$. We have, for example,

$$(\cos z)^m = \left(\frac{e^{zi} + e^{-zi}}{2}\right)^m.$$

Combining the terms at equal distances from the extremities of the expansion of the numerator, and then applying Euler's formulæ, we find at once

$$(2 \cos z)^m = 2 \cos mz + 2\,m \cos(m - 2)z + 2\,\frac{m(m - 1)}{1 \cdot 2} \cos(m - 4)z + \cdots.$$

If m is odd, the last term contains $\cos z$; if m is even, the term which ends the expansion is independent of z and is equal to $m!/[(m/2)!]^2$. In the same way, if m is odd,

$$(2\,i \sin z)^m = 2\,i \sin mz - 2\,im \sin(m - 2)z + 2\,i\,\frac{m(m - 1)}{1 \cdot 2} \sin(m - 4)z \cdots;$$

and if m is even,

$$(2\,i \sin z)^m = 2 \cos mz - 2\,m \cos(m - 2)z + \cdots + (-1)^{\frac{m}{2}}\frac{m!}{\left(\frac{m}{2}!\right)^2}.$$

These formulæ show at once that the primitive functions of $(\sin z)^m$ and of $(\cos z)^m$ are periodic functions of z when m is *odd*, and only then.

Note. When the function $F(\sin z, \cos z)$ has the period π, we can express it rationally in terms of e^{2zi} and can take for the simple elements ctn $(z - \alpha)$, ctn $(z - \beta)$, $\cdots$.

17. Expansion of Log $(1 + z)$. The transcendental functions which we have defined are of two kinds : those which, like e^z, $\sin z$, $\cos z$, are analytic in the whole plane, and those which, like Log z, arc tan z, $\cdots$, have singular points and cannot be represented by developments in power series convergent in the whole plane. Nevertheless, such functions may have developments holding for certain parts of the plane. We shall now show this for the logarithmic function.

Simple division leads to the elementary formula

$$\frac{1}{1+z} = 1 - z + z^2 - z^3 + \cdots + (-1)^n z^n \pm \frac{z^{n+1}}{1+z};$$

and if $|z| < 1$, the remainder $z^{n+1}/(1+z)$ approaches zero when n increases indefinitely. Hence, in the interior of a circle C of radius 1 we have

$$\frac{1}{1+z} = 1 - z + z^2 - z^3 + \cdots + (-1)^n z^n \pm \cdots.$$

Let $F(z)$ be the series obtained by integrating this series term by term:

$$F(z) = \frac{z}{1} - \frac{z^2}{2} + \frac{z^3}{3} - \frac{z^4}{4} + \cdots + (-1)^n \frac{z^{n+1}}{n+1} + \cdots;$$

this new series is convergent inside the unit circle and represents an analytic function whose derivative $F'(z)$ is $1/(1+z)$. We know, however, a function which has the same derivative, Log $(1 + z)$. It follows that the difference Log $(1 + z) - F(z)$ reduces to a constant.* In order to determine this constant it will be necessary to fix precisely the determination chosen for the logarithm. If we take the one which becomes zero for $z = 0$, we have for every point inside C

$$(28) \qquad \text{Log}\,(1+z) = \frac{z}{1} - \frac{z^2}{2} + \frac{z^3}{3} - \frac{z^4}{4} + \cdots.$$

Let us join the point A to the point M, which represents z (Fig. 8). The absolute value of $1 + z$ is represented by the length $r = AM$. For the angle of $1 + z$ we can take the angle α which AM makes with AO, an angle which lies between $-\pi/2$ and $+\pi/2$ as long as the point M remains inside the circle C. That determination of the

---

* In order that the derivative of an analytic function $X + Yi$ be zero, it is necessary that we have (§ 3) $\partial X/\partial x = 0$, $\partial Y/\partial x = 0$, and consequently $\partial Y/\partial y = \partial X/\partial y = 0$; X and Y are therefore constants.

logarithm which becomes zero for $z = 0$ is $\log r + i\alpha$; hence the formula (28) is not ambiguous.

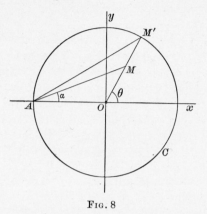

Fig. 8

Changing z to $-z$ in this formula and then subtracting the two expressions, we obtain

$$\operatorname{Log}\left(\frac{1+z}{1-z}\right) = 2\left(\frac{z}{1} + \frac{z^3}{3} + \frac{z^5}{5} + \cdots\right).$$

If we now replace z by iz, we shall obtain again the development of arc tan z

$$\operatorname{arc\,tan} z = \frac{1}{2\,i} \operatorname{Log}\left(\frac{1+iz}{1-iz}\right) = \frac{z}{1} - \frac{z^3}{3} + \frac{z^5}{5} - \cdots.$$

The series (28) remains convergent at every point on the circle of convergence except the point A (footnote, p. 19), and consequently the two series

$$\cos\theta - \frac{\cos 2\,\theta}{2} + \frac{\cos 3\,\theta}{3} - \frac{\cos 4\,\theta}{4} + \cdots,$$

$$\sin\theta - \frac{\sin 2\,\theta}{2} + \frac{\sin 3\,\theta}{3} - \frac{\sin 4\,\theta}{4} + \cdots$$

are both convergent except for $\theta = (2\,k + 1)\,\pi$ (cf. I, § 166). By Abel's theorem the sum of the series at M' is the limit approached by the sum of the series at a point M as M approaches M' along the radius OM'. If we suppose θ always between $-\pi$ and $+\pi$, the angle α will have for its limit $\theta/2$, and the absolute value AM will have for its limit $2\cos(\theta/2)$. We can therefore write

$$\log\left(2\cos\frac{\theta}{2}\right) = \cos\theta - \frac{\cos 2\,\theta}{2} + \frac{\cos 3\,\theta}{3} - \frac{\cos 4\,\theta}{4} + \cdots,$$

$$\frac{\theta}{2} = \sin\theta - \frac{\sin 2\,\theta}{2} + \frac{\sin 3\,\theta}{3} - \cdots, \qquad (-\pi < \theta < \pi).$$

If in the last formula we replace θ by $\theta - \pi$, we obtain again a formula previously established (I, § 204, 2d ed.; § 198, 1st ed.).

18. Extension of the binomial formula. In a fundamental paper on power series, Abel set for himself the problem of determining the sum of the convergent series

$$(29) \quad \begin{cases} \phi(m, z) = 1 + \dfrac{m}{1} z + \dfrac{m(m-1)}{1 \cdot 2} z^2 + \cdots \\ \qquad\qquad + \dfrac{m(m-1)\cdots(m-p+1)}{p\,!} z^p + \cdots \end{cases}$$

for all the values of m and z, real or imaginary, provided we have $|z| < 1$. We might accomplish this by means of a differential equation, in the manner indicated in the case of real variables (I, § 183, 2d ed.; § 179, 1st ed.). The following method, which gives an application of § 11, is more closely related to the method followed by Abel. We shall suppose z fixed and $|z| < 1$, and we shall study the properties of $\phi(m, z)$ considered as a function of m. If m is a positive integer, the function evidently reduces to the polynomial $(1 + z)^m$. *If m and m' are any two values whatever of the parameter m, we have always*

$$(30) \qquad \phi(m, z)\,\phi(m', z) = \phi(m + m', z).$$

In fact, let us multiply the two series $\phi(m, z)$, $\phi(m', z)$ by the ordinary rule. The coefficient of z^p in the product is equal to

$$(31) \quad m_p + m_{p-1} m_1' + m_{p-2} m_2' + \cdots + m_1 m_{p-1}' + m_p',$$

where we have set for abbreviation

$$m_k = \frac{m(m-1)\cdots(m-k+1)}{k\,!}.$$

The proposed functional relation will be established if we show that the expression (31) is identical with the coefficient of z^p in $\phi(m + m', z)$, that is, with $(m + m')_p$. We could easily verify directly the identity

$$(32) \qquad (m + m')_p = m_p + m_{p-1} m_1' + \cdots + m_p',$$

but the computation is unnecessary if we notice that the relation (30) is always satisfied whenever m and m' are positive integers. The two sides of the equation (32) are polynomials in m and m' which are equal whenever m and m' are positive integers; they are therefore identical.

On the other hand, $\phi(m, z)$ can be expanded in a power series of increasing powers of m. In fact, if we carry out the indicated products, $\phi(m, z)$ can be considered as the sum of a double series

$$(33) \quad \begin{cases} \phi(m, z) = 1 + \dfrac{m}{1} z - \dfrac{m}{2} z^2 + \dfrac{m}{3} z^3 - \cdots \pm \dfrac{m}{p} z^p \mp \cdots \\[2ex] \qquad\qquad + \dfrac{m^2}{2} z^2 - \dfrac{m^2}{2} z^3 + \cdots \\[2ex] \qquad\qquad\qquad + \dfrac{m^3}{6} z^3 - \cdots + \dfrac{m^p}{p!} z^p + \cdots \end{cases}$$

if we sum it by columns. This double series is absolutely convergent. For, let $|z| = \rho$ and $|m| = \sigma$; if we replace each term by its absolute value, the sum of the terms of the new series included in the $(p + 1)$th column is equal to

$$\frac{\sigma(\sigma + 1) \cdots (\sigma + p - 1)}{p!} \rho^p,$$

which is the general term of a convergent series. We can therefore sum the double series by rows, and we thus obtain for $\phi(m, z)$ a development in power series

$$\phi(m, z) = 1 + \frac{a_1}{1} m + \frac{a_2}{1 \cdot 2} m^2 + \cdots.$$

From the relation (30) and the results established above (§ 11), this series must be identical with that for $e^{a_1 m}$. Now for the coefficient of m we have

$$a_1 = \frac{z}{1} - \frac{z^2}{2} + \frac{z^3}{3} - \cdots = \mathrm{Log}\,(1 + z);$$

hence

$$(34) \qquad\qquad \phi(m, z) = e^{m\,\mathrm{Log}\,(1 + z)},$$

where the determination of the logarithm to be understood is that one which becomes zero when $z = 0$. We can again represent the last expression by $(1 + z)^m$; but in order to know without ambiguity the value in question, it is convenient to make use of the expression $e^{m\,\mathrm{Log}\,(1 + z)}$.

Let $m = \mu + \nu i$; if r and α have the same meanings as in the preceding paragraph, we have

$$e^{m\,\mathrm{Log}\,(1 + z)} = e^{(\mu + \nu i)(\log r + i\alpha)}$$
$$= e^{\mu \log r - \nu \alpha}[\cos(\mu\alpha + \nu \log r) + i \sin(\mu\alpha + \nu \log r)].$$

In conclusion, let us study the series on the circle of convergence. Let U_n be the absolute value of the general term for a point z on the circle. The ratio of two consecutive terms of the series of absolute values is equal to $|(m - n + 1)/n|$, that is, if $m = \mu + \nu i$, to

$$\frac{\sqrt{(\mu + 1 - n)^2 + \nu^2}}{n} = 1 - \frac{\mu + 1}{n} + \frac{\phi(n)}{n^2},$$

where the function $\phi(n)$ remains finite when n increases indefinitely. By a known rule for convergence (I, § 163) this series is convergent when $\mu + 1 > 1$ and divergent in every other case. *The series* (29) *is therefore absolutely convergent at all the points on the circle of convergence when μ is positive.*

If $\mu + 1$ is negative or zero, the absolute value of the general term never decreases, since the ratio U_{n+1}/U_n is never less than unity. *The series is divergent at all the points on the circle when $\mu \leqq -1$.*

It remains to study the case where $-1 < \mu \leqq 0$. Let us consider the series whose general term is U_n^p; the ratio of two consecutive terms is equal to

$$\left[1 - \frac{\mu + 1}{n} + \frac{\phi(n)}{n^2}\right]^p = 1 - \frac{p(\mu + 1)}{n} + \frac{\phi_1(n)}{n^2},$$

and if we choose p large enough so that $p(\mu + 1) > 1$, this series will be convergent. It follows that U_n^p, and consequently the absolute value of the general term U_n, approaches zero. This being the case, in the identity

$$\phi(m, z)(1 + z) = \phi(m + 1, z)$$

let us retain on each side only the terms of degree less than or equal to n; there remains the relation

$$S_n(1 + z) = S_n' + \frac{m(m - 1) \cdots (m - n + 1)}{n!} z^{n+1},$$

where S_n and S_n' indicate respectively the sum of the first $(n + 1)$ terms of $\phi(m, z)$ and of $\phi(m + 1, z)$. If the real part of m lies between -1 and 0, the real part of $m + 1$ is positive. Suppose $|z| = 1$; when the number n increases indefinitely, S_n' approaches a limit, and the last term on the right approaches zero; it follows that S_n also approaches a limit, unless $1 + z = 0$. Therefore, *when $-1 < \mu \leqq 0$, the series is convergent at all the points on the circle of convergence, except at the point $z = -1$.*

III. CONFORMAL REPRESENTATION

19. Geometric interpretation of the derivative. Let $u = X + Yi$ be a function of the complex variable z, analytic within a closed curve C. We shall represent the value of u by the point whose coördinates are X, Y with respect to a system of rectangular axes. To simplify the following statements we shall suppose that the axes OX, OY are parallel respectively to the axes Ox and Oy and arranged in the same order of rotation in the same plane or in a plane parallel to the plane xOy.

When the point z describes the region A bounded by the closed curve C, the point u with the coördinates (X, Y) describes in its plane a region A'; the relation $u = f(z)$ defines then a certain correspondence between the points of the two planes or of two portions of a plane. On account of the relations which connect the derivatives of the functions X, Y, it is clear that this correspondence should possess special properties. We shall now show that *the angles are unchanged.*

Let z and z_1 be two neighboring points of the region A, and u and u_1 the corresponding points of the region A'. By the original definition of the derivative the quotient $(u_1 - u)/(z_1 - z)$ has for its limit $f'(z)$ when the absolute value of $z_1 - z$ approaches zero in any manner whatever. Suppose that the point z_1 approaches the point z along a curve C, whose tangent at the point z makes an angle α with the parallel to the direction Ox; the point u_1 will itself describe a curve C' passing through u. Let us discard the case in which $f'(z)$ is zero, and let ρ and ω be the absolute value and the angle of $f'(z)$ respectively. Likewise let r and r' be the distances zz_1 and uu_1, α' the angle which the direction zz_1 makes with the parallel zx' to Ox, and β' the angle which the direction uu_1 makes with the parallel uX' to OX. The absolute value of the quotient

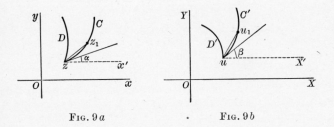

FIG. 9 a   .   FIG. 9 b

$(u_1 - u)/(z_1 - z)$ is equal to r_1/r, and the angle of the quotient is equal to $\beta' - \alpha'$. We have then the two relations

$$(35) \qquad \lim \frac{r_1}{r} = \rho, \qquad \lim (\beta' - \alpha') = \omega + 2\,k\pi.$$

Let us consider only the second of these relations. We may suppose $k = 0$, since a change in k simply causes an increase in the angle ω by a multiple of 2π. When the point z_1 approaches the point z along the curve C, α' approaches the limit α, β' approaches a limit β, and we have $\beta = \alpha + \omega$. That is to say, *in order to obtain the direction of the tangent to the curve described by the point u, it suffices to turn the direction of the tangent to the curve described by z through a constant angle ω.* It is naturally understood in this statement that those directions of the two tangents are made to correspond which correspond to the same sense of motion of the points z and u.

Let D be another curve of the plane xOy passing through the point z, and let D' be the corresponding curve of the plane XOY. If the letters γ and δ denote respectively the angles which the corresponding directions of the tangents to these two curves make with zx' and uX' (Figs. 9 a and 9 b), we have

$$\beta = \alpha + \omega, \qquad \delta = \gamma + \omega,$$

and consequently $\delta - \beta = \gamma - \alpha$. *The curves C' and D' cut each other in the same angle as the curves C and D.* Moreover, we see that the sense of rotation is preserved. It should be noticed that if $f'(z) = 0$, the demonstration no longer applies.

If, in particular, we consider, in one of the two planes xOy or XOY, two families of orthogonal curves, the corresponding curves in the other plane also will form two families of orthogonal curves. For example, the two families of curves $X = C$, $Y = C'$, and the two families of curves

$$(36) \qquad |f(z)| = C, \qquad \text{angle} \, f(z) = C'$$

form orthogonal nets in the plane xOy, for the corresponding curves in the plane XOY are, in the first case, two systems of parallels to the axes of coördinates, and, in the other, circles having the origin for center and straight lines proceeding from the origin.

Example 1. Let $z' = z^\alpha$, where α is a real positive number. Indicating by r and θ the polar coördinates of z, and by r' and θ' the polar coördinates of z', the preceding relation becomes equivalent to the two relations $r' = r^\alpha$, $\theta' = \alpha\theta$. We pass then from the point z to the point z' by raising the radius vector to the power α and by multiplying the angle by α. The angles are preserved, except those which have their vertices at the origin, and these are multiplied by the constant factor α.

Example 2. Let us consider the general linear transformation

$$(37) \qquad\qquad z' = \frac{az + b}{cz + d},$$

where a, b, c, d are any constants whatever. In certain particular cases it is easily seen how to pass from the point z to the point z'. Take for example the transformation $z' = z + b$; let $z = x + yi$, $z' = x' + y'i$, $b = \alpha + \beta i$; the preceding relation gives $x' = x + \alpha$, $y' = y + \beta$, which shows that we pass from the point z to the point z' by a translation.

Let now $z' = az$; if ρ and ω indicate the absolute value and angle of a respectively, then we have $r' = \rho r$, $\theta' = \omega + \theta$. Hence we pass from the point z to the point z' by multiplying the radius vector by the constant factor ρ and then turning this new radius vector through a constant angle ω. We obtain then the transformation defined by the formula $z' = az$ by combining an expansion with a rotation.

Finally, let us consider the relation

$$z' = \frac{1}{z},$$

where r, θ, r', θ' have the same meanings as above. We must have $rr' = 1$, $\theta + \theta' = 0$. The product of the radii vectores is therefore equal to unity, while the polar angles are equal and of opposite signs. Given a circle C with center A and radius R, we shall use the expression *inversion with respect to the given circle* to denote the transformation by which the polar angle is unchanged but the radius vector of the new point is R^2/r. We obtain then the transformation defined by the relation $z'z = 1$ by carrying out first an inversion with respect to a circle of unit radius and with the origin as center, and then taking the symmetric point to the point obtained with respect to the axis Ox.

The most general transformation of the form (37) can be obtained by combining the transformations which we have just studied. If $c = 0$, we can replace the transformation (37) by the succession of transformations

$$z_1 = \frac{a}{d}z, \qquad z' = z_1 + \frac{b}{d}.$$

If c is *not* zero, we can carry out the indicated division and write

$$z' = \frac{a}{c} + \frac{bc - ad}{c^2z + cd},$$

and the transformation can be replaced by the succession of transformations

$$z_1 = z + \frac{d}{c}, \qquad z_2 = c^2z_1, \qquad z_3 = \frac{1}{z_2},$$

$$z_4 = (bc - ad)z_3, \qquad z' = z_4 + \frac{a}{c}.$$

All these special transformations leave the angles and the sense of rotation unchanged, and change circles into circles. Hence the same thing is then true of the general transformation (37), which is therefore often called a *circular transformation*. In the above statement straight lines should be regarded as circles with infinite radii.

Example 3. Let

$$z' = (z - e_1)^{m_1}(z - e_2)^{m_2} \cdots (z - e_p)^{m_p},$$

where $e_1, e_2, \cdots, e_p$ are any quantities whatever, and where the exponents $m_1, m_2, \cdots, m_p$ are any real numbers, positive or negative. Let $M, E_1, E_2, \cdots, E_p$ be the points which represent the quantities $z, e_1, e_2, \cdots, e_p$; let also $r_1, r_2, \cdots, r_p$ denote the distances $ME_1, ME_2, \cdots, ME_p$ and $\theta_1, \theta_2, \cdots, \theta_p$ the angles which $E_1M, E_2M, \cdots, E_pM$ make with the parallels to Ox. The absolute value and the angle of z' are respectively $r_1^{m_1}r_2^{m_2} \cdots r_p^{m_p}$ and $m_1\theta_1 + m_2\theta_2 + \cdots + m_p\theta_p$. Then the two families of curves

$$r_1^{m_1}r_2^{m_2} \cdots r_p^{m_p} = C, \qquad m_1\theta_1 + m_2\theta_2 + \cdots + m_p\theta_p = C'$$

form an orthogonal system. When the exponents $m_1, m_2, \cdots, m_p$ are rational numbers, all the curves are algebraic. If, for example, $p = 2, m_1 = m_2 = 1$, one of the families is composed of Cassinian ovals with two foci, and the second family is a system of equilateral hyperbolas.

20. Conformal transformations in general. The examination of the converse of the proposition which we have just established leads us to treat a more general problem. Two surfaces, Σ, Σ', being given, let us set up between them any point-to-point correspondence whatever (except for certain broad restrictions which will be made later), and let us examine the cases in which the angles are unaltered in that transformation. Let x, y, z be the rectangular coördinates of a point of Σ, and let x', y', z' be the rectangular coördinates of a point of Σ'. We shall suppose the six coördinates x, y, z, x', y', z' expressed as functions of two variable parameters u, v in such a way that corresponding points of the two surfaces correspond to the same pair of values of the parameters u, v:

$$(38) \qquad \Sigma \begin{cases} x = f(u, v), \\ y = \phi(u, v), \\ z = \psi(u, v), \end{cases} \qquad \Sigma' \begin{cases} x' = f'(u, v), \\ y' = \phi'(u, v), \\ z' = \psi'(u, v). \end{cases}$$

Moreover, we shall suppose that the functions f, ϕ, $\cdots$, together with their partial derivatives of the first order, are continuous when the points (x, y, z) and (x', y', z') remain in certain regions of the two surfaces Σ and Σ'. We shall employ the usual notations (I, § 131):

$$(39) \quad \begin{cases} E = S\left(\dfrac{\partial x}{\partial u}\right)^2, & F = S\dfrac{\partial x}{\partial u}\dfrac{\partial x}{\partial v}, & G = S\left(\dfrac{\partial x}{\partial v}\right)^2, \\[2mm] E' = S\left(\dfrac{\partial x'}{\partial u}\right)^2, & F' = S\dfrac{\partial x'}{\partial u}\dfrac{\partial x'}{\partial v}, & G' = S\left(\dfrac{\partial x'}{\partial v}\right)^2, \\[2mm] \multicolumn{3}{c}{ds^2 = E\,du^2 + 2\,F\,du\,dv + G\,dv^2,} \\[1mm] \multicolumn{3}{c}{ds'^2 = E'\,du^2 + 2\,F'\,du\,dv + G'\,dv^2.} \end{cases}$$

Let C and D (Figs. 10 a and 10 b) be two curves on the surface Σ, passing through a point m of that surface, and C' and D' the corresponding curves on the surface Σ' passing through the point m'.

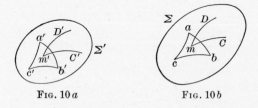

FIG. 10 a FIG. 10 b

Along the curve C the parameters u, v are functions of a single auxiliary variable t, and we shall indicate their differentials by du and dv. Likewise, along D, u and v are functions of a variable t', and we shall denote their differentials here by δu and δv. In general, we shall distinguish by the letters d and δ the differentials relative to a displacement on the curve C and to one on the curve D. The following total differentials are proportional to the direction cosines of the tangent to the curve C,

$$dx = \frac{\partial x}{\partial u} du + \frac{\partial x}{\partial v} dv, \quad dy = \frac{\partial y}{\partial u} du + \frac{\partial y}{\partial v} dv, \quad dz = \frac{\partial z}{\partial u} du + \frac{\partial z}{\partial v} dv,$$

and the following are proportional to the direction cosines of the tangent to the curve D,

$$\delta x = \frac{\partial x}{\partial u} \delta u + \frac{\partial x}{\partial v} \delta v, \quad \delta y = \frac{\partial y}{\partial u} \delta u + \frac{\partial y}{\partial v} \delta v, \quad \delta z = \frac{\partial z}{\partial u} \delta u + \frac{\partial z}{\partial v} \delta v.$$

Let ω be the angle between the tangents to the two curves C and D. The value of $\cos \omega$ is given by the expression

$$\cos \omega = \frac{dx\, \delta x + dy\, \delta y + dz\, \delta z}{\sqrt{dx^2 + dy^2 + dz^2} \sqrt{\delta x^2 + \delta y^2 + \delta z^2}},$$

which can be written, making use of the notation (39), in the form

$$(40) \quad \cos \omega = \frac{E\, du\, \delta u + F(du\, \delta v + dv\, \delta u) + G\, dv\, \delta v}{\sqrt{E\, du^2 + 2 F\, du\, dv + G\, dv^2} \sqrt{E\, \delta u^2 + 2 F\, \delta u\, \delta v + G\, \delta v^2}}.$$

If we let ω' denote the angle between the tangents to the two curves C' and D', we have also

$$(41) \quad \cos \omega' = \frac{E'\, du\, \delta u + F'(du\, \delta v + dv\, \delta u) + G'\, dv\, \delta v}{\sqrt{E'\, du^2 + 2 F'\, du\, dv + G'\, dv^2} \sqrt{E'\, \delta u^2 + 2 F'\, \delta u\, \delta v + G'\, \delta v^2}}.$$

In order that the transformation considered shall not change the value of the angles, it is necessary that $\cos \omega' = \cos \omega$, whatever du, dv, δu, δv may be. The two sides of the equality

$$\cos^2 \omega' = \cos^2 \omega$$

are rational functions of the ratios $\delta v/\delta u$, dv/du, and these functions must be equal whatever the values of these ratios. Hence the corresponding coefficients of the two fractions must be proportional; that is, we must have

$$(42) \qquad \frac{E'}{E} = \frac{F'}{F} = \frac{G'}{G} = \lambda^2,$$

where λ is any function whatever of the parameters u, v. These conditions are evidently also sufficient, for $\cos \omega$, for example, is a homogeneous function of E, F, G, of degree zero.

The conditions (42) can be replaced by a single relation $ds'^2 = \lambda^2 ds^2$, or

$$(43) \qquad ds' = \lambda ds.$$

This relation states that the ratio of two corresponding infinitesimal arcs approach a limit independent of du and of dv, when these two arcs approach zero. This condition makes the reasoning almost intuitive. For, let abc be an infinitesimal triangle on the first surface, and $a'b'c'$ the corresponding triangle on the second surface. Imagine these two curvilinear triangles replaced by rectilinear triangles that approximate them. Since the ratios $a'b'/ab$, $a'c'/ac$, $b'c'/bc$ approach the same limit $\lambda(u, v)$, these two triangles approach similarity and the corresponding angles approach equality.

We see that any two corresponding infinitesimal figures on the two surfaces can be considered as similar, since the lengths of the arcs are proportional and the angles equal; it is on this account that the term *conformal representation* is often given to every correspondence which does not alter the angles.

Given two surfaces Σ, Σ' and a definite relation which establishes a point-to-point correspondence between these two surfaces, we can always determine whether the conditions (42) are satisfied or not, and therefore whether we have a conformal representation of one of the surfaces on the other.

But we may consider other problems. For example, given the surfaces Σ and Σ', we may propose the problem of determining all the correspondences between the points of the two surfaces which preserve the angles. Suppose that the coördinates (x, y, z) of a point of Σ are expressed as functions of two parameters (u, v), and that the coördinates (x', y', z') of a point of Σ' are expressed as functions of two other parameters (u', v'). Let

$$ds^2 = E\,du^2 + 2\,F\,du\,dv + G\,dv^2, \quad ds'^2 = E'\,du'^2 + 2\,F'\,du'\,dv' + G'\,dv'^2$$

be the expressions for the squares of the linear elements. The problem in question amounts to this: *To find two functions* $u' = \pi_1(u, v)$, $v' = \pi_2(u, v)$ *such that we have identically*

$$E'\,d\pi_1^2 + 2\,F'\,d\pi_1\,d\pi_2 + G'\,d\pi_2^2 = \lambda^2(E\,du^2 + 2\,F\,du\,dv + G\,dv^2),$$

λ *being any function of the variables* u, v. The general theory of differential equations shows that this problem always admits an infinite number of solutions; we shall consider only certain special cases.

21. Conformal representation of one plane on another plane. Every correspondence between the points of two planes is defined by relations such as

$$(44) \qquad\qquad X = P(x, y), \qquad Y = Q(x, y),$$

where the two planes are referred to systems of rectangular coördinates (x, y) and (X, Y). From what we have just seen, in order that this transformation shall preserve the angles, it is necessary and sufficient that we have

$$dX^2 + dY^2 = \lambda^2 (dx^2 + dy^2),$$

where λ is any function whatever of x, y independent of the differentials. Developing the differentials dX, dY and comparing the two sides, we find that the two functions $P(x, y)$ and $Q(x, y)$ must satisfy the two relations

(45) $\quad \left(\dfrac{\partial P}{\partial x}\right)^2 + \left(\dfrac{\partial Q}{\partial x}\right)^2 = \left(\dfrac{\partial P}{\partial y}\right)^2 + \left(\dfrac{\partial Q}{\partial y}\right)^2, \quad \dfrac{\partial P}{\partial x}\dfrac{\partial P}{\partial y} + \dfrac{\partial Q}{\partial x}\dfrac{\partial Q}{\partial y} = 0.$

The partial derivatives $\partial P / \partial y$, $\partial Q / \partial y$ cannot both be zero, for the first of the relations (45) would give also $\partial Q / \partial x = \partial P / \partial x = 0$, and the functions P and Q would be constants. Consequently we can write according to the last relation,

$$\frac{\partial P}{\partial x} = \mu\, \frac{\partial Q}{\partial y}, \qquad \frac{\partial Q}{\partial x} = -\, \mu\, \frac{\partial P}{\partial y},$$

where μ is an auxiliary unknown. Putting these values in the first condition (45), it becomes

$$(\mu^2 - 1)\left[\left(\frac{\partial P}{\partial y}\right)^2 + \left(\frac{\partial Q}{\partial y}\right)^2\right] = 0,$$

and from it we derive the result $\mu = \pm 1$. We must then have either

(46) $\qquad \dfrac{\partial P}{\partial x} = \dfrac{\partial Q}{\partial y}, \qquad \dfrac{\partial P}{\partial y} = -\dfrac{\partial Q}{\partial x}$

or

(47) $\qquad \dfrac{\partial P}{\partial x} = -\dfrac{\partial Q}{\partial y}, \qquad \dfrac{\partial P}{\partial y} = \dfrac{\partial Q}{\partial x}.$

The first set of conditions state that $P + Qi$ is an analytic function of $x + yi$. As for the second set, we can reduce it to the first by changing Q to $- Q$, that is, by taking the figure symmetric to the transformed figure with respect to the axis OX. Thus we see, finally, that to every conformal representation of a plane on a plane there corresponds a solution of the system (46), and consequently an analytic function. If we suppose the axes OX and OY parallel respectively to the axes Ox and Oy, the sense of rotation of the angles is preserved or not, according as the functions P and Q satisfy the relations (46) or (47).

22. Riemann's theorem. Given in the plane of the variable z a region A bounded by a single curve (or simple boundary), and in the plane of the variable u a circle C, Riemann proved that there exists an analytic function $u = f(z)$, analytic in the region A, such that to each point of the region A corresponds a point of the circle, and that, conversely, to a point of the circle corresponds one and only one point of A. The function $f(z)$ depends also upon three arbitrary real constants, which we can dispose of in such a way that the center of the circle corresponds to a given point of the region A, while an arbitrarily chosen point on the circumference corresponds to a given point of the boundary of A. We shall not give here the demonstration of this theorem, of which we shall indicate only some examples.

We shall point out only that the circle can be replaced by a half-plane. Thus, let us suppose that, in the plane of u, the circumference passes through the origin; the transformation $u' = 1/u$ replaces that circumference by a straight line, and the circle itself by the portion of the u'-plane situated on one side of the straight line extended indefinitely in both directions.

Example 1. Let $u = z^{1/\alpha}$, where α is real and positive. Consider the portion A of the plane included between the direction Ox and a ray through the origin making an angle of $\alpha\pi$ with Ox ($\alpha \lessgtr 2$). Let $z = re^{i\theta}$, $u = Re^{i\omega}$; we have

$$R = r^{\frac{1}{\alpha}}, \qquad \omega = \frac{\theta}{\alpha}.$$

When the point z describes the portion A of the plane, r varies from 0 to $+\infty$ and θ from 0 to $\alpha\pi$; hence R varies from 0 to $+\infty$ and ω from 0 to π.

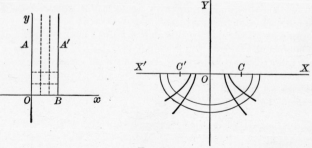

Fig. 11

The point u therefore describes the half-plane situated above the axis OX, and to a point of that half-plane corresponds only one point of A, for we have, inversely, $r = R^\alpha$, $\theta = \alpha\omega$.

Let us next take the portion B of the z-plane bounded by two arcs of circles which intersect. Let z_0, z_1 be the points of intersection; if we carry out first the transformation

$$z' = \frac{z - z_0}{z - z_1},$$

the region B goes over into a portion A of the z'-plane included between two rays from the origin, for along the arc of a circle passing through the points

z_0, z_1, the angle of $(z - z_0)/(z - z_1)$ remains constant. Applying now the pre-ceding transformation $u = (z')^{1/\alpha}$, we see that the function

$$u = \left(\frac{z - z_0}{z - z_1}\right)^{\frac{1}{\alpha}}$$

enables us to realize the conformal representation of the region B on a half-plane by suitably choosing α.

Example 2. Let $u = \cos z$. Let us cause z to describe the infinite half-strip R, or $AOBA'$ (Fig. 11), defined by the inequalities $0 \leqq x \leqq \pi$, $y \geqq 0$, and let us examine the region described by the point $u = X + Yi$. We have here (§ 12)

$$(48) \qquad X = \cos x \frac{e^y + e^{-y}}{2}, \qquad Y = - \sin x \frac{e^y - e^{-y}}{2}.$$

When x varies from 0 to π, Y is always negative and the point u remains in the half-plane below the axis $X'OX$. Hence, to every point of the region R corresponds a point of the u half-plane, and when the point z is on the bound-ary of R, we have $Y = 0$, for one of the two factors $\sin x$ or $(e^y - e^{-y})/2$ is zero. Conversely, to every point of the u half-plane below OX corresponds one and only one point of the strip R in the z-plane. In fact, if z' is a root of the equa-tion $u = \cos z$, all the other roots are included in the expression $2 k\pi \pm z'$. If the coefficient of i in z' is positive, there cannot be but one of these points in the strip R, for all the points $2 k\pi - z'$ are below Ox. There is always one of the points $2 k\pi + z'$ situated in R, for there is always one of these points whose abscissa lies between 0 and 2π. That abscissa cannot be included between π and 2π, for the corresponding value of Y would then be positive. The point is therefore located in R.

It is easily seen from the formulæ (48) that when the point z describes the portion of a parallel to Ox in R, the point u describes half of an ellipse. When the point z describes a parallel to Oy, the point u describes a half-branch of a hyperbola. All these conics have as foci the points C, C' of the axis OX, with the abscissas $+ 1$ and $- 1$.

Example 3. Let

$$(49) \qquad u = \frac{e^{\frac{\pi z}{2a}} - 1}{e^{\frac{\pi z}{2a}} + 1}$$

where a is real and positive. In order that $|u|$ shall be less than unity, it is easy to show that it is necessary and sufficient, that $\cos[(\pi y)/(2 a)] > 0$. If y varies from $- a$ to $+ a$, we see that to the infinite strip included between the two straight lines $y = - a$, $y = + a$ corresponds in the u-plane the circle C described about the origin as center with unit radius. Conversely, to every point of this circle corresponds one and only one point of the infinite strip, for the values of z which correspond to a given value of u form an arithmetical pro-gression with the constant difference of $4 ai$. Hence there cannot be more than one value of z in the strip considered. Moreover, there is always one of these roots in which the coefficient of i lies between $- a$ and $3 a$, and that coefficient cannot lie between a and $3 a$, for the corresponding value of $|u|$ would then be greater than *unity*.

23. Geographic maps. To make a conformal map of a surface means to make the points of the surface correspond to those of a plane in such a way that the angles are unaltered. Suppose that the coördinates of a point of the surface Σ under consideration be expressed as functions of two variable parameters (u, v), and let

$$ds^2 = E\,du^2 + 2\,F\,du\,dv + G\,dv^2$$

be the square of the linear element for this surface. Let (α, β) be the rectangular coördinates of the point of the plane P which corresponds to the point (u, v) of the surface. The problem here is to find two functions

$$u = \pi_1(\alpha, \beta), \qquad v = \pi_2(\alpha, \beta)$$

of such a nature that we have identically

$$E\,du^2 + 2\,F\,du\,dv + G\,dv^2 = \lambda(d\alpha^2 + d\beta^2),$$

where λ is any function whatever of α, β not containing the differentials. This problem admits an infinite number of solutions, which can all be deduced from one of them by means of the conformal transformations, already studied, of one plane on another. Suppose that we actually have at the same time

$$ds^2 = \lambda(d\alpha^2 + d\beta^2), \qquad ds^2 = \lambda'(d\alpha'^2 + d\beta'^2);$$

then we shall also have

$$d\alpha^2 + d\beta^2 = \frac{\lambda'}{\lambda}(d\alpha'^2 + d\beta'^2),$$

so that $\alpha + \beta i$, or $\alpha - \beta i$, will be an analytic function of $\alpha' + \beta' i$. The converse is evident.

Example 1. *Mercator's projection.* We can always make a map of a surface of revolution in such a way that the meridians and the parallels of latitude correspond to the parallels to the axes of coördinates. Thus, let

$$x = \rho\cos\omega, \qquad y = \rho\sin\omega, \qquad z = f(\rho)$$

be the coördinates of a point of a surface of revolution about the axis Oz; we have

$$ds^2 = d\rho^2[1 + f'^2(\rho)] + \rho^2 d\omega^2 = \rho^2\left[d\omega^2 + \frac{1 + f'^2(\rho)}{\rho^2}\,d\rho^2\right],$$

which can be written

$$ds^2 = \rho^2(dX^2 + dY^2)$$

if we set

$$X = \omega, \qquad Y = \int\frac{\sqrt{1 + f'^2(\rho)}}{\rho}\,d\rho.$$

In the case of a sphere of radius R we can write the coördinates in the form

$$x = R \sin \theta \cos \phi, \qquad y = R \sin \theta \sin \phi, \qquad z = R \cos \theta,$$

$$ds^2 = R^2(d\theta^2 + \sin^2 \theta d\phi^2) = R^2 \sin^2 \theta\left(d\phi^2 + \frac{d\theta^2}{\sin^2 \theta}\right),$$

and we shall set

$$X = \phi, \qquad Y = \int \frac{d\theta}{\sin \theta} = \log\left(\tan \frac{\theta}{2}\right).$$

We obtain thus what is called *Mercator's projection*, in which the meridians are represented by parallels to the axis OY, and the parallels of latitude by segments of straight lines parallel to OX. To obtain the whole surface of the sphere it is sufficient to let ϕ vary from 0 to 2π, and θ from 0 to π; then X varies from 0 to 2π and Y from $-\infty$ to $+\infty$. The map has then the appearance of an infinite strip of breadth 2π. The curves on the surface of the sphere which cut the meridians at a constant angle are called *loxodromic curves* or *rhumb lines*, and are represented on the map by straight lines.

Example 2. Stereographic projection. Again, we may write the square of the linear element of the sphere in the form

$$ds^2 = 4 \cos^4 \frac{\theta}{2}\left(\frac{R^2 d\theta^2}{4 \cos^4 \dfrac{\theta}{2}} + R^2 \tan^2 \frac{\theta}{2} d\phi^2\right),$$

or

$$ds^2 = 4 \cos^4 \frac{\theta}{2}(d\rho^2 + \rho^2 d\omega^2),$$

if we set

$$\rho = R \tan \frac{\theta}{2}, \qquad \omega = \phi.$$

But $d\rho^2 + \rho^2 d\omega^2$ represents the square of the linear element of the plane in polar coördinates (ρ, ω); hence it is sufficient, in order to obtain a conformal representation of the sphere, to make a point of the plane with polar coördinates (ρ, ω) correspond to the point (θ, ϕ) of the surface of the sphere. It is seen immediately, on drawing the figure, that ρ and ω are the polar coördinates of the stereographic projection of the point (θ, ϕ) of the sphere on the plane of the equator, the center of projection being one of the poles.*

---

* The center of projection is the south pole if θ is measured from the north pole to the radius. Using the north pole as the center of projection, the point $(R^2/\rho, \omega)$, symmetric to the first point (see Ex. 17, p. 58), would be obtained. — TRANS.

Example 3. *Map of an anchor ring.* Consider the anchor ring generated by the revolution of a circle of radius R about an axis situated in its own plane at a distance a from its center, where $a > R$. Taking the axis of revolution for the axis of z, and the median plane of the anchor ring for the xy-plane, we can write the coördinates of a point of the surface in the form

$$x = (a + R\cos\theta)\cos\phi, \qquad y = (a + R\cos\theta)\sin\phi, \qquad z = R\sin\theta,$$

and it is sufficient to let θ and ϕ vary from $-\pi$ to $+\pi$. From these formulæ we deduce

$$ds^2 = (a + R\cos\theta)^2\left[d\phi^2 + \frac{R^2\,d\theta^2}{(a + R\cos\theta)^2}\right];$$

and, to obtain a map of the surface, we may set

$$X = \phi,$$
$$Y = e\int_0^\theta \frac{d\theta}{1 + e\cos\theta} = \frac{2e}{\sqrt{1-e^2}}\arctan\left(\sqrt{\frac{1-e}{1+e}}\tan\frac{\theta}{2}\right),$$

where

$$e = \frac{R}{a} < 1.$$

Thus the total surface of the anchor ring corresponds point by point to that of a rectangle whose sides are 2π and $2\pi e/\sqrt{1-e^2}$.

24. Isothermal curves. Let $U(x, y)$ be a solution of Laplace's equation

$$\Delta U = \frac{\partial^2 U}{\partial x^2} + \frac{\partial^2 U}{\partial y^2} = 0;$$

the curves represented by the equation

(50) $$U(x, y) = C,$$

where C is an arbitrary constant, form a family of *isothermal* curves. With every solution $U(x, y)$ of Laplace's equation we can associate another solution, $V(x, y)$, such that $U + Vi$ is an analytic function of $x + yi$. The relations

$$\frac{\partial U}{\partial x} = \frac{\partial V}{\partial y}, \qquad \frac{\partial U}{\partial y} = -\frac{\partial V}{\partial x}$$

show that the two families of isothermal curves

$$U(x, y) = C, \qquad V(x, y) = C'$$

are orthogonal, for the slopes of the tangents to the two curves C and C' are respectively

$$-\frac{\partial U}{\partial x} \div \frac{\partial U}{\partial y}, \qquad -\frac{\partial V}{\partial x} \div \frac{\partial V}{\partial y}.$$

Thus the orthogonal trajectories of a family of isothermal curves form another family of isothermal curves. We obtain all the conjugate systems of isothermal curves by considering all analytic functions $f(z)$ and taking the curves for which the real part of $f(z)$ and the coefficient of i have constant values. The curves for which the absolute value R and the angle Ω of $f(z)$ remain constant also form two conjugate isothermal systems; for the real part of the analytic function $\mathrm{Log}\,[f(z)]$ is $\log R$, and the coefficient of i is Ω.

Likewise we obtain conjugate isothermal systems by considering the curves described by the point whose coördinates are X, Y, where $f(z) = X + Yi$, when we give to x and y constant values. This is seen by regarding $x + yi$ as an analytic function of $X + Yi$. More generally, every transformation of the points of one plane on the other, which preserves the angles, changes one family of isothermal curves into a new family of isothermal curves. Let

$$x = p(x', y'), \qquad y = q(x', y')$$

be equations defining a transformation which preserves angles, and let $F(x', y')$ be the result obtained on substituting $p(x', y')$ and $q(x', y')$ for x and y in $U(x, y)$. The proof consists in showing that $F(x', y')$ is a solution of Laplace's equation, provided that $U(x, y)$ is a solution. The verification of this fact does not offer any difficulty (see Vol. I, Chap. III, Ex. 8, 2d ed.; Chap. II, Ex. 9, 1st ed.), but the theorem can be established without any calculation. Thus, we can suppose that the functions $p(x', y')$ and $q(x', y')$ satisfy the relations

$$\frac{\partial p}{\partial x'} = \frac{\partial q}{\partial y'}, \qquad \frac{\partial p}{\partial y'} = -\frac{\partial q}{\partial x'},$$

for a symmetric transformation evidently changes a family of isothermal curves into a new family of isothermal curves. The function $x + yi = p + qi$ is then an analytic function of $z' = x' + y'i$, and, after the substitution, $U + Vi$ also becomes an analytic function $F(x', y') + i\Phi(x', y')$ of the same variable z' (§ 5). Hence the two families of curves

$$F(x', y') = C, \qquad \Phi(x', y') = C'$$

give a new orthogonal net formed by two conjugate isothermal families.

For example, concentric circles and the rays from the center form two conjugate isothermal families, as we see at once by considering the analytic function $\text{Log } z$. Carrying out an inversion, we have the result that the circles passing through two fixed points also form an isothermal system. The conjugate system is also composed of circles.

Likewise, confocal ellipses form an isothermal system. Indeed, we have seen above that the point $u = \cos z$ describes confocal ellipses when the point z is made to describe parallels to the axis Ox (§ 22). The conjugate system is made up of confocal and orthogonal hyperbolas.

Note. In order that a family of curves represented by an equation $P(x, y) = C$ may be isothermal, it is not necessary that the function $P(x, y)$ be a solution of Laplace's equation. Indeed, these curves are represented also by the equation $\phi[P(x, y)] = C$, whatever be the function ϕ; hence it is sufficient to take for the function ϕ a form such that $U(x, y) = \phi(P)$ satisfies Laplace's equation. Making the calculation, we find that we must have

$$\frac{d^2\phi}{dP^2}\left[\left(\frac{\partial P}{\partial x}\right)^2 + \left(\frac{\partial P}{\partial y}\right)^2\right] + \frac{d\phi}{dP}\left(\frac{\partial^2 P}{\partial x^2} + \frac{\partial^2 P}{\partial y^2}\right) = 0 ;$$

hence it is necessary that the quotient

$$\frac{\dfrac{\partial^2 P}{\partial x^2} + \dfrac{\partial^2 P}{\partial y^2}}{\left(\dfrac{\partial P}{\partial x}\right)^2 + \left(\dfrac{\partial P}{\partial y}\right)^2}$$

depend only on P, and if that condition is satisfied, the function ϕ can be obtained by two quadratures.

EXERCISES

1. Determine the analytic function $f(z) = X + Yi$ whose real part X is equal to
$$\frac{2 \sin 2x}{e^{2y} + e^{-2y} - 2 \cos 2x}.$$
Consider the same question, given that $X + Y$ is equal to the preceding function.

2. Let $\phi(m, p) = 0$ be the tangential equation of a real algebraic curve, that is to say, the condition that the straight line $y = mx + p$ be tangent to that curve. The roots of the equation $\phi(i, -zi) = 0$ are the real foci of the curve.

3. If p and q are two integers prime to each other, the two expressions $(\sqrt[q]{z})^p$ and $\sqrt[q]{z^p}$ are equivalent. What happens when p and q have a greatest common divisor $d > 1$?

4. Find the absolute value and the angle of e^{x+yi} by considering it as the limit of the polynomial $[1 + (x + yi)/m]^m$ when the integer m increases indefinitely.

5. Prove the formulæ
$$\cos a + \cos(a + b) + \cdots + \cos(a + nb) = \frac{\sin\left(\frac{n+1}{2}b\right)}{\sin\left(\frac{b}{2}\right)} \cos\left(a + \frac{nb}{2}\right),$$

$$\sin a + \sin(a + b) + \cdots + \sin(a + nb) = \frac{\sin\left(\frac{n+1}{2}b\right)}{\sin\left(\frac{b}{2}\right)} \sin\left(a + \frac{nb}{2}\right).$$

6. What is the final value of arc $\sin z$ when the variable z describes the segment of a straight line from the origin to the point $1 + i$, if the initial value of arc $\sin z$ is taken as 0?

7. Prove the continuity of a power series by means of the formula (12) (§ 8)
$$f(z + h) - f(z) = hf_1(z) + \frac{h^2}{2!}f_2(z) + \cdots + \frac{h^n}{n!}f_n(z) + \cdots.$$
[Take a suitable dominant function for the series of the right-hand side.]

8. Calculate the integrals
$$\int x^m e^{ax} \cos bx\, dx, \qquad \int x^m e^{ax} \sin bx\, dx,$$
$$\int \operatorname{ctn}(x - a) \operatorname{ctn}(x - b) \cdots \operatorname{ctn}(x - l)\, dx.$$

9. Given in the plane xOy a closed curve C having any number whatever of double points and described in a determined sense, a numerical coefficient is assigned to each region of the plane determined by the curve according to the rule of Volume I (§ 97, 2d ed.; § 96, 1st ed.). Thus, let R, R' be two contiguous regions separated by the arc ab of the curve described in the sense of a to b; the coefficient of the region to the left is greater by unity than the coefficient of the region to the right, and the region exterior to the curve has the coefficient 0.

Let z_0 be a point taken in one of the regions and N the corresponding coefficient. Prove that $2N\pi$ represents the variation of the angle of $z - z_0$ when the point z describes the curve C in the sense chosen.

10. By studying the development of $\mathrm{Log}\,[(1 + z)/(1 - z)]$ on the circle of convergence, prove that the sum of the series

$$\frac{\sin\theta}{1} + \frac{\sin 3\,\theta}{3} + \frac{\sin 5\,\theta}{5} + \cdots + \frac{\sin (2\,n + 1)\,\theta}{2\,n + 1} + \cdots$$

is equal to $\pm\,\pi/4$, according as $\sin\theta \gtrless 0$. (Cf. Vol. I, § 204, 2d ed.; § 198, 1st ed.)

11. Study the curves described by the point $Z = z^2$ when the point z describes a straight line or a circle.

12. The relation $2Z = z + c^2/z$ effects the conformal representation of the region inclosed between two confocal ellipses on the ring-shaped region bounded by two concentric circles.

[Take, for example, $z = Z + \sqrt{Z^2 - c^2}$, make in the Z-plane a straight-line cut $(- c, c)$, and choose for the radical a positive value when Z is real and greater than c.]

13. Every circular transformation $z' = (az + b)/(cz + d)$ can be obtained by the combination of an *even* number of inversions. Prove also the converse.

14. Every transformation defined by the relation $z' = (az_0 + b)/(cz_0 + d)$, where z_0 indicates the conjugate of z, results from an *odd* number of inversions. Prove also the converse.

15. Fuchsian transformations. Every linear transformation (§ 19, Ex. 2) $z' = (az + b)/(cz + d)$, where a, b, c, d are real numbers satisfying the relation $ad - bc = 1$, is called a *Fuchsian transformation*. Such a transformation sets up a correspondence such that to every point z situated above Ox corresponds a point z' situated on the same side of Ox'.

The two definite integrals

$$\int \frac{\sqrt{dx^2 + dy^2}}{y}, \qquad \iint \frac{dx\,dy}{y^2}$$

are *invariants* with respect to all these transformations.

The preceding transformation has two double points which correspond to the roots α, β of the equation $cz^2 + (d - a)z - b = 0$. If α and β are real and distinct, we can write the equation $z' = (az + b)/(cz + d)$ in the equivalent form

$$\frac{z' - \alpha}{z' - \beta} = k\,\frac{z - \alpha}{z - \beta}$$

where k is real. Such a transformation is called *hyperbolic*.

If α and β are conjugate imaginaries, we can write the equation

$$\frac{z' - \alpha}{z' - \beta} = e^{i\omega}\frac{z - \alpha}{z - \beta},$$

where ω is real. Such a transformation is called *elliptic*.

If $\beta = \alpha$, we can write

$$\frac{1}{z' - \alpha} = \frac{1}{z - \alpha} + k,$$

where α and k are real. Such a transformation is called *parabolic*.

16. Let $z' = f(z)$ be a Fuchsian transformation. Put

$$z_1 = f(z), \qquad z_2 = f(z_1), \qquad \cdots, \qquad z_n = f(z_{n-1}).$$

Prove that all the points $z, z_1, z_2, \cdots, z_n$ are on the circumference of a circle. Does the point z_n approach a limiting position as n increases indefinitely?

17. Given a circle C with the center O and radius R, two points M, M' situated on a ray from the center O are said to be *symmetric* with respect to that circle if $OM \times OM' = R^2$.

Let now C, C' be two circles in the same plane and M any point whatever in that plane. Take the point M_1 symmetric to M with respect to the circle C, then the point M_1' symmetric to M_1 with respect to C', then the point M_2 symmetric to M_1' with respect to C, and so on forever. Study the distribution of the points M_1, M_1', M_2, M_2', $\cdots$.

18. Find the analytic function $Z = f(z)$ which enables us to pass from Mercator's projection to the stereographic projection.

19*. All the isothermal families composed of circles are made up of circles passing through two fixed points, distinct or coincident, real or imaginary.

[Setting $z = x + yi, z_0 = x - yi$, the equation of a family of circles depending upon a single parameter λ may be written in the form

$$zz_0 + az + bz_0 + c = 0,$$

where a, b, c are functions of the parameter λ. In order that this family be isothermal, it is necessary that $\partial^2 \lambda / \partial z \partial z_0 = 0$. Making the calculation, the theorem stated is proved.]

20*. If $|q| < 1$, we have the identity

$$(1 + q)(1 + q^2) \cdots (1 + q^n) \cdots = \frac{1}{(1 - q)(1 - q^3) \cdots (1 - q^{2n+1}) \cdots},$$

. . . .

[EULER.]

[In order to prove this, transform the infinite product on the left into an infinite product with two indices by putting in the first row the factors $1 + q$, $1 + q^2$, $1 + q^4$, $\cdots$, $1 + q^{2n}$, $\cdots$; in the second row the factors $1 + q^3$, $1 + q^6$, $\cdots$, $1 + (q^3)^{2n}$, $\cdots$; and then apply the formula (16) of the text.]

21. Develop in powers of z the infinite products

$$F(z) = (1 + xz)(1 + x^2z) \cdots (1 + x^nz) \cdots,$$
$$\Phi(z) = (1 + xz)(1 + x^3z) \cdots (1 + x^{2n+1}z) \cdots.$$

[It is possible, for example, to make use of the relation

$$F(xz)(1 + xz) = F(z), \qquad \Phi(x^2z)(1 + xz) = \Phi(z).]$$

22*. Supposing $|x| < 1$, prove Euler's formula

$$(1 - x)(1 - x^2)(1 - x^3) \cdots (1 - x^n) \cdots$$
$$= 1 - x - x^2 + x^5 - x^7 + x^{12} - \cdots + x^{\frac{3n^2-n}{2}} - x^{\frac{3n^2+n}{2}} + \cdots.$$

(See J. BERTRAND, *Calcul différentiel*, p. 328.)

23*. Given a sphere of unit radius, the stereographic projection of that sphere is made on the plane of the equator, the center of projection being one of the poles. To a point M of the sphere is made to correspond the complex number $s = x + yi$, where x and y are the rectangular coördinates of the projection m of M with respect to two rectangular axes of the plane of the equator, the origin being the center of the sphere. To two diametrically opposite points of the sphere correspond two complex numbers, $s, -1/s_0$, where s_0 is the conjugate imaginary to s. Every linear transformation of the form

$$\text{(A)} \qquad \frac{s' - \alpha}{s' - \beta} = e^{i\omega}\frac{s - \alpha}{s - \beta},$$

where $\beta\alpha_0 + 1 = 0$, defines a rotation of the sphere about a diameter. To groups of rotations which make a regular polyhedron coincide with itself correspond the groups of finite order of linear substitutions of the form (A). (See KLEIN, *Das Ikosaeder*.)

CHAPTER II

THE GENERAL THEORY OF ANALYTIC FUNCTIONS ACCORDING TO CAUCHY

I. DEFINITE INTEGRALS TAKEN BETWEEN IMAGINARY LIMITS

25. Definitions and general principles. The results presented in the preceding chapter are independent of the work of Cauchy and, for the most part, prior to that work. We shall now make a systematic study of analytic functions, and determine the logical consequences of the definition of such functions. Let us recall that a function $f(z)$ is analytic in a region A : 1) if to every point taken in the region A corresponds a definite value of $f(z)$; 2) if that value varies continuously with z; 3) if for every point z taken in A the quotient

$$\frac{f(z+h)-f(z)}{h}$$

approaches a limit $f'(z)$ when the absolute value of h approaches zero.

The consideration of definite integrals, when the variable passes through a succession of complex values, is due to Cauchy [*]; it was the origin of new and fruitful methods.

Let $f(z)$ be a continuous function of z along the curve AMB (Fig. 12). Let us mark off on this curve a certain number of points of division $z_0, z_1, z_2, \cdots, z_{n-1}, z'$, which follow each other in the order of increasing indices when the arc is traversed from A to B, the points z_0 and z' coinciding with the extremities A and B.

Let us take next a second series of points $\zeta_1, \zeta_2, \cdots, \zeta_n$ on the arc AB, the point ζ_k being situated on the arc $z_{k-1}z_k$, and let us consider the sum

$$S = f(\zeta_1)(z_1 - z_0) + f(\zeta_2)(z_2 - z_1) + \cdots$$
$$+ f(\zeta_k)(z_k - z_{k-1}) + \cdots + f(\zeta_n)(z' - z_{n-1}).$$

When the number of points of division $z_1, \cdots, z_{n-1}$ increases indefinitely in such a way that the absolute values of all the differences

---

[*] *Mémoire sur les intégrales définies, prises entre des limites imaginaires*, 1825. This memoir is reprinted in Volumes VII and VIII of the *Bulletin des Sciences mathématiques* (1st series).

$z_1 - z_0$, $z_2 - z_1$, $\cdots$ become and remain smaller than any positive number arbitrarily chosen, the sum S approaches a limit, which is called the definite integral of $f(z)$ taken along AMB and which is represented by the symbol

$$\int_{(AMB)} f(z)\, dz.$$

To prove this, let us separate the real part and the coefficient of i in S, and let us set

$$f(z) = X + Yi, \qquad z_k = x_k + y_k i, \qquad \zeta_k = \xi_k + \eta_k i,$$

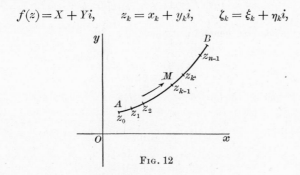

FIG. 12

where X and Y are continuous functions along AMB. Uniting the similar terms, we can write the sum S in the form

$$
\begin{aligned}
S = {}& X(\xi_1, \eta_1)(x_1 - x_0) + \cdots \\
& + X(\xi_k, \eta_k)(x_k - x_{k-1}) + \cdots + X(\xi_n, \eta_n)(x' - x_{n-1}) \\
& - [\, Y(\xi_1, \eta_1)(y_1 - y_0) + \cdots + Y(\xi_k, \eta_k)(y_k - y_{k-1}) + \cdots] \\
& + i[X(\xi_1, \eta_1)(y_1 - y_0) + \cdots] + i\,[\, Y(\xi_1, \eta_1)(x_1 - x_0) + \cdots].
\end{aligned}
$$

When the number of divisions increases indefinitely, the sum of the terms in the same row has for its limit a line integral taken along AMB, and the limit of S is equal to the sum of four line integrals:*

$$\int_{(AMB)} f(z)\, dz = \int_{(AMB)} (X dx - Y dy) + i \int_{(AMB)} (Y dx + X dy).$$

---

* In order to avoid useless complications in the proofs, we suppose that the coördinates x, y of a point of the arc AMB are continuous functions $x = \phi\,(t)$, $y = \psi\,(t)$ of a parameter t, which have only a finite number of maxima and minima between A and B. We can then break up the path of integration into a finite number of arcs which are each represented by an equation of the form $y = F(x)$, the function F being continuous between the corresponding limits; or into a finite number of arcs which are each represented by an equation of the form $x = G(y)$. There is no disadvantage in making this hypothesis, for in all the applications there is always a certain amount of freedom in the choice of the path of integration. Moreover, it would suffice to suppose that $\phi\,(x)$ and $\psi\,(x)$ are functions of limited variation. We have seen that in this case the curve AMB is then rectifiable (I, ftns., §§ 73, 82, 95, 2d ed.).

From the definition it results immediately that

$$\int_{(AMB)} f(z)\,dz + \int_{(BMA)} f(z)\,dz = 0.$$

It is often important to know an upper bound for the absolute value of an integral. Let s be the length of the arc AM, L the length of the arc AB, s_{k-1}, s_k, σ_k the lengths of the arcs Az_{k-1}, Az_k, $A\zeta_k$ of the path of integration. Setting $F(s) = |f(z)|$, we have

$$|f(\zeta_k)(z_k - z_{k-1})| = F(\sigma_k)\,|z_k - z_{k-1}| \leqq F(\sigma_k)(s_k - s_{k-1}),$$

for $|z_k - z_{k-1}|$ represents the length of the chord, and $s_k - s_{k-1}$ the length of the arc. Hence the absolute value of S is less than or at most equal to the sum $\Sigma\, F(\sigma_k)(s_k - s_{k-1})$; whence, passing to the limit, we find

$$\left| \int_{(AMB)} f(z)\,dz \right| \leqq \int_0^L F(s)\,ds.$$

Let M be an upper bound for the absolute value of $f(z)$ along the curve AB. It is clear that the absolute value of the integral on the right is less than ML, and we have, a fortiori,

$$\left| \int_{(AMB)} f(z)\,dz \right| < ML.$$

26. Change of variables. Let us consider the case that occurs frequently in applications, in which the coördinates x, y of a point of the arc AB are continuous functions of a variable parameter t, $x = \phi(t)$, $y = \psi(t)$, possessing continuous derivatives $\phi'(t)$, $\psi'(t)$; and let us suppose that the point (x, y) describes the path of integration from A to B as t varies from α to β. Let $P(t)$ and $Q(t)$ be the functions of t obtained by substituting $\phi(t)$ and $\psi(t)$, respectively, for x and y in X and Y.

By the formula established for line integrals (I, § 95, 2d ed.; § 93, 1st ed.) we have

$$\int_{(AB)} X\,dx - Y\,dy = \int_\alpha^\beta [P(t)\,\phi'(t) - Q(t)\,\psi'(t)]\,dt,$$

$$\int_{(AB)} X\,dy + Y\,dx = \int_\alpha^\beta [P(t)\,\psi'(t) + Q(t)\,\phi'(t)]\,dt.$$

Adding these two relations, after having multiplied the two sides of the second by i, we obtain

$$(1) \qquad \int_{(AB)} f(z)\,dz = \int_\alpha^\beta [P(t) + iQ(t)][\phi'(t) + i\psi'(t)]\,dt.$$

This is precisely the result obtained by applying to the integral $\int f(z)\,dz$ the formula established for definite integrals in the case of real functions of real variables; that is, in order to calculate the integral $\int f(z)\,dz$ we need only substitute $\phi(t) + i\psi(t)$ for z and $[\phi'(t) + i\psi'(t)]dt$ for dz in $f(z)\,dz$. The evaluation of $\int f(z)\,dz$ is thus reduced to the evaluation of two ordinary definite integrals. If the path AMB is composed of several pieces of distinct curves, the formula should be applied to each of these pieces separately.

Let us consider, for example, the definite integral

$$\int_{-1}^{+1} \frac{dz}{z^2}.$$

We cannot integrate along the axis of reals, since the function to be integrated becomes infinite for $z = 0$, but we can follow any path whatever which does not pass through the origin. Let z describe a semicircle of unit radius about the origin as center. This path is given by setting $z = e^{ti}$ and letting t vary from π to 0. Then the integral takes the form

$$\int_{-1}^{+1} \frac{dz}{z^2} = \int_{\pi}^{0} ie^{-ti}dt = i\int_{\pi}^{0} \cos t\,dt + \int_{\pi}^{0} \sin t\,dt = -2.$$

This is precisely the result that would be obtained by substituting the limits of integration directly in the primitive function $-1/z$ according to the fundamental formula of the integral calculus (I, § 78, 2d ed.; § 76, 1st ed.).

More generally, let $z = \phi(u)$ be a continuous function of a new complex variable $u = \xi + \eta i$ such that, when u describes in its plane a path CND, the variable z describes the curve AMB. To the points of division of the curve AMB correspond on the curve CND the points of division $u_0, u_1, u_2, \cdots, u_{k-1}, u_k, \cdots, u'$. If the function $\phi(u)$ possesses a derivative $\phi'(u)$ along the curve CND, we can write

$$\frac{z_k - z_{k-1}}{u_k - u_{k-1}} = \phi'(u_{k-1}) + \epsilon_k,$$

where ϵ_k approaches zero when u_k approaches u_{k-1} along the curve CND. Taking $\zeta_{k-1} = z_{k-1}$ and replacing $z_k - z_{k-1}$ by the expression derived from the preceding equality, the sum S, considered above, becomes

$$S = \sum_{k=1}^{n} f(z_{k-1})\,\phi'(u_{k-1})\,(u_k - u_{k-1}) + \sum_{k=1}^{n} \epsilon_k f(z_{k-1})\,(u_k - u_{k-1}).$$

The first part of the right-hand side has for its limit the definite integral

$$\int_{(CND)} f[\phi(u)]\,\phi'(u)\,du.$$

As for the remaining term, its absolute value is smaller than $\eta ML'$, where η is a positive number greater than each of the absolute values $|\epsilon_k|$ and where L' is the length of the curve CND. If the points of division can be taken so close that all the absolute values $|\epsilon_k|$ will be less than an arbitrarily chosen positive number, the remaining term will approach zero, and the general formula for the change of variable will be

$$(2) \qquad \int_{(AMB)} f(z)\, dz = \int_{(CND)} f[\phi(u)]\, \phi'(u)\, du.$$

This formula is always applicable when $\phi(u)$ is an analytic function; in fact, it will be shown later that the derivative of an analytic function is also an analytic function* (see § 34).

27. The formulæ of Weierstrass and Darboux. The proof of the law of the mean for integrals (I, § 76, 2d ed.; § 74, 1st ed.) rests upon certain inequalities which cease to have a precise meaning when applied to complex quantities. Weierstrass and Darboux, however, have obtained some interesting results in this connection by considering integrals taken along a segment of the axis of reals. We have seen above that the case of any path whatever can be reduced to this particular case, provided certain mild restrictions are placed upon the path of integration.

Let I be a definite integral of the following form:

$$I = \int_\alpha^\beta f(t)[\phi(t) + i\psi(t)]\, dt,$$

---

* If this property is admitted, the following proposition can easily be proved.

Let $f(z)$ be an analytic function in a finite region A of the plane. For every positive number ϵ another positive number η can be found such that

$$\left|\frac{f(z+h)-f(z)}{h} - f'(z)\right| < \epsilon,$$

when z and $z+h$ are two points of A whose distance from each other $|h|$ is less than η.

For, let $f(z) = P(x, y) + iQ(x, y)$, $h = \Delta x + i\Delta y$. From the calculation made in § 3, to find the conditions for the existence of a unique derivative, we can write

$$\frac{f(z+h)-f(z)}{h} - f'(z) = \frac{[P'_x(x+\theta\Delta x, y) - P'_x(x, y)]\Delta x}{\Delta x + i\Delta y}$$
$$+ \frac{[P'_y(x+\Delta x, y+\theta\Delta y) - P'_y(x, y)]\Delta y}{\Delta x + i\Delta y}$$
$$+ \cdots\cdots\cdots\cdots\cdots\cdots\cdots\cdots$$

Since the derivatives P'_x, P'_y, Q'_x, Q'_y are continuous in the region A, we can find a number η such that the absolute values of the coefficients of Δx and of Δy are less than $\epsilon/4$, when $\sqrt{\Delta x^2 + \Delta y^2}$ is less than η. Hence the inequality written down above will be satisfied if we have $|h| < \eta$. This being the case, if the function $\phi(u)$ is analytic in the region A, all the absolute values $|\epsilon_k|$ will be smaller than a given positive number ϵ, provided the distance between two consecutive points of division of the curve CND is less than the corresponding number η, and the formula (2) will be established.

where $f(t)$, $\phi(t)$, $\psi(t)$ are three real functions of the real variable t continuous in the interval (α, β). From the very definition of the integral we evidently have

$$I = \int_\alpha^\beta f(t)\,\phi(t)\,dt + i\int_\alpha^\beta f(t)\,\psi(t)\,dt.$$

Let us suppose, for definiteness, that $\alpha < \beta$; then $t - \alpha$ is the length of the path of integration measured from α, and the general formula which gives an upper bound for the absolute value of a definite integral becomes

$$|I| \leqq \int_\alpha^\beta |f(t)\,[\phi(t) + i\psi(t)]|\,dt,$$

or, supposing that $f(t)$ is positive between α and β,

$$|I| \leqq \int_\alpha^\beta f(t)\,|\phi(t) + i\psi(t)|\,dt.$$

Applying the law of the mean to this new integral, and indicating by ξ a value of t lying between α and β, we have also

$$|I| \leqq |\phi(\xi) + i\psi(\xi)|\int_\alpha^\beta f(t)\,dt.$$

Setting $F(t) = \phi(t) + i\psi(t)$, this result may also be written in the form

(3) $$I = \lambda F(\xi)\int_\alpha^\beta f(t)\,dt,$$

where λ is a complex number *whose absolute value is less than or equal to unity;* this is Darboux's formula.

To Weierstrass is due a more precise expression, which has a relation to some elementary facts of statics. When t varies from α to β, the point with the coördinates $x = \phi(t)$, $y = \psi(t)$ describes a certain curve L. Let (x_0, y_0), (x_1, y_1), $\cdots$, (x_{k-1}, y_{k-1}), $\cdots$ be the points of L which correspond to the values α, t_1, $\cdots$, t_{k-1}, $\cdots$ of t; and let us set

$$X = \frac{\Sigma\phi(t_{k-1}).f(t_{k-1})(t_k - t_{k-1})}{\Sigma f(t_{k-1})(t_k - t_{k-1})},$$

$$Y = \frac{\Sigma\psi(t_{k-1}).f(t_{k-1})(t_k - t_{k-1})}{\Sigma f(t_{k-1})(t_k - t_{k-1})}.$$

According to a known theorem, X and Y are the coördinates of the center of gravity of a system of masses placed at the points (x_0, y_0), (x_1, y_1), $\cdots$, (x_{k-1}, y_{k-1}), $\cdots$ of the curve L, the mass placed at the point (x_{k-1}, y_{k-1}) being equal to $f(t_{k-1})(t_k - t_{k-1})$, where $f(t)$ is still supposed to be positive. It is clear that the center of gravity lies within every closed convex curve C that envelops the curve L. When the number of intervals increases indefinitely, the point (X, Y) will have for its limit a point whose coördinates (u, v) are given by the equations

$$u = \frac{\int_\alpha^\beta f(t)\,\phi(t)\,dt}{\int_\alpha^\beta f(t)\,dt}, \qquad v = \frac{\int_\alpha^\beta f(t)\,\psi(t)\,dt}{\int_\alpha^\beta f(t)\,dt},$$

which is itself within the curve C. We can state these two formulæ as one by writing

$$(4) \qquad I = (u + iv) \int_\alpha^\beta f(t)\,dt = Z \int_\alpha^\beta f(t)\,dt,$$

where Z is a point of the complex plane *situated within every closed convex curve enveloping the curve L*. It is clear that, in the general case, the factor Z of Weierstrass is limited to a much more restricted region than the factor $\lambda F(\xi)$ of Darboux.

28. Integrals taken along a closed curve. In the preceding paragraphs, it suffices to suppose that $f(z)$ is a continuous function of the complex variable z along the path of integration. We shall now suppose also that $f(z)$ is an analytic function, and we shall first consider how the value of the definite integral is affected by the path followed by the variable in going from A to B.

If a function $f(z)$ is analytic within a closed curve and also on the curve itself, the integral $\int f(z)\,dz$, taken around that curve, is equal to zero.

In order to demonstrate this fundamental theorem, which is due to Cauchy, we shall first establish several lemmas:

1) The integrals $\int dz$, $\int z\,dz$, taken along any closed curve whatever, are zero. In fact, by definition, the integral $\int dz$, taken along any path whatever between the two points a, b, is equal to $b - a$, and the integral is zero if the path is closed, since then $b = a$. As for the integral $\int z\,dz$, taken along any curve whatever joining two points a, b, if we take successively $\zeta_k = z_{k-1}$, then $\zeta_k = z_k$ (§ 25), we see that the integral is also the limit of the sum

$$\sum_i \frac{z_i(z_{i+1} - z_i) + z_{i+1}(z_{i+1} - z_i)}{2} = \sum_i \frac{z_{i+1}^2 - z_i^2}{2} = \frac{b^2 - a^2}{2};$$

hence it is equal to zero if the curve is closed.

2) If the region bounded by any curve C whatever be divided into smaller parts by transversal curves drawn arbitrarily, the sum of the integrals $\int f(z)\,dz$ taken in the same sense along the boundary

of each of these parts is equal to the integral $\int f(z)\,dz$ taken along
the complete boundary C. It is clear that each portion of the auxiliary curves separates two contiguous regions and must be described
twice in integration in opposite senses. Adding all these integrals, there will remain then only the integrals taken along the
boundary curve, whose sum is the integral $\int_{(C)}f(z)\,dz$.

Let us now suppose that the region A is divided up, partly in
smaller regular parts, which shall be squares having their sides
parallel to the axes Ox, Oy; partly in irregular parts, which shall be
portions of squares of which the remaining part lies beyond the
boundary C. These squares need not necessarily be equal. For example, we might suppose that two sets of parallels to Ox and Oy
have been drawn, the distance between two neighboring parallels
being constant and equal to l; then some of the squares thus obtained
might be divided up into smaller squares by new parallels to the
axes. Whatever may be the manner of subdivision adopted, let us
suppose that there are N regular parts and N' irregular parts; let
us number the regular parts in any order whatever from 1 to N, and
the irregular parts from 1 to N'. Let l_i be the length of the side of
the ith square and l_k' that of the square to which the kth irregular
part belongs, L the length of the boundary C, and $\mathcal{A}$ the area of a
polygon which contains within it the curve C.

Let $abcd$ be the ith square (Fig. 13), let z_i be a point taken in its
interior or on one of its sides, and let z be any point on its boundary.
Then we have

$$(5) \qquad \frac{f(z)-f(z_i)}{z-z_i}=f'(z_i)+\epsilon_i,$$

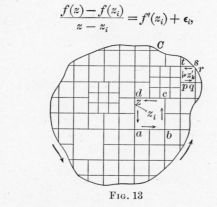

Fig. 13

where $|\epsilon_i|$ is small, provided that the side of the square is itself
small. It follows that

$$f(z)=zf'(z_i)+f(z_i)-z_if'(z_i)+\epsilon_i(z-z_i),$$

$$\int_{(c_i)} f(z)\,dz = f'(z_i) \int_{(c_i)} z\,dz + [f(z_i) - z_i f'(z_i)] \int_{(c_i)} dz + \int_{(c_i)} \epsilon_i (z - z_i)\,dz,$$

where the integrals are to be taken along the perimeter c_i of the square. By the first lemma stated above, this reduces to the form

(6) $$\int_{(c_i)} f(z)\,dz = \int_{(c_i)} \epsilon_i (z - z_i)\,dz.$$

Again, let $pqrst$ be the kth irregular part, let z_k' be a point taken in its interior or on its perimeter, and let z be any point of its perimeter. Then we have, as above,

(7) $$\frac{f(z) - f(z_k')}{z - z_k'} = f'(z_k') + \epsilon_k',$$

where ϵ_k' is infinitesimal at the same time as l_k'; whence we find

(8) $$\int_{(c_k')} f(z)\,dz = \int_{(c_k')} \epsilon_k' (z - z_k')\,dz.$$

Let η be a positive number greater than the absolute values of all the factors ϵ_i and ϵ_k'. The absolute value of $z - z_i$ is less than $l_i \sqrt{2}$; hence, by (6), we find

$$\left| \int_{(c_i)} f(z)\,dz \right| < 4\,l_i^2 \eta\,\sqrt{2} = 4\,\eta\,\sqrt{2}\,\omega_i,$$

where ω_i denotes the area of the ith regular part. From (8) we find, in the same way,

$$\left| \int_{(c_k')} f(z)\,dz \right| < \eta l_k'\,\sqrt{2}\,(4\,l_k' + \text{arc } rs) = 4\,\eta\,\sqrt{2}\,\omega_k' + \eta l_k'\,\sqrt{2}\,\text{arc } rs,$$

where ω_k' is the area of the square which contains the kth irregular part. Adding all these integrals, we obtain, a fortiori, the inequality

(9) $$\left| \int_{(C)} f(z)\,dz \right| < \eta \left[4\,\sqrt{2}\,(\Sigma \omega_i + \Sigma \omega_k') + \lambda\,\sqrt{2}\,L \right],$$

where λ is an upper bound for the sides l_k'. When the number of squares is increased indefinitely in such a way that all the sides l_i and l_k' approach zero, the sum $\Sigma \omega_i + \Sigma \omega_k'$ finally becomes less than A. On the right-hand side of the inequality (9) we have, then, the product of a factor which remains finite and another factor η which can be supposed smaller than any given positive number. This can be true only if the left-hand side is zero; we have then

$$\int_{(C)} f(z)\,dz = 0.$$

29. In order that the preceding conclusion may be legitimate, we must make sure that we can take the squares so small that the absolute values of all the quantities ϵ_i, ϵ_k' will be less than a positive number η given in advance, if the points z_i and z_k' are suitably chosen.* We shall say for brevity that a region bounded by a closed curve γ, situated in a region of the plane inclosed by the curve C, satisfies the condition (α) with respect to the number η if it is possible to find in the interior of the curve γ or on the curve itself a point z' such that we always have

$$(\alpha) \qquad |f(z) - f(z') - (z - z')f'(z')| \leqq |z - z'|\,\eta,$$

when z describes the curve γ. The proof depends on showing that *we can choose the squares so small that all the parts considered, regular and irregular, satisfy the condition (α) with respect to the number η.*

We shall establish this new lemma by the well-known process of successive subdivisions. Suppose that we have first drawn two sets of parallels to the axes Ox, Oy, the distance between two adjacent parallels being constant and equal to l. Of the parts obtained, some may satisfy the condition (α), while others do not. Without changing the parts which do satisfy the condition (α), we shall divide the others into smaller parts by joining the middle points of the opposite sides of the squares which form these parts or which inclose them. If, after this new operation, there are still parts which do not satisfy the condition (α), we will repeat the operation on those parts, and so on. Continuing in this way, there can be only two cases : either we shall end by having only regions which satisfy the condition (α), in which case the lemma is proved ; or, however far we go in the succession of operations, we shall always find some parts which do not satisfy that condition.

In the latter case, in at least one of the regular or irregular parts obtained by the first division, the process of subdivision just described never leads us to a set of regions all of which satisfy the condition (α) ; let A_1 be such a part. After the second subdivision, the part A_1 contains at least one subdivision A_2 which cannot be subdivided into regions all of which satisfy the condition (α). Since it is possible to continue this reasoning indefinitely, we shall have a succession of regions

$$A_1, A_2, A_3, \cdots, A_n, \cdots$$

which are squares, or portions of squares, such that each is included in the preceding, and whose dimensions approach zero as n becomes infinite. There is, therefore, a limit point z_0 situated in the interior of the curve or on the curve itself. Since, by hypothesis, the function $f(z)$ possesses a derivative $f'(z_0)$ for $z = z_0$, we can find a number ρ such that

$$|f(z) - f(z_0) - (z - z_0)f'(z_0)| \leqq \eta|z - z_0|,$$

provided that $|z - z_0|$ is less than ρ. Let c be the circle with radius ρ described about the point z_0 as center. For large enough values of n, the region A_n will lie within the circle c, and we shall have for all the points of the boundary of A_n

$$|f(z) - f(z_0) - (z - z_0)f'(z_0)| \leqq |z - z_0|\,\eta.$$

---

* GOURSAT, *Transactions of the American Mathematical Society*, 1900, Vol. I, p. 14.

Moreover, it is clear that the point z_0 is in the interior of A_n or on the boundary; hence that region must satisfy the condition (α) with respect to η. We are therefore led to a contradiction in supposing that the lemma is not true.

30. By means of a suitable convention as to the sense of integration the theorem can be extended also to boundaries formed by several distinct closed curves. Let us consider, for example, a function $f(z)$ analytic within the region A bounded by the closed curve C and the two interior curves C', C'', and on these curves themselves (Fig. 14). The complete boundary Γ of the region A is formed by these three distinct curves, and we shall say that that boundary is described in the positive sense if the region A is on the left hand with respect to this sense of motion; the arrows on the figure indicate the positive sense of description for each of the curves. With this agreement, we have always

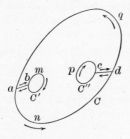

Fig. 14

$$\int_{(\Gamma)} f(z)\,dz = 0,$$

the integral being taken along the complete boundary in the positive sense. The proof given for a region with a simple boundary can be applied again here; we can also reduce this case to the preceding by drawing the transversals ab, cd and by applying the theorem to the closed curve $abmbandcpcdqa$ (I, § 153).

It is sometimes convenient in the applications to write the preceding formula in the form

$$\int_{(C)} f(z)\,dz = \int_{(C')} f(z)\,dz + \int_{(C'')} f(z)\,dz,$$

where the three integrals are now taken in the same sense; that is, the last two must be taken in the reverse direction to that indicated by the arrows.

Let us return to the question proposed at the beginning of § 28; the answer is now very easy. Let $f(z)$ be an analytic function in a region A of the plane. Given two paths AMB, ANB, having the same extremities and lying entirely in that region, they will give the same value for the integral $\int f(z)\,dz$ if the function $f(z)$ is analytic within the closed curve formed by the path AMB followed by the path BNA. We shall suppose, for definiteness, that that closed curve does not have any double points. Indeed, since the sum of the two integrals along AMB and along BNA is zero, the two integrals along AMB and along ANB must be equal. We can state this result again as follows : *Two paths AMB and ANB, having the same extremities, give the same value for the integral $\int f(z)\,dz$ if we can pass from one to the other by a continuous deformation without encountering any point where the function ceases to be analytic.*

This statement holds true even when the two paths have any number whatever of common points besides the two extremities (I, § 152). From this we conclude that, when $f(z)$ is analytic in a region bounded by *a single* closed curve, the integral $\int f(z)\,dz$ is equal to zero when taken along any closed curve whatever situated in that region. But we must not apply this result to the case of a region bounded by several distinct closed curves. Let us consider, for example, a function $f(z)$ analytic in the ring-shaped region between two concentric circles C, C'. Let C'' be a circle having the same center and lying between C and C' ; the integral $\int f(z)\,dz$, taken along C'', is not in general zero. Cauchy's theorem shows only that the value of that integral remains the same when the radius of the circle C'' is varied.*

---

* Cauchy's theorem remains true without any hypothesis upon the existence of the function $f(z)$ beyond the region A limited by the curve C, or upon the existence of a derivative at each point of the curve C itself. It is sufficient that the function $f(z)$ shall be analytic at every point of the region A, and *continuous on the boundary* C, that is, that the value $f(Z)$ of the function in a point Z of C varies continuously with the position of Z on that boundary, and that the difference $f(Z) - f(z)$, where z is an interior point, approaches zero uniformly with $|Z - z|$. In fact, let us first suppose that every straight line from a fixed point a of A meets the boundary in a single point. When the point z describes C, the point $a + \theta\,(z - a)$ (where θ is a real number between 0 and 1) describes a closed curve C' situated in A. The difference between the two integrals, along the curves C and C', is equal to

$$\delta = \int_{(C)} \{f(z) - \theta f[z - (z - a)\,(1 - \theta)]\}\,dz,$$

and we can take the difference $1 - \theta$ so small that $|\delta|$ will be less than any given positive number, for we can write the function under the integral sign in the form

$$f(z) - f[z - (z - a)\,(1 - \theta)] + (1 - \theta) f[z - (z - a)\,(1 - \theta)].$$

Since the integral along C' is zero, we have, then, also

$$\int_{(C)} f(z)\,dz = 0.$$

In the case of a boundary of any form whatever, we can replace this boundary by a succession of closed curves that fulfill the preceding condition by drawing suitably placed transversals.

31. Generalization of the formulæ of the integral calculus. Let $f(z)$ be an analytic function in the region A limited by a simple boundary curve C. The definite integral

$$\Phi(Z) = \int_{z_0}^{Z} f(z)\,dz,$$

taken from a fixed point z_0 up to a variable point Z along a path lying in the region A, is, from what we have just seen, a definite function of the upper limit Z. We shall now show that this function $\Phi(Z)$ is also an analytic function of Z whose derivative is $f(Z)$. For let $Z + h$ be a point near Z; then we have

$$\Phi(Z + h) - \Phi(Z) = \int_{Z}^{Z+h} f(z)\,dz,$$

and we may suppose that this last integral is taken along the segment of a straight line joining the two points Z and $Z + h$. If the two points are very close together, $f(z)$ differs very little from $f(Z)$ along that path, and we can write

$$f(z) = f(Z) + \delta,$$

where $|\delta|$ is less than any given positive number η, provided that $|h|$ is small enough. Hence we have, after dividing by h,

$$\frac{\Phi(Z + h) - \Phi(Z)}{h} = f(Z) + \frac{1}{h} \int_{Z}^{Z+h} \delta\,dz.$$

The absolute value of the last integral is less than $\eta |h|$, and therefore the left-hand side has for its limit $f(Z)$ when h approaches zero.

If a function $F(Z)$ whose derivative is $f(Z)$ is already known, the two functions $\Phi(Z)$ and $F(Z)$ differ only by a constant (footnote, p. 38), and we see that the fundamental formula of integral calculus can be extended to the case of complex variables:

$$(10) \qquad \int_{z_0}^{z_1} f(z)\,dz = F(z_1) - F(z_0).$$

This formula, established by supposing that the two functions $f(z)$, $F(z)$ were analytic in the region A, is applicable in more general cases. It may happen that the function $F(z)$, or both $f(z)$ and $F(z)$ at the same time, are multiple-valued; the integral has a precise meaning if the path of integration does not pass through any of the critical points of these functions. In the application of the formula it will be necessary to pick out an initial determination $F(z_0)$ of the primitive function, and to follow the continuous variation of that function when the variable z describes the path of integration. Moreover, if $f(z)$ is itself a multiple-valued function, it will be necessary to choose, among the determinations of $F(z)$, that one whose derivative is equal to the determination chosen for $f(z)$.

Whenever the path of integration can be inclosed within a region with a simple boundary, in which the branches of the two functions $f(z)$, $F(z)$ under consideration are analytic, the formula may be regarded as demonstrated. Now in any case, whatever may be the path of integration, we can break it up into several pieces for which the preceding condition is satisfied, and apply the formula (10) to each of them separately. Adding the results, we see that the formula is true in general, provided that we apply it with the necessary precautions.

Let us, for example, calculate the definite integral $\int_{z_0}^{z_1} z^m \, dz$, taken along any path whatever not passing through the origin, where m is a real or a complex number different from -1. One primitive function is $z^{m+1}/(m+1)$, and the general formula (10) gives

$$\int_{z_0}^{z_1} z^m \, dz = \frac{z_1^{m+1} - z_0^{m+1}}{m+1}.$$

In order to remove the ambiguity present in this formula when m is not an integer, let us write it in the form:

$$\int_{z_0}^{z_1} z^m \, dz = \frac{e^{(m+1)\,\mathrm{Log}\,(z_1)} - e^{(m+1)\,\mathrm{Log}\,(z_0)}}{m+1}.$$

The initial value $\mathrm{Log}\,(z_0)$ having been chosen, the value of z^m is thereby fixed along the whole path of integration, as is also the final value $\mathrm{Log}\,(z_1)$. The value of the integral depends both upon the initial value chosen for $\mathrm{Log}\,(z_0)$ and upon the path of integration. Similarly, the formula

$$\int_{z_0}^{z_1} \frac{f'(z)}{f(z)} \, dz = \mathrm{Log}\,[f(z_1)] - \mathrm{Log}\,[f(z_0)]$$

does not present any difficulty in interpretation if the function $f(z)$ is continuous and does not vanish along the path of integration. The point $u = f(z)$ describes in its plane an arc of a curve not passing through the origin, and the right-hand side is equal to the variation of $\mathrm{Log}\,(u)$ along this arc. Finally, we may remark in passing that the formula for integration by parts, since it is a consequence of the formula (10), can be extended to integrals of functions of a complex variable.

32. Another proof of the preceding results. The properties of the integral $\int f(z)\,dz$ present a great analogy to the properties of line integrals when the condition for integrability is fulfilled (I, § 152). Riemann has shown, in fact, that Cauchy's theorem results immediately from the analogous theorem relative to line integrals. Let $f(z) = X + Yi$ be an analytic function of z within a region A with a simple boundary; the integral taken along a closed curve C lying in that region is the sum of two line integrals:

$$\int_{(C)} f(z)\,dz = \int_{(C)} X\,dx - Y\,dy + i\int_{(C)} Y\,dx + X\,dy,$$

and, from the relations which connect the derivatives of the functions X, Y,

$$\frac{\partial X}{\partial x} = \frac{\partial Y}{\partial y}, \qquad \frac{\partial X}{\partial y} = -\frac{\partial Y}{\partial x},$$

we see that both of these line integrals are zero * (I, § 152).

It follows that the integral $\int_{z_0}^{z} f(z)\,dz$, taken from a fixed point z_0 to a variable point z, is a single-valued function $\Phi(z)$ in the region A. Let us separate the real part and the coefficient of i in that function:

$$\Phi(z) = P(x, y) + iQ(x, y),$$

$$P(x, y) = \int_{(x_0, y_0)}^{(x, y)} X\,dx - Y\,dy, \qquad Q(x, y) = \int_{(x_0, y_0)}^{(x, y)} Y\,dx + X\,dy.$$

The functions P and Q have partial derivatives,

$$\frac{\partial P}{\partial x} = X, \qquad \frac{\partial P}{\partial y} = -Y, \qquad \frac{\partial Q}{\partial x} = Y, \qquad \frac{\partial Q}{\partial y} = X,$$

which satisfy the conditions

$$\frac{\partial P}{\partial x} = \frac{\partial Q}{\partial y}, \qquad \frac{\partial P}{\partial y} = -\frac{\partial Q}{\partial x}.$$

Consequently, $P + Qi$ is an analytic function of z whose derivative is $X + Yi$ or $f(z)$.

If the function $f(z)$ is discontinuous at a certain number of points of A, the same thing will be true of one or more of the functions X, Y, and the line integrals $P(x, y)$, $Q(x, y)$ will in general have periods that arise from loops described about points of discontinuity (I, § 153). The same thing will then be true of the integral $\int_{z_0}^{z} f(z)\,dz$. We shall resume the study of these periods, after having investigated the nature of the singular points of $f(z)$.

---

* It should be noted that Riemann's proof assumes the continuity of the derivatives $\partial X/\partial x$, $\partial Y/\partial y$, $\cdots$; that is, of $f'(z)$.

To give at least one example of this, let us consider the integral $\int_1^z dz/z$. After separating the real part and the coefficient of i, we have

$$\int_1^z \frac{dz}{z} = \int_{(1,0)}^{(x,y)} \frac{dx + idy}{x + iy} = \int_{(1,0)}^{(x,y)} \frac{x\,dx + y\,dy}{x^2 + y^2} + i \int_{(1,0)}^{(x,y)} \frac{x\,dy - y\,dx}{x^2 + y^2}.$$

The real part is equal to $[\log (x^2 + y^2)]/2$, whatever may be the path followed. As for the coefficient of i, we have seen that it has the period 2π; it is equal to the angle through which the radius vector joining the origin to the point (x, y) has turned. We thus find again the various determinations of $\mathrm{Log}\,(z)$.

II. CAUCHY'S INTEGRAL.   TAYLOR'S AND LAURENT'S SERIES.   SINGULAR POINTS.   RESIDUES

We shall now present a series of new and important results, which Cauchy deduced from the consideration of definite integrals taken between imaginary limits.

33. The fundamental formula.   Let $f(z)$ be an analytic function in the finite region A limited by a boundary Γ, composed of one or of several distinct closed curves, and continuous on the boundary itself. If x is a point * of the region A, the function

$$\frac{f(z)}{z - x}$$

is analytic in the same region, except at the point $z = x$.

With the point x as center, let us describe a circle γ with the radius ρ, lying entirely in the region A; the preceding function is then analytic in the region of the plane limited by the boundary Γ and the circle γ, and we can apply to it the general theorem (§ 28). Suppose, for definiteness, that the boundary Γ is composed of two closed curves C, C' (Fig. 15).   Then we have

$$\int_{(C)} \frac{f(z)\,dz}{z - x} = \int_{(C')} \frac{f(z)\,dz}{z - x} + \int_{(\gamma)} \frac{f(z)\,dz}{z - x},$$

where the three integrals are taken in the sense indicated by the arrows.   We can write this in the form

$$\int_{(\Gamma)} \frac{f(z)\,dz}{z - x} = \int_{(\gamma)} \frac{f(z)\,dz}{z - x},$$

---

* In what follows we shall often have to consider several complex quantities at the same time. We shall denote them indifferently by the letters $x, z, u, \cdots$. Unless it is expressly stated, the letter x will no longer be reserved to denote a real variable.

where the integral $\int_{(\Gamma)}$ denotes the integral taken along the total boundary Γ in the positive sense. If the radius ρ of the circle γ is very small, the value of $f(z)$ at any point of this circle differs very little from $f(x)$:

$$f(z) = f(x) + \delta,$$

where $|\delta|$ is very small. Replacing $f(z)$ by this value, we find

$$(11) \qquad \int_{(\Gamma)} \frac{f(z)\,dz}{z-x} = f(x) \int_{(\gamma)} \frac{dz}{z-x} + \int_{(\gamma)} \frac{\delta\,dz}{z-x}.$$

The first integral of the right-hand side is easily evaluated; if we put $z = x + \rho e^{\theta i}$, it becomes

$$\int_{(\gamma)} \frac{dz}{z-x} = \int_0^{2\pi} \frac{i\rho e^{\theta i}\,d\theta}{\rho e^{\theta i}} = 2\,\pi i.$$

The second integral $\int_{(\gamma)} \delta\,dz/(z-x)$ is therefore independent of the radius ρ of the circle γ; on the other hand, if $|\delta|$ remains less than

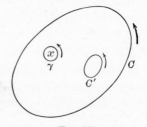

FIG. 15

a positive number η, the absolute value of this integral is less than $(\eta/\rho)\,2\,\pi\rho = 2\,\pi\eta$. Now, since the function $f(z)$ is continuous for $z = x$, we can choose the radius ρ so small that η also will be as small as we wish. Hence this integral must be zero. Dividing the two sides of the equation (11) by $2\,\pi i$, we obtain

$$(12) \qquad f(x) = \frac{1}{2\,\pi i} \int_{(\Gamma)} \frac{f(z)\,dz}{z-x}.$$

This is Cauchy's fundamental formula. It expresses the value of the function $f(z)$ at any point x whatever within the boundary by means of the values of the same function taken only along that boundary.

Let $x + \Delta x$ be a point near x, which, for example, we shall suppose lies in the interior of the circle γ of radius ρ. Then we have also

$$f(x + \Delta x) = \frac{1}{2\,\pi i} \int_{(\Gamma)} \frac{f(z)\,dz}{z - x - \Delta x},$$

and consequently, subtracting the sides of (12) from the corresponding sides of this equation and dividing by Δx, we find

$$\frac{f(x + \Delta x) - f(x)}{\Delta x} = \frac{1}{2\pi i} \int_{(\Gamma)} \frac{f(z)\, dz}{(z - x)(z - x - \Delta x)}.$$

When Δx approaches zero, the function under the integral sign approaches the limit $f(z)/(z - x)^2$. In order to prove rigorously that we have the right to apply the usual formula for differentiation, let us write the integral in the form

$$\int_{(\Gamma)} \frac{f(z)\, dz}{(z - x)(z - x - \Delta x)} = \int_{(\Gamma)} \frac{f(z)\, dz}{(z - x)^2} + \int_{(\Gamma)} \frac{\Delta x\, f(z)\, dz}{(z - x)^2 (z - x - \Delta x)}.$$

Let M be an upper bound for $|f(z)|$ along Γ, L the length of the boundary, and δ a lower bound for the distance of any point whatever of the circle γ to any point whatever of Γ. The absolute value of the last integral is less than $ML|\Delta x|/\delta^3$ and consequently approaches zero with $|\Delta x|$. Passing to the limit, we obtain the result

$$(13) \qquad f'(x) = \frac{1}{2\pi i} \int_{(\Gamma)} \frac{f(z)\, dz}{(z - x)^2}.$$

It may be shown in the same way that the usual method of differentiation under the integral sign can be applied to this new integral * and to all those which can be deduced from it, and we obtain successively

$$f''(x) = \frac{2!}{2\pi i} \int_{(\Gamma)} \frac{f(z)\, dz}{(z - x)^3}, \qquad f'''(x) = \frac{3!}{2\pi i} \int_{(\Gamma)} \frac{f(z)\, dz}{(z - x)^4},$$

and, in general,

$$(14) \qquad f^{(n)}(x) = \frac{n!}{2\pi i} \int_{(\Gamma)} \frac{f(z)\, dz}{(z - x)^{n+1}}.$$

Hence, if a function $f(z)$ is analytic in a certain region of the plane, the sequence of successive derivatives of that function is unlimited, and all these derivatives are also analytic functions in the same region. It is to be noticed that we have arrived at this result by assuming only the existence of the first derivative.

Note. The reasoning of this paragraph leads to more general conclusions. Let $\phi(z)$ be a continuous function (but not necessarily

---

* The general formula for differentiation under the integral sign will be established later (Chapter V).

analytic) of the complex variable z along the curve Γ, closed or not. The integral

$$F(x) = \int_{(\Gamma)} \frac{\phi(z)\,dz}{z - x}$$

has a definite value for every value of x that does not lie on the path of integration. The evaluations just made prove that the limit of the quotient $[F(x + \Delta x) - F(x)]/\Delta x$ is the definite integral

$$F'(x) = \int_{(\Gamma)} \frac{\phi(z)\,dz}{(z - x)^2},$$

when $|\Delta x|$ approaches zero. Hence $F(x)$ is an analytic function for every value of x, except for the points of the curve Γ, which are in general singular points for that function (see § 90). Similarly, we find that the nth derivative $F^{(n)}(x)$ has for its value

$$F^{(n)}(x) = n! \int_{(\Gamma)} \frac{\phi(z)\,dz}{(z - x)^{n+1}}.$$

34. Morera's theorem. A converse of Cauchy's fundamental theorem which was first proved by Morera may be stated as follows : *If a function $f(z)$ of a complex variable z is continuous in a region A, and if the definite integral $\int_{(C)} f(z)\,dz$, taken along any closed curve C lying in A, is zero, then $f(z)$ is an analytic function in A.*

For the definite integral $F(z) = \int_{z_0}^{z} f(t)\,dt$, taken between the two points z_0, z of the region A along any path whatever lying in that region, has a definite value independent of the path. If the point z_0 is supposed fixed, the integral is a function of z. The reasoning of § 31 shows that the quotient $\Delta F/\Delta z$ has $f(z)$ for its limit when Δz approaches zero. Hence the function $F(z)$ is an analytic function of z having $f(z)$ for its derivative, and that derivative is therefore also an analytic function.

35. Taylor's series. *Let $f(z)$ be an analytic function in the interior of a circle with the center a ; the value of that function at any point x within the circle is equal to the sum of the convergent series*

$$(15) \quad \begin{cases} f(x) = f(a) + \dfrac{x - a}{1} f'(a) \\[2mm] \quad + \dfrac{(x - a)^2}{2!} f''(a) + \cdots + \dfrac{(x - a)^n}{n!} f^{(n)}(a) + \cdots. \end{cases}$$

In the demonstration we can suppose that the function $f(z)$ is analytic on the circumference of the circle itself ; in fact, if x is any point in the interior of the circle C, we can always find a circle C', with center a and with a radius less than that of C, which contains the point x within it, and we would reason with the circle C' just as we are about to do with the circle C. With this understanding, x being an interior point of C, we have, by the fundamental formula,

$$(12') \qquad f(x) = \frac{1}{2\pi i} \int_{(C)} \frac{f(z)}{z-x}\, dz.$$

Let us now write $1/(z-x)$ in the following way:

$$\frac{1}{z-x} = \frac{1}{z-a-(x-a)} = \frac{1}{z-a}\left(\frac{1}{1-\dfrac{x-a}{z-a}}\right),$$

or, carrying out the division up to the remainder of degree $n+1$ in $x-a$,

$$\frac{1}{z-x} = \frac{1}{z-a} + \frac{x-a}{(z-a)^2} + \frac{(x-a)^2}{(z-a)^3} + \cdots$$
$$+ \frac{(x-a)^n}{(z-a)^{n+1}} + \frac{(x-a)^{n+1}}{(z-x)(z-a)^{n+1}}.$$

Let us replace $1/(z-x)$ in the formula $(12')$ by this expression, and let us bring the factors $x-a$, $(x-a)^2$, $\cdots$, independent of z, outside of the integral sign. This gives

$$f(x) = J_0 + J_1(x-a) + \cdots + J_n(x-a)^n + R_n,$$

where the coefficients J_0, J_1, $\cdots$, J_n and the remainder R_n have the values

$$(16) \quad \begin{cases} J_0 = \dfrac{1}{2\pi i} \displaystyle\int_{(C)} \dfrac{f(z)\,dz}{z-a}, & J_1 = \dfrac{1}{2\pi i} \displaystyle\int_{(C)} \dfrac{f(z)\,dz}{(z-a)^2}, & \cdots, \\[3mm] J_n = \dfrac{1}{2\pi i} \displaystyle\int_{(C)} \dfrac{f(z)\,dz}{(z-a)^{n+1}}, & R_n = \dfrac{1}{2\pi i} \displaystyle\int_{(C)} \left(\dfrac{x-a}{z-a}\right)^{n+1} \dfrac{f(z)\,dz}{z-x}. \end{cases}$$

As n becomes infinite the remainder R_n approaches zero. For let M be an upper bound for the absolute value of $f(z)$ along the circle C, R the radius of that circle, and r the absolute value of $x-a$. We have $|z-x| \geqq R-r$, and therefore $|1/(z-x)| \leqq 1/(R-r)$, when z describes the circle C. Hence the absolute value of R_n is less than

$$\frac{1}{2\pi}\left(\frac{r}{R}\right)^{n+1} \frac{M}{R-r}\, 2R\pi = \frac{MR}{R-r}\left(\frac{r}{R}\right)^{n+1},$$

and the factor $(r/R)^{n+1}$ approaches zero as n becomes infinite. From this it follows that $f(x)$ is equal to the convergent series

$$f(x) = J_0 + J_1(x-a) + \cdots + J_n(x-a)^n + \cdots.$$

Now, if we put $x = a$ in the formulæ (12), (13), (14), the boundary Γ being here the circle C, we find

$$J_0 = f(a), \qquad J_1 = f'(a), \qquad \cdots, \qquad J_n = \frac{f^{(n)}(a)}{n!}, \qquad \cdots.$$

The series obtained is therefore identical with the series (15); that is, with Taylor's series.

The circle C is a circle with center a, in the interior of which the function is analytic; it is clear that we would obtain the greatest circle satisfying that condition by taking for radius the distance from the point a to that singular point of $f(z)$ nearest a. This is also the circle of convergence for the series on the right.*

This important theorem brings out the identity of the two definitions for analytic functions which we have given (I, § 197, 2d ed.; § 191, 1st ed.; and II, § 3). In fact, every power series represents an analytic function inside of its circle of convergence (§ 8); and, conversely, as we have just seen, every function analytic in a circle with the center a can be developed in a power series proceeding according to powers of $x - a$ and convergent inside of that circle. Let us also notice that a certain number of results previously established become now almost intuitive; for example, applying the theorem to the functions $\text{Log}\,(1 + z)$ and $(1 + z)^m$, which are analytic inside of the circle of unit radius with the origin as center, we find again the formulæ of §§ 17 and 18.

Let us now consider the quotient of two power series $f(x)/\phi(x)$, each convergent in a circle of radius R. If the series $\phi(x)$ does not vanish for $x = 0$, since it is continuous we can describe a circle of radius $r \leqq R$ in the whole interior of which it does not vanish. The function $f(x)/\phi(x)$ is therefore analytic in this circle of radius r and can therefore be developed in a power series in the neighborhood of the origin (I, § 188, 2d ed.; § 183, 1st ed.). In the same way, the theorem relative to the substitution of one series in another series can be proved, etc.

Note. Let $f(z)$ be an analytic function in the interior of a circle C with the center a and the radius r and continuous on the circle itself. The absolute value $|f(z)|$ of the function on the circle is a continuous function, the maximum value of which we shall indicate by $\mathcal{M}(r)$. On the other hand, the coefficient a_n of $(x - a)^n$ in the

---

* This last conclusion requires some explanation on the nature of singular points, which will be given in the chapter devoted to analytic extension.

development of $f(z)$ is equal to $f^{(n)}(a)/n!$, that is, to

$$\frac{1}{2\pi i}\int_{(C)}\frac{f(z)\,dz}{(z-a)^{n+1}};$$

we have, then,

(17) $A_n = |a_n| < \dfrac{1}{2\pi}\dfrac{\mathscr{M}(r)}{r^{n+1}}2\pi r = \dfrac{\mathscr{M}(r)}{r^n},$

so that $\mathscr{M}(r)$ is greater than all the products $A_n r^n$.* We could use $\mathscr{M}(r)$ instead of M in the expression for the dominant function (I, § 186, 2d ed.; § 181, 1st ed.).

36. Liouville's theorem. If the function $f(x)$ is analytic for every finite value of x, then Taylor's expansion is valid, whatever a may be, in the whole extent of the plane, and the function considered is called an *integral function*. From the expressions obtained for the coefficients we easily derive the following proposition, due to Liouville:

Every integral function whose absolute value is always less than a fixed number M is a constant.

For let us develop $f(x)$ in powers of $x - a$, and let a_n be the coefficient of $(x - a)^n$. It is clear that $\mathscr{M}(r)$ is less than M, whatever may be the radius r, and therefore $|a_n|$ is less than M/r^n. But the radius r can be taken just as large as we wish; we have, then, $a_n = 0$ if $n \geqq 1$, and $f(x)$ reduces to a constant $f(a)$.

More generally, let $f(x)$ be an integral function such that the absolute value of $f(x)/x^m$ remains less than a fixed number M for values of x whose absolute value is greater than a positive number R; then *the function $f(x)$ is a polynomial of degree not greater than m.* For suppose we develop $f(x)$ in powers of x, and let a_n be the coefficient of x^n. If the radius r of the circle C is greater than R, we have $\mathscr{M}(r) < Mr^m$, and consequently $|a_n| < Mr^{m-n}$. If $n > m$, we have then $a_n = 0$, since Mr^{m-n} can be made smaller than any given number by choosing r large enough.

37. Laurent's series. The reasoning by which Cauchy derived Taylor's series is capable of extended generalizations. Thus, let $f(z)$ be an analytic function in the ring-shaped region between the

---

* The inequalities (17) are interesting, especially since they establish a relation between the order of magnitude of the coefficients of a power series and the order of magnitude of the function; $\mathscr{M}(r)$ is not, in general, however, the smallest number which satisfies these inequalities, as is seen at once when all the coefficients a_n are real and positive. These inequalities (17) can be established without making use of Cauchy's integral (MÉRAY, *Leçons nouvelles sur l'analyse infinitésimale*, Vol. I, p. 99).

two concentric circles C, C' having the common center a. We shall show that *the value $f(x)$ of the function at any point x taken in that region is equal to the sum of two convergent series, one proceeding in positive powers of $x - a$, the other in positive powers of $1/(x - a)$.*[*]

We can suppose, just as before, that the function $f(z)$ is analytic on the circles C, C' themselves. Let R, R' be the radii of these circles and r the absolute value of $x - a$; if C' is the interior circle, we have $R' < r < R$. About x as center let us describe a small circle γ lying entirely between C and C'. We have the equality

$$\int_{(C)} \frac{f(z)\,dz}{z - x} = \int_{(C')} \frac{f(z)\,dz}{z - x} + \int_{(\gamma)} \frac{f(z)\,dz}{z - x},$$

the integrals being taken in a suitable sense; the last integral, taken along γ, is equal to $2\pi i f(x)$, and we can write the preceding relation in the form

$$(18) \qquad f(x) = \frac{1}{2\pi i} \int_{(C)} \frac{f(z)\,dz}{z - x} + \frac{1}{2\pi i} \int_{(C')} \frac{f(z)\,dz}{x - z},$$

where the integrals are all taken in the same sense.

Repeating the reasoning of § 35, we find again that we have

$$(19) \qquad \frac{1}{2\pi i} \int_{(C)} \frac{f(z)\,dz}{z - x} = J_0 + J_1(x - a) + \cdots + J_n(x - a)^n + \cdots,$$

where the coefficients $J_0, J_1, \cdots, J_n, \cdots$ are given by the formulæ (16). In order to develop the second integral in a series, let us notice that

$$\frac{1}{x - z} = \frac{1}{x - a}\left(\frac{1}{1 - \dfrac{z - a}{x - a}}\right) = \frac{1}{x - a} + \frac{z - a}{(x - a)^2} + \cdots$$
$$+ \frac{(z - a)^{n-1}}{(x - a)^n} + \frac{(z - a)^n}{(x - z)(x - a)^n},$$

and that the integral of the complementary term,

$$\frac{1}{2\pi i} \int_{(C')} \left(\frac{z - a}{x - a}\right)^n \frac{f(z)}{x - z}\,dz,$$

approaches zero when n increases indefinitely. In fact, if M' is the maximum of the absolute value of $f(z)$ along C', the absolute value of this integral is less than

$$\frac{1}{2\pi}\left(\frac{R'}{r}\right)^n \frac{M'}{r - R'}\, 2\pi R' = \frac{M'R'}{r - R'}\left(\frac{R'}{r}\right)^n,$$

---

[*] *Comptes rendus de l'Académie des Sciences*, Vol. XVII. See *Œuvres de Cauchy*, 1st series, Vol. VIII, p. 115.

and the factor R'/r is less than unity. We have, then, also

$$(20) \quad \frac{1}{2\pi i}\int_{(C')}\frac{f(z)\,dz}{x-z}=\frac{K_1}{x-a}+\frac{K_2}{(x-a)^2}+\cdots+\frac{K_n}{(x-a)^n}+\cdots,$$

where the coefficient K_n is equal to the definite integral

$$(21) \quad K_n=\frac{1}{2\pi i}\int_{(C')}(z-a)^{n-1}f(z)\,dz.$$

Adding the two developments (19) and (20), we obtain the proposed development of $f(x)$.

In the formulæ (16) and (21), which give the coefficients J_n and K_n, we can take the integrals along any circle Γ whatever lying between C and C' and having the point a for center, for the functions under the integral sign are analytic in the ring. Hence, if we agree to let the index n vary from $-\infty$ to $+\infty$, we can write the development of $f(x)$ in the form

$$(22) \quad f(x)=\sum_{n=-\infty}^{+\infty}J_n(x-a)^n,$$

where the coefficient J_n, whatever the sign of n, is given by the formula

$$(23) \quad J_n=\frac{1}{2\pi i}\int_{(\Gamma)}\frac{f(z)\,dz}{(z-a)^{n+1}}.$$

Example. The same function $f(x)$ can have developments which are entirely different, according to the region considered. Let us take, for example, a rational fraction $f(x)$, of which the denominator has only simple roots with different absolute values. Let $a, b, c, \cdots, l$ be these roots arranged in the order of increasing absolute values. Disregarding the integral part, which does not interest us here, we have

$$f(x)=\frac{A}{x-a}+\frac{B}{x-b}+\frac{C}{x-c}+\cdots+\frac{L}{x-l}.$$

In the circle of radius a about the origin as center, each of the simple fractions can be developed in positive powers of x, and the development of $f(x)$ is identical with that given by Maclaurin's expansion

$$f(x)=-\left(\frac{A}{a}+\cdots+\frac{L}{l}\right)-\left(\frac{A}{a^2}+\cdots+\frac{L}{l^2}\right)x-\cdots-\left(\frac{A}{a^{n+1}}+\cdots+\frac{L}{l^{n+1}}\right)x^n-\cdots.$$

In the ring between the two circles of radii $|a|$ and $|b|$ the fractions $1/(x-b)$, $1/(x-c), \cdots, 1/(x-l)$ can be developed in positive powers of x, but $1/(x-a)$ must be developed in positive powers of $1/x$, and we have

$$f(x)=-\left(\frac{B}{b}+\cdots+\frac{L}{l}\right)-\left(\frac{B}{b^2}+\cdots+\frac{L}{l^2}\right)x-\cdots$$
$$-\left(\frac{B}{b^{n+1}}+\cdots+\frac{L}{l^{n+1}}\right)x^n-\cdots+\frac{A}{x}+\frac{Aa}{x^2}+\cdots+\frac{Aa^{n-1}}{x^n}+\cdots.$$

In the next ring we shall have an analogous development, and so on. Finally, exterior to the circle of radius $|l|$, we shall have only positive powers of $1/x$:

$$f(x) = \frac{A + \cdots + L}{x} + \frac{Aa + \cdots + Ll}{x^2} + \cdots + \frac{Aa^{n-1} + \cdots + Ll^{n-1}}{x^n} + \cdots .$$

38. Other series. The proofs of Taylor's series and of Laurent's series are based essentially on a particular development of the simple fraction $1/(z - x)$ when the point x remains inside or outside a fixed circle. Appell has shown that we can again generalize these formulæ by considering a function $f(x)$ analytic in the interior of a region A bounded by any number whatever of arcs of

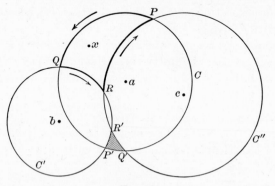

Fig. 16

circles or of entire circumferences.* Let us consider, for example, a function $f(x)$ analytic in the curvilinear triangle PQR (Fig. 16) formed by the three arcs of circles PQ, QR, RP, belonging respectively to the three circumferences C, C', C''. Denoting by x any point within this curvilinear triangle, we have

$$(24) \quad f(x) = \frac{1}{2\pi i} \int_{(PQ)} \frac{f(z)\,dz}{z-x} + \frac{1}{2\pi i} \int_{(QR)} \frac{f(z)\,dz}{z-x} + \frac{1}{2\pi i} \int_{(RP)} \frac{f(z)\,dz}{z-x} .$$

Along the arc PQ we can write

$$\frac{1}{z-x} = \frac{1}{z-a} + \frac{x-a}{(z-a)^2} + \cdots + \frac{(x-a)^n}{(z-a)^{n+1}} + \frac{1}{z-a}\left(\frac{x-a}{z-a}\right)^{n+1},$$

where a is the center of C; but when z describes the arc PQ, the absolute value of $(x-a)/(z-a)$ is less than unity, and therefore the absolute value of the integral

$$\frac{1}{2\pi i} \int_{(PQ)} \frac{f(z)}{z-x}\left(\frac{x-a}{z-a}\right)^{n+1} dz$$

approaches zero as n becomes infinite. We have, therefore,

$$(\alpha) \quad \frac{1}{2\pi i} \int_{(PQ)} \frac{f(z)\,dz}{z-x} = J_0 + J_1(x-a) + \cdots + J_n(x-a)^n + \cdots ,$$

---

* *Acta mathematica*, Vol. I, p. 145.

where the coefficients are constants whose expressions it would be easy to write out. Similarly, along the arc QR we can write

$$\frac{1}{x-z} = \frac{1}{x-b} + \frac{z-b}{(x-b)^2} + \cdots + \frac{(z-b)^{n-1}}{(x-b)^n} + \frac{1}{x-z}\left(\frac{z-b}{x-b}\right)^n,$$

where b is the center of C'. Since the absolute value of $(z-b)^n/(x-b)^n$ approaches zero as n becomes infinite, we can deduce from the preceding equation a development for the second integral of the form

$$(\beta) \qquad \frac{1}{2\pi i}\int_{(QR)}\frac{f(z)\,dz}{z-x} = \frac{K_1}{x-b} + \frac{K_2}{(x-b)^2} + \cdots + \frac{K_n}{(x-b)^n} + \cdots.$$

Similarly, we find

$$(\gamma) \qquad \frac{1}{2\pi i}\int_{(RP)}\frac{f(z)\,dz}{z-x} = \frac{L_1}{x-c} + \frac{L_2}{(x-c)^2} + \cdots + \frac{L_n}{(x-c)^n} + \cdots,$$

where c is the center of the circle C''. Adding the three expressions (α), (β), (γ), we obtain for $f(x)$ the sum of three series, proceeding respectively according to positive powers of $x-a$, of $1/(x-b)$, and of $1/(x-c)$. It is clear that we can transform this sum into a series of which all the terms are rational functions of x, for example, by uniting all the terms of the same degree in $x-a$, $1/(x-b)$, $1/(x-c)$. The preceding reasoning applies whatever may be the number of arcs of circles.

It is seen in the preceding example that the three series, (α), (β), (γ), are still convergent when the point x is inside the triangle $P'Q'R'$, and the sum of these three series is again equal to the integral

$$\int\frac{f(z)\,dz}{z-x}$$

taken along the boundary of the triangle PQR in the positive sense. Now, when the point x is in the triangle $P'Q'R'$, the function $f(z)/(z-x)$ is analytic in the interior of the triangle PQR, and the preceding integral is therefore zero. Hence we obtain in this way a series of rational fractions which is convergent when x is within one of the two triangles PQR, $P'Q'R'$, and for which *the sum is equal to $f(x)$ or to zero, according as the point x is in the triangle PQR or in the triangle $P'Q'R'$.*

Painlevé has obtained more general results along the same lines.* Let us consider, in order to limit ourselves to a very simple case, a convex closed curve Γ having a tangent which changes continuously and a radius of curvature which remains under a certain upper bound. It is easy to see that we can associate with each point M of Γ a circle C tangent to Γ at that point and inclosing that curve entirely in its interior, and this may be done in such a way that the center of the circle moves in a continuous manner with M. Let $f(z)$ be a function analytic in the interior of the boundary Γ and continuous on the boundary itself. Then, in the fundamental formula

$$f(x) = \frac{1}{2\pi i}\int_{(\Gamma)}\frac{f(z)\,dz}{z-x},$$

---

* *Sur les lignes singulières des fonctions analytiques* (*Annales de la Faculté de Toulouse*, 1888).

where x is an interior point to Γ, we can write

$$\frac{1}{z-x} = \frac{1}{z-a} + \frac{x-a}{(z-a)^2} + \cdots + \frac{(x-a)^n}{(z-a)^{n+1}} + \frac{1}{z-x}\left(\frac{x-a}{z-a}\right)^{n+1},$$

where a denotes the center of the circle C which corresponds to the point z of the boundary ; a is no longer constant, as in the case already examined, but it is a continuous function of z when the point M describes the curve Γ. Nevertheless, the absolute value of $(x-a)/(z-a)$, which is a continuous function of z, remains less than a fixed number ρ less than unity, since it cannot reach the value unity, and therefore the integral of the last term approaches zero as n becomes infinite. Hence we have

$$(25) \qquad f(x) = \frac{1}{2\,\pi i} \sum_{n=0}^{+\infty} \int_{(\Gamma)} \frac{(x-a)^n}{(z-a)^{n+1}}\, f(z)\, dz,$$

and it is clear that the general term of this series is a polynomial $P_n(x)$ of degree not greater than n. *The function $f(x)$ is then developable in a series of polynomials in the interior of the boundary Γ.*

The theory of conformal transformations enables us to obtain another kind of series for the development of analytic functions. Let $f(x)$ be an analytic function in the interior of the region A, which may extend to infinity. Suppose that we know how to represent the region A conformally on the region inclosed by a circle C such that to a point of the region A corresponds one and only one point of the circle, and conversely ; let $u = \phi(z)$ be the analytic function which establishes a correspondence between the region A and the circle C having the point $u = 0$ for center in the u-plane. When the variable u describes this circle, the corresponding value of z is an analytic function of u. The same is true of $f(z)$, which can therefore be developed in a convergent series of powers of u, or of $\phi(z)$, when the variable z remains in the interior of A.

Suppose, for example, that the region A consists of the infinite strip included between the two parallels to the axis of reals $y = \pm a$. We have seen (§ 22) that by putting $u = (e^{\pi z/2a} - 1)/(e^{\pi z/2a} + 1)$ this strip is made to correspond to a circle of unit radius having its center at the point $u = 0$. Every function analytic in this strip can therefore be developed in this strip in a convergent series of the following form :

$$f(z) = \sum_{n=0}^{+\infty} A_n \left(\frac{e^{\frac{\pi z}{2a}} - 1}{e^{\frac{\pi z}{2a}} + 1}\right)^n.$$

39. Series of analytic functions. The sum of a uniformly convergent series whose terms are analytic functions of z is a continuous function of z, but we could not say without further proof that that sum is also an analytic function. It must be proved that the sum has a unique derivative at every point, and this is easy to do by means of Cauchy's integral.

Let us first notice that a uniformly convergent series whose terms are continuous functions of a complex variable z can be integrated term by term, as in the case of a real variable. The proof given in the case of the real variable (I, § 114, 2d ed.; § 174, 1st ed.) applies here without change, provided the path of integration has a finite length.

The theorem which we wish to prove is evidently included in the following more general proposition:

Let

$$(26) \qquad f_1(z) + f_2(z) + \cdots + f_n(z) + \cdots$$

be a series all of whose terms are analytic functions in a region A bounded by a closed curve Γ and continuous on the boundary. If the series (26) *is uniformly convergent on* Γ, *it is convergent in every point of A, and its sum is an analytic function $F(z)$ whose pth derivative is represented by the series formed by the pth derivatives of the terms of the series* (26).

Let $\phi(z)$ be the sum of (26) in a point of Γ; $\phi(z)$ is a continuous function of z along the boundary, and we have seen (§ 33, *Note*) that the definite integral

$$(27) \qquad F(x) = \frac{1}{2\pi i} \int_{(\Gamma)} \frac{\phi(z)\,dz}{z - x} = \frac{1}{2\pi i} \int_{(\Gamma)} \frac{\sum\limits_{\nu=1}^{+\infty} f_\nu(z)}{z - x}\, dz,$$

where x is any point of A, represents an analytic function in the region A, whose pth derivative is the expression

$$(28) \qquad F^{(p)}(x) = \frac{p\,!}{2\pi i} \int_{(\Gamma)} \frac{\phi(z)\,dz}{(z - x)^{p+1}} = \frac{p\,!}{2\pi i} \int_{(\Gamma)} \frac{\sum\limits_{\nu=1}^{+\infty} f_\nu(z)}{(z - x)^{p+1}}\, dz.$$

Since the series (26) is uniformly convergent on Γ, the same thing is true of the series obtained by dividing each of its terms by $z - x$, and we can write

$$F(x) = \sum_{\nu=1}^{+\infty} \frac{1}{2\pi i} \int_{(\Gamma)} \frac{f_\nu(z)\,dz}{z - x};$$

or again, since $f_\nu(z)$ is an analytic function in the interior of Γ, we have, by formula (12),

$$F(x) = f_1(x) + f_2(x) + \cdots + f_\nu(x) + \cdots.$$

Similarly, the expression (28) can be written in the form

$$F^{(p)}(x) = f_1^{(p)}(x) + \cdots + f_\nu^{(p)}(x) + \cdots.$$

Hence, if the series (26) is uniformly convergent in a region A of the plane, x being any point of that region, it suffices to apply the preceding theorem to a closed curve Γ lying in A and surrounding the point x. This leads to the following proposition :

Every series uniformly convergent in a region A of the plane, whose terms are all analytic functions in A, represents an analytic function $F(z)$ in the same region. The pth derivative of $F(z)$ is equal to the series obtained by differentiating p times each term of the series which represents $F(z)$.*

40. Poles. Every function analytic in a circle with the center a is equal, in the interior of that circle, to the sum of a power series

$$(29) \qquad f(z) = A_0 + A_1(z-a) + \cdots + A_m(z-a)^m + \cdots.$$

We shall say, for brevity, that the function is *regular* at the point a, or that a is an *ordinary point* for the given function. We shall call the interior of a circle C, described about a as a center with the radius ρ, the *neighborhood* of the point a, when the formula (29) is applicable. It is, moreover, not necessary that this shall be the largest circle in the interior of which the formula (29) is true; the radius ρ of the neighborhood will often be defined by some other particular property.

If the first coefficient A_0 is zero, we have $f(a) = 0$, and the point a is a zero of the function $f(z)$. The order of a zero is defined in the same way as for polynomials; if the development of $f(z)$ commences with a term of degree m in $z - a$,

$$f(z) = A_m(z-a)^m + A_{m+1}(z-a)^{m+1} + \cdots, \qquad (m > 0),$$

where A_m is not zero, we have

$$f(a) = 0, \quad f'(a) = 0, \quad \cdots, \quad f^{(m-1)}(a) = 0, \quad f^{(m)}(a) \neq 0,$$

and the point a is said to be a *zero of order m*. We can also write the preceding formula in the form

$$f(z) = (z-a)^m \phi(z),$$

$\phi(z)$ being a power series which does not vanish when $z = a$. Since this series is a continuous function of z, we can choose the radius ρ of the neighborhood so small that $\phi(z)$ does not vanish in that neighborhood, and we see that the function $f(z)$ will not have any other zero than the point a in the interior of that neighborhood. *The zeros of an analytic function are therefore isolated points.*

Every point which is not an ordinary point for a single-v function $f(z)$ is said to be a *singular point*. A singular point

---

* This proposition is usually attributed to Weierstrass.

function $f(z)$ is a *pole* if that point is an ordinary point for the reciprocal function $1/f(z)$. The development of $1/f(z)$ in powers of $z - a$ cannot contain a constant term, for the point a would then be an ordinary point for the function $f(z)$. Let us suppose that the development commences with a term of degree m in $z - a$,

$$(30) \qquad \frac{1}{f(z)} = (z - a)^m \phi(z),$$

where $\phi(z)$ denotes a regular function in the neighborhood of the point a which is not zero when $z = a$. From this we derive

$$(31) \qquad f(z) = \frac{1}{(z - a)^m} \frac{1}{\phi(z)} = \frac{\psi(z)}{(z - a)^m},$$

where $\psi(z)$ denotes a regular function in the neighborhood of the point a which is not zero when $z = a$. This formula can be written in the equivalent form

$$(31') \quad f(z) = \frac{B_m}{(z - a)^m} + \frac{B_{m-1}}{(z - a)^{m-1}} + \cdots + \frac{B_1}{z - a} + P(z - a),$$

where we denote by $P(z - a)$, as we shall often do hereafter, a regular function for $z = a$, and by $B_m, B_{m-1}, \cdots, B_1$ certain constants. Some of the coefficients $B_1, B_2, \cdots, B_{m-1}$ may be zero, but the coefficient B_m is surely different from zero. The integer m is called the *order of the pole*. It is seen that a pole of order m of $f(z)$ is a zero of order m of $1/f(z)$, and conversely.

In the neighborhood of a pole a the development of $f(z)$ is composed of a regular part $P(z - a)$ and of a polynomial in $1/(z - a)$; this polynomial is called the *principal part* of $f(z)$ in the neighborhood of the pole. *When the absolute value of $z - a$ approaches zero, the absolute value of $f(z)$ becomes infinite in whatever way the point z approaches the pole.* In fact, since the function $\psi(z)$ is not zero for $z = a$, suppose the radius of the neighborhood so small that the absolute value of $\psi(z)$ remains greater than a positive number M in this neighborhood. Denoting by r the absolute value of $z - a$, we have $|f(z)| > M/r^m$, and therefore $|f(z)|$ becomes infinite when r approaches zero. Since the function $\psi(z)$ is regular for $z = a$, there exists a circle C with the center a in the interior of which $\psi(z)$ is analytic. The quotient $\psi(z)/(z - a)^m$ is an analytic function for all the points of this circle except for the point a itself. In the neighborhood of a pole a, the function $f(z)$ has therefore no other singular point than the pole itself; in other words, *poles are isolated singular points.*

41. Functions analytic except for poles. Every function which is analytic at all the points of a region A, except only for singular points that are poles, is said to be *analytic except for poles in that region*.* A function analytic in the whole plane except for poles may have an infinite number of poles, but it can have only a finite number in any finite region of the plane. The proof depends on a general theorem, which we must now recall : *If in a finite region A of the plane there exist an infinite number of points possessing a particular property, there exists at least one limit point in the region A or on its boundary.* (We mean by *limit point* a point in every neighborhood of which there exist an infinite number of points possessing the given property.) This proposition is proved by the process of successive subdivisions that we have employed so often. For brevity, let us indicate by (E) the assemblage of points considered, and let us suppose that the region A is divided into squares, or portions of squares, by parallels to the axes Ox, Oy. There will be at least one region A_1 containing an infinite number of points of the assemblage (E). By subdividing the region A_1 in the same way, and by continuing this process indefinitely, we can form an infinite sequence of regions A_1, A_2, $\cdots$, A_n, $\cdots$ that become smaller and smaller, each of which is contained in the preceding and contains an infinite number of the points of the assemblage. All the points of A_n approach a limit point Z lying in the interior of or on the boundary of A. The point Z is necessarily a limit point of (E), since there are always an infinite number of points of (E) in the interior of a circle having Z for center, however small the radius of that circle may be.

Let us now suppose that the function $f(z)$ is analytic except for poles in the interior of a finite region A and also on the boundary Γ of that region. If it has an infinite number of poles in the region, it will have, by the preceding theorem, at least one point Z situated in A or on Γ, in every neighborhood of which it will have an infinite number of poles. Hence the point Z can be neither a pole nor an ordinary point. It is seen in the same way that the function $f(z)$ can have only a finite number of zeros in the same region. It follows that we can state the following theorem :

Every function analytic except for poles in a finite region A and on its boundary has in that region only a finite number of zeros and only a finite number of poles.

---

* Such functions are said by some writers to be *meromorphic.* — TRANS.

In the neighborhood of any point a, a function $f(z)$ analytic except for poles can be put in the form

$$(32) \qquad f(z) = (z - a)^\mu \phi(z),$$

where $\phi(z)$ is a regular function not zero for $z = a$. The exponent μ is called the *order* of $f(z)$ at the point a. The order is zero if the point a is neither a pole nor a zero for $f(z)$; it is equal to m if the point a is a zero of order m for $f(z)$, and to $-n$ if a is a pole of order n for $f(z)$.

42. Essentially singular points. Every singular point of a single-valued analytic function, which is not a pole, is called an *essentially singular point*. An essentially singular point a is isolated if it is possible to describe about a as a center a circle C in the interior of which the function $f(z)$ has no other singular point than the point a itself; we shall limit ourselves for the moment to such points.

Laurent's theorem furnishes at once a development of the function $f(z)$ that holds in the neighborhood of an essentially singular point. Let C be a circle, with the center a, in the interior of which the function $f(z)$ has no other singular point than a; also let c be a circle concentric with and interior to C. In the circular ring included between the two circles C and c the function $f(z)$ is analytic and is therefore equal to the sum of a series of positive and negative powers of $z - a$,

$$(33) \qquad f(z) = \sum_{m=-\infty}^{+\infty} A_m (z - a)^m.$$

This development holds true for all the points interior to the circle C except the point a, for we can always take the radius of the circle c less than $|z - a|$ for any point z whatever that is different from a and lies in C. Moreover, the coefficients A_m do not depend on this radius (§ 37). The development (33) contains first a part regular at the point a, say $P(z - a)$, formed by the terms with positive exponents, and then a series of terms in powers of $1/(z - a)$,

$$(34) \qquad \frac{A_{-1}}{z - a} + \frac{A_{-2}}{(z - a)^2} + \cdots + \frac{A_{-m}}{(z - a)^m} + \cdots.$$

This is the *principal part* of $f(z)$ in the neighborhood of the singular point. This principal part does not reduce to a polynomial in $(z - a)^{-1}$, for the point $z = a$ would then be a pole, contrary to the hypothesis.* It is an *integral transcendental function* of $1/(z-a)$. In fact, let r be any positive number less than the radius of the circle C; the coefficient A_{-m} of the series (34) is given by the expression (§ 37)

$$A_{-m} = \frac{1}{2\pi i}\int_{(C')}(z-a)^{m-1}f(z)\,dz,$$

the integral being taken along the circle C' with the center a and the radius r. We have, then,

(35) $$|A_{-m}| < \mathcal{M}(r)\,r^m,$$

where $\mathcal{M}(r)$ denotes the maximum of the absolute value of $f(z)$ along the circle C'. The series is then convergent, provided that $|z-a|$ is greater than r, and since r is a number which we may suppose as small as we wish, the series (34) is convergent for every value of z different from a, and we can write

$$f(z) = P(z-a) + G\left(\frac{1}{z-a}\right),$$

where $P(z-a)$ is a regular function at the point a, and $G[1/(z-a)]$ an integral transcendental function† of $1/(z-a)$.

When the absolute value of $z-a$ approaches zero, the value of $f(z)$ does not approach any definite limit. More precisely, *if a circle C is described with the point a as a center and with an arbitrary radius ρ, there always exists in the interior of this circle points z for which f(z) differs as little as we please from any number given in advance* (WEIERSTRASS).

Let us first prove that, given any two positive numbers ρ and M, there exist values of z for which both the inequalities, $|z-a| < \rho$, $|f(z)| > M$, hold. For, if the absolute value of $f(z)$ were at most equal to M when we have $|z-a| < \rho$, $\mathcal{M}(r)$ would be less than or equal to M for $r < \rho$, and, from the inequality (35), all the coefficients A_{-m} would be zero, for the product $\mathcal{M}(r)\,r^m \leqq Mr^m$ would approach zero with r.

Let us consider now any value A whatever. If the equation $f(z)=A$ has roots within the circle C, however small the radius ρ

---

* To avoid overlooking any hypothesis, it would be necessary to examine also the case in which the development of $f(z)$ in the interior of C contains only positive powers of $z-a$, the value $f(a)$ of the function at the point a being different from the term independent of $z-a$ in the series. The point $z=a$ would be a *point of discontinuity* for $f(z)$. We shall disregard this kind of singularity, which is of an entirely artificial character (see below, Chapter IV).

† We shall frequently denote an integral function of x by $G(x)$.

may be, the theorem is proved. If the equation $f(z) = A$ does not have an infinite number of roots in the neighborhood of the point a, we can take the radius ρ so small that in the interior of the circle C with the radius ρ and the center a this equation does not have any roots. The function $\phi(z) = 1/[f(z) - A]$ is then analytic for every point z within C except for the point a; this point a cannot be anything but an essentially singular point for $\phi(z)$, for otherwise the point would be either a pole or an ordinary point for $f(z)$. Therefore, from what we have just proved, there exist values of z in the interior of the circle C for which we have

$$|\phi(z)| > \frac{1}{\epsilon} \quad \text{or} \quad |f(z) - A| < \epsilon,$$

however small the positive number ϵ may be.

This property sharply distinguishes poles from essentially singular points. While the absolute value of the function $f(z)$ becomes infinite in the neighborhood of a pole, the value of $f(z)$ is completely indeterminate for an essentially singular point.

Picard * has demonstrated a more precise proposition by showing that every equation $f(z) = A$ has an infinite number of roots in the neighborhood of an essentially singular point, there being no exception except for, at most, one particular value of A.

Example. The point $z = 0$ is an essentially singular point for the function

$$e^{\frac{1}{z}} = 1 + \frac{1}{z} + \frac{1}{2!}\frac{1}{z^2} + \cdots + \frac{1}{n!}\frac{1}{z^n} + \cdots.$$

It is easy to prove that the equation $e^{1/z} = A$ has an infinite number of roots with absolute values less than ρ, however small ρ may be, provided that A is not zero. Setting $A = r(\cos\theta + i\sin\theta)$, we derive from the preceding equation

$$\frac{1}{z} = \log r + i(\theta + 2k\pi).$$

We shall have $|z| < \rho$, provided that

$$(\log r)^2 + (\theta + 2k\pi)^2 \geqq \frac{1}{\rho^2}.$$

There are evidently an infinite number of values of the integer k which satisfy this condition. In this example there is one exceptional value of A, that is, $A = 0$. But it may also happen that there are no exceptional values; such is the case, for example, for the function $\sin(1/z)$, near $z = 0$.

---

* *Annales de l'École Normale supérieure*, 1880.

43. Residues. Let a be a pole or an isolated essentially singular point of a function $f(z)$. Let us consider the question of evaluating the integral $\int f(z)\,dz$ along the circle C drawn in the neighborhood of the point a with the center a. The regular part $P(z - a)$ gives zero in the integration. As for the principal part $G[1/(z - a)]$, we can integrate it term by term, for, even though the point a is an essentially singular point, this series is uniformly convergent. The integral of the general term

$$\int_{(C)} \frac{A_{-m}\,dz}{(z - a)^m}$$

is zero if the exponent m is greater than unity, for the primitive function $-A_{-m}/[(m - 1)(z - a)^{m-1}]$ takes on again its original value after the variable has described a closed path. If, on the contrary, $m = 1$, the definite integral $A_{-1}\int dz/(z - a)$ has the value $2\pi i A_{-1}$, as was shown by the previous evaluation made in § 34. We have then the result

$$2\pi i A_{-1} = \int_{(C)} f(z)\,dz,$$

which is essentially only a particular case of the formula (23) for the coefficients of the Laurent development. The coefficient A_{-1} is called the *residue* of the function $f(z)$ with respect to the singular point a.

Let us consider now a function $f(z)$ continuous on a closed boundary curve Γ and having in the interior of that curve Γ only a finite number of singular points $a, b, c, \cdots, l$. Let $A, B, C, \cdots, L$ be the corresponding residues; if we surround each of these singular points with a circle of very small radius, the integral $\int f(z)\,dz$, taken along Γ in the positive sense, is equal to the sum of the integrals taken along the small curves in the same sense, and we have the very important formula

$$(36) \qquad \int_{(\Gamma)} f(z)\,dz = 2\pi i (A + B + C + \cdots + L),$$

which says that *the integral $\int f(z)\,dz$, taken along Γ in the positive sense, is equal to the product of $2\pi i$ and the sum of the residues with respect to the singular points of $f(z)$ within the curve Γ.*

It is clear that the theorem is also applicable to boundaries Γ composed of several distinct closed curves. The importance of residues is now evident, and it is useful to know how to calculate them rapidly. If a point a is a pole of order m for $f(z)$, the product $(z - a)^m f(z)$ is regular at the point a, and the residue of $f(z)$ is evidently the coefficient of $(z - a)^{m-1}$ in the development of that product. The rule becomes simple in the case of a simple pole; the residue is then equal to the limit of the product $(z - a)f(z)$ for $z = a$. Quite frequently the function $f(z)$ appears under the form

$$f(z) = \frac{P(z)}{Q(z)},$$

where the functions $P(z)$ and $Q(z)$ are regular for $z = a$, and $P(a)$ is different from zero, while a is a simple zero for $Q(z)$. Let $Q(z) = (z - a)R(z)$; then the residue is equal to the quotient $P(a)/R(a)$, or again, as it is easy to show, to $P(a)/Q'(a)$.

III. APPLICATIONS OF THE GENERAL THEOREMS

The applications of the last theorem are innumerable. We shall now give some of them which are related particularly to the evaluation of definite integrals and to the theory of equations.

44. Introductory remarks. Let $f(z)$ be a function such that the product $(z - a)f(z)$ approaches zero with $|z - a|$. The integral of this function along a circle γ, with the center a and the radius ρ, approaches zero with the radius of that circle. Indeed, we can write

$$\int_{(\gamma)} f(z)\,dz = \int_{(\gamma)} (z - a)f(z)\frac{dz}{z - a}.$$

If η is the maximum of the absolute value of $(z - a)f(z)$ along the circle γ, the absolute value of the integral is less than $2\pi\eta$, and consequently approaches zero, since η itself is infinitesimal with ρ. We could show in the same way that, when the product $(z - a)f(z)$ approaches zero as the absolute value of $z - a$ becomes infinite, the integral $\int_{(C)} f(z)\,dz$, taken along a circle C with the center a, approaches zero as the radius of the circle becomes infinite. These statements are still true if, instead of integrating along the entire circumference, we integrate along only a part of it, provided that the product $(z - a)f(z)$ approaches zero along that part.

Frequently we have to find an upper bound for the absolute value of a definite integral of the form $\int_a^b f(x)\,dx$, taken along the axis of reals. Let us suppose for definiteness $a < b$. We have seen above (§ 25) that the absolute value of that integral is at most equal to the integral $\int_a^b |f(x)|\,dx$, and, consequently, is less than $M(b - a)$ if M is an upper bound of the absolute value of $f(x)$.

45. Evaluation of elementary definite integrals. The definite integral $\int_{-\infty}^{+\infty} F(x)\,dx$, taken along the real axis, where $F(x)$ is a rational function, has a sense, provided that the denominator does not vanish for any real value of x and that the degree of the numerator is less than the degree of the denominator by at least two units. With the origin as center let us describe a circle C with a radius R large enough to include all the roots of the denominator of $F(z)$, and let us consider a path of integration formed by the diameter BA, traced along the real axis, and the semicircumference C', lying above the real axis. The only singular points of $F(z)$ lying in the interior of this path are poles, which come from the roots of the denominator of $F(z)$ for which the coefficient of i is positive. Indicating by ΣR_k the sum of the residues relative to these poles, we can then write

$$\int_{-R}^{+R} F(z)\,dz + \int_{(C')} F(z)\,dz = 2\,\pi i \Sigma R_k.$$

As the radius R becomes infinite the integral along C' approaches zero, since the product $zF(z)$ is zero for z infinite; and, taking the limit, we obtain

$$\int_{-\infty}^{+\infty} F(x)\,dx = 2\,\pi i \Sigma R_k.$$

We easily reduce to the preceding case the definite integrals

$$\int_{0}^{2\pi} F(\sin x,\ \cos x)\,dx,$$

where F is a rational function of $\sin x$ and $\cos x$ that does not become infinite for any real value of x, and where the integral is to be taken along the axis of reals. Let us first notice that we do not change the value of this integral by taking for the limits x_0 and $x_0 + 2\pi$, where x_0 is any real number whatever. It follows that we can take for the limits $-\pi$ and $+\pi$, for example. Now the classic change of variable $\tan(x/2) = t$ reduces the given integral to the integral of a rational function of t taken between the limits $-\infty$ and $+\infty$, for $\tan(x/2)$ increases from $-\infty$ to $+\infty$ when x increases from $-\pi$ to $+\pi$.

We can also proceed in another way. By putting $e^{xi} = z$ we have $dx = dz/iz$, and Euler's formulæ give

$$\cos x = \frac{z^2 + 1}{2z}, \qquad \sin x = \frac{z^2 - 1}{2iz},$$

so that the given integral takes the form

$$\int F\left(\frac{z^2-1}{2\,iz},\ \frac{z^2+1}{2\,z}\right)\frac{dz}{iz}.$$

As for the new path of integration, when x increases from 0 to $2\,\pi$ the variable z describes in the positive sense the circle of unit radius about the origin as center. It will suffice, then, to calculate the residues of the new rational function of z with respect to the poles whose absolute values are less than unity.

Let us take for example the integral $\int_0^{2\pi}\text{ctn}\,[(x-a-bi)/2]\,dx$, which has a finite value if b is not zero. We have

$$\text{ctn}\left(\frac{x-a-bi}{2}\right)=i\,\frac{e^{i\left(\frac{x-a-bi}{2}\right)}+e^{-i\left(\frac{x-a-bi}{2}\right)}}{e^{i\left(\frac{x-a-bi}{2}\right)}-e^{-i\left(\frac{x-a-bi}{2}\right)}},$$

or

$$\text{ctn}\left(\frac{x-a-bi}{2}\right)=i\,\frac{e^{ix}+e^{-b+ai}}{e^{ix}-e^{-b+ai}}.$$

Hence the change of variable $e^{xi}=z$ leads to the integral

$$\int_{(C)}\frac{z+e^{-b+ai}}{z-e^{-b+ai}}\frac{dz}{z}.$$

The function to be integrated has two simple poles

$$z=0,\qquad z=e^{-b+ai},$$

and the corresponding residues are -1 and $+2$. If b is positive, the two poles are in the interior of the path of integration, and the integral is equal to $2\,\pi i$; if b is negative, the pole $z=0$ is the only one within the path, and the integral is equal to $-2\,\pi i$. The proposed integral is therefore equal to $\pm\,2\,\pi i$, according as b is positive or negative. We shall now give some examples which are less elementary.

46. Various definite integrals. *Example* 1. The function $e^{imz}/(1+z^2)$ has the two poles $+i$ and $-i$, with the residues $e^{-m}/2\,i$ and $-e^m/2\,i$. Let us suppose for definiteness that m is positive, and let us consider the boundary formed by a large semicircle of radius R about the origin as center and above the real axis, and by the diameter which falls along the axis of reals. In the interior of this boundary the function $e^{miz}/(1+z^2)$ has the single pole $z=i$, and the integral taken along the total boundary is equal to πe^{-m}. Now the integral along the semicircle approaches zero as the radius R becomes infinite, for the absolute value of the product $ze^{imz}/(1+z^2)$ along that curve approaches zero. Indeed, if we replace z by $R(\cos\theta+i\sin\theta)$, we have

$$e^{miz}=e^{-mR\sin\theta+imR\cos\theta},$$

and the absolute value $e^{-mR\sin\theta}$ remains less than unity when θ varies from 0 to π. As for the absolute value of the factor $z/(1+z^2)$, it approaches zero as z becomes infinite. We have, then, in the limit

$$\int_{-\infty}^{+\infty}\frac{e^{mix}}{1+x^2}dx = \pi e^{-m}.$$

If we replace e^{mix} by $\cos mx + i\sin mx$, the coefficient of i on the left-hand side is evidently zero, for the elements of the integral cancel out in pairs. Since we have also $\cos(-mx) = \cos mx$, we can write the preceding formula in the form

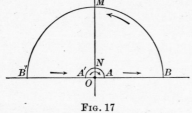

Fig. 17

$$(37)\quad \int_0^{+\infty}\frac{\cos mx}{1+x^2}dx = \frac{\pi}{2}e^{-m}.$$

Example 2. The function e^{iz}/z is analytic in the interior of the boundary $ABMB'A'NA$ (Fig. 17) formed by the two semicircles BMB', $A'NA$, described about the origin as center with the radii R and r, and the straight lines AB, $B'A'$.

We have, then, the relation

$$\int_r^R\frac{e^{ix}}{x}dx + \int_{(BMB')}\frac{e^{iz}}{z}dz + \int_{-R}^{-r}\frac{e^{ix}}{x}dx + \int_{(A'NA)}\frac{e^{iz}}{z}dz = 0,$$

which we can write also in the form

$$\int_r^R\frac{e^{ix}-e^{-ix}}{x}dx + \int_{(BMB')}\frac{e^{iz}}{z}dz + \int_{(A'NA)}\frac{e^{iz}}{z}dz = 0.$$

When r approaches zero, the last integral approaches $-\pi i$; we have, in fact,

$$\frac{e^{iz}}{z} = \frac{1}{z} + P(z),$$

where $P(z)$ is a regular function at the origin, so that

$$\int_{(A'NA)}\frac{e^{iz}}{z}dz = \int_{(A'NA)}P(z)\,dz + \int_{(A'NA)}\frac{dz}{z}.$$

The integral of the regular part $P(z)$ becomes infinitesimal with the length of the path of integration; as for the last integral, it is equal to the variation of $\mathrm{Log}(z)$ along $A'NA$, that is, to $-\pi i$.

The integral along BMB' approaches zero as R becomes infinite. For if we put $z = R(\cos\theta + i\sin\theta)$, we find

$$\int_{(BMB')}\frac{e^{iz}}{z}dz = i\int_0^\pi e^{-R\sin\theta + iR\cos\theta}\,d\theta,$$

and the absolute value of this integral is less than

$$\int_0^\pi e^{-R\sin\theta}\,d\theta = 2\int_0^{\frac{\pi}{2}}e^{-R\sin\theta}\,d\theta.$$

When θ increases from 0 to $\pi/2$, the quotient $\sin\theta/\theta$ decreases from 1 to $2/\pi$, and we have

$$R\sin\theta > \frac{2}{\pi}R\theta \, ;$$

hence

$$e^{-R\sin\theta} < e^{-\frac{2R\theta}{\pi}},$$

$$\int_0^{\frac{\pi}{2}} e^{-R\sin\theta}\, d\theta < \int_0^{\frac{\pi}{2}} e^{-\frac{2R\theta}{\pi}}\, d\theta = -\frac{\pi}{2R}\left[e^{-\frac{2R\theta}{\pi}} \right]_0^{\frac{\pi}{2}} = \frac{\pi}{2R}(1 - e^{-R}) \, ;$$

which establishes the proposition stated above.

Passing to the limit, we have, then (see I, § 100, 2d ed.),

$$\int_0^{+\infty} \frac{e^{ix} - e^{-ix}}{x}\, dx = \pi i,$$

or

$$\int_0^{+\infty} \frac{\sin x}{x}\, dx = \frac{\pi}{2}.$$

Example 3. The integral of the integral transcendental function e^{-z^2} along the boundary $OABO$ formed by the two radii OA and OB, making an angle of 45°, and by the arc of a circle AB (Fig. 18), is equal to zero, and this fact can be expressed as follows :

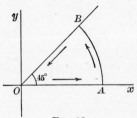

FIG. 18

$$\int_0^R e^{-x^2}\, dx + \int_{(AB)} e^{-z^2}\, dz = \int_{(OB)} e^{-z^2}\, dz.$$

When the radius R of the circle to which the arc AB belongs becomes infinite, the integral along the arc AB approaches zero. In fact, if we put $z = R[\cos(\phi/2) + i\sin(\phi/2)]$, that integral becomes

$$\frac{iR}{2}\int_0^{\frac{\pi}{2}} e^{-R^2(\cos\phi + i\sin\phi)} e^{\frac{i\phi}{2}}\, d\phi,$$

and its absolute value is less than the integral

$$\frac{R}{2}\int_0^{\frac{\pi}{2}} e^{-R^2\cos\phi}\, d\phi.$$

As in the previous example, we have

$$\frac{R}{2}\int_0^{\frac{\pi}{2}} e^{-R^2\cos\phi}\, d\phi = \frac{R}{2}\int_0^{\frac{\pi}{2}} e^{-R^2\sin\phi}\, d\phi < \frac{R}{2}\int_0^{\frac{\pi}{2}} e^{-\frac{2R^2\phi}{\pi}}\, d\phi.$$

The last integral has the value

$$-\frac{\pi}{4R}\left[e^{-\frac{2R^2\phi}{\pi}} \right]_0^{\frac{\pi}{2}} = \frac{\pi}{4R}(1 - e^{-R^2})$$

and approaches zero when R becomes infinite.

Along the radius OB we can put $z = \rho\,[\cos(\pi/4) + i\sin(\pi/4)]$, which gives $e^{-z^2} = e^{-i\rho^2}$, and as R becomes infinite we have at the limit (see I, § 135, 2d ed.; § 134, 1st ed.)

$$\int_0^{+\infty} e^{-i\rho^2}\left(\cos\frac{\pi}{4} + i\sin\frac{\pi}{4}\right) d\rho = \int_0^{+\infty} e^{-x^2}dx = \frac{\sqrt{\pi}}{2},$$

or, again,

$$\int_0^{+\infty} e^{-i\rho^2}d\rho = \frac{\sqrt{\pi}}{2}\left(\cos\frac{\pi}{4} - i\sin\frac{\pi}{4}\right).$$

Equating the real parts and the coefficients of i, we obtain the values of Fresnel's integrals,

$$(38)\qquad \int_0^{+\infty}\cos\rho^2 d\rho = \frac{1}{2}\sqrt{\frac{\pi}{2}},\qquad \int_0^{+\infty}\sin\rho^2 d\rho = \frac{1}{2}\sqrt{\frac{\pi}{2}}.$$

47. Evaluation of $\Gamma(p)\,\Gamma(1-p)$. The definite integral

$$\int_0^{+\infty}\frac{x^{p-1}dx}{1+x},$$

where the variable x and the exponent p are real, has a finite value, provided that p is positive and less than one; it is equal to the product $\Gamma(p)\,\Gamma(1-p)$.*

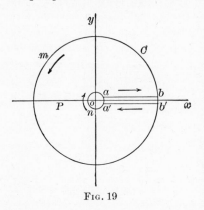

In order to evaluate this integral, let us consider the function $z^{p-1}/(1+z)$, which has a pole at the point $z = -1$ and a branch point at the point $z = 0$. Let us consider the boundary $abmb'a'na$ (Fig. 19) formed by the two circles C and C', described about the origin with the radii r and ρ respectively, and the two straight lines ab and $a'b'$, lying as near each other as we please above and below a cut along the axis Ox. The function $z^{p-1}/(1+z)$ is single-valued within this boundary, which contains only one singular point, the pole $z = -1$.

In order to calculate the value of the integral along this path, we shall agree to take for the angle of z that one which lies between 0 and 2π. If R denotes the residue with respect to the pole $z = -1$, we have then

$$\int_{ab}\frac{z^{p-1}}{1+z}dz + \int_{(C)}\frac{z^{p-1}dz}{1+z} + \int_{b'a'}\frac{z^{p-1}}{1+z}dz + \int_{(C')}\frac{z^{p-1}dz}{1+z} = 2\,i\pi R.$$

The integrals along the circles C and C' approach zero as r becomes infinite and as ρ approaches zero respectively, for the product $z^p/(1+z)$ approaches zero in either case, since $0 < p < 1$.

---

*Replace t by $1/(1+x)$ in the last formula of § 135, Vol. I, 2d ed.; § 134, 1st ed. The formula (39), derived by supposing p to be real, is correct, provided the real part of p lies between 0 and 1.

Along ab, z is real. For simplicity let us replace z by x. Since the angle of z is zero along ab, z^{p-1} is equal to the numerical value of x^{p-1}. Along $a'b'$ also z is real, but since its angle is 2π, we have

$$z^{p-1} = e^{(p-1)(\log x + 2\pi i)} = e^{2\pi i(p-1)}x^{p-1}.$$

The sum of the two integrals along ab and along $b'a'$ therefore has for its limit

$$[1 - e^{2\pi i(p-1)}]\int_0^{+\infty}\frac{x^{p-1}}{1+x}dx.$$

The residue R is equal to $(-1)^{p-1}$, that is, to $e^{(p-1)\pi i}$, if π is taken as the angle of -1. We have, then,

$$\int_0^{+\infty}\frac{x^{p-1}}{1+x}dx = \frac{2\pi i e^{(p-1)\pi i}}{1 - e^{2\pi i(p-1)}} = \frac{2\pi i}{e^{-(p-1)\pi i} - e^{(p-1)\pi i}} = \frac{-\pi}{\sin(p-1)\pi},$$

or, finally,

$$(39) \qquad\qquad \int_0^{+\infty}\frac{x^{p-1}}{1+x}dx = \frac{\pi}{\sin p\pi}.$$

48. Application to functions analytic except for poles. Given two functions, $f(z)$ and $\phi(z)$, let us suppose that one of them, $f(z)$, is analytic except for poles in the interior of a closed curve C, that the other, $\phi(z)$, is everywhere analytic within the same curve, and that the three functions $f(z)$, $f'(z)$, $\phi(z)$ are continuous on the curve C; and let us try to find the singular points of the function $\phi(z)f'(z)/f(z)$ within C. A point a which is neither a pole nor a zero for $f(z)$ is evidently an ordinary point for the function $f'(z)/f(z)$ and consequently for the function $\phi(z)f'(z)/f(z)$. If a point a is a pole or a zero of $f(z)$, we shall have, in the neighborhood of that point,

$$f(z) = (z - a)^\mu \psi(z),$$

where μ denotes a positive or negative integer equal to the order of the function at that point (§ 41), and where $\psi(z)$ is a regular function which is not zero for $z = a$. Taking the logarithmic derivatives on both sides, we find

$$\frac{f'(z)}{f(z)} = \frac{\mu}{z - a} + \frac{\psi'(z)}{\psi(z)}.$$

Since, on the other hand, we have, in the neighborhood of the point a,

$$\phi(z) = \phi(a) + (z - a)\phi'(a) + \cdots,$$

it follows that the point a is a pole of the first order for the product $\phi(z)f'(z)/f(z)$, and its residue is equal to $\mu\phi(a)$, that is, to $m\phi(a)$, if the point a is a zero of order m for $f(z)$, and to $-n\phi(a)$ if the point a is a pole of order n for $f(z)$. Hence, by the general theorem of residues, provided there are no roots of $f(z)$ on the curve C, we have

$$(40) \qquad \frac{1}{2\pi i}\int_{(C)} \phi(z)\,\frac{f'(z)}{f(z)}\,dz = \Sigma\phi(a) - \Sigma\phi(b),$$

where a is any one of the zeros of $f(z)$ inside the boundary C, b any one of the poles of $f(z)$ within C, and where each of the poles and zeros are counted a number of times equal to its degree of multiplicity. The formula (40) furnishes an infinite number of relations, since we may take for $\phi(z)$ any analytic function.

Let us take in particular $\phi(z) = 1$; then the preceding formula becomes

$$(41) \qquad N - P = \frac{1}{2\pi i}\int_{(C)} \frac{f'(z)}{f(z)}\,dz,$$

where N and P denote respectively the number of zeros and the number of poles of $f(z)$ within the boundary C. This formula leads to an important theorem. In fact, $f'(z)/f(z)$ is the derivative of $\mathrm{Log}\,[f(z)]$; to calculate the definite integral on the right-hand side of the formula (41) it is therefore sufficient to know the variation of

$$\log|f(z)| + i \,\text{angle}\,[f(z)]$$

when the variable z describes the boundary C in the positive sense. But $|f(z)|$ returns to its initial value, while the angle of $f(z)$ increases by $2K\pi$, K being a positive or negative integer. We have, therefore,

$$(42) \qquad N - P = \frac{2K\pi i}{2\pi i} = K;$$

that is, *the difference $N - P$ is equal to the quotient obtained by the division of the variation of the angle of $f(z)$ by 2π when the variable z describes the boundary C in the positive sense.*

Let us separate the real part and the coefficient of i in $f(z)$:

$$f(z) = X + Yi.$$

When the point $z = x + yi$ describes the curve C in the positive sense, the point whose coördinates are X, Y, with respect to a system of rectangular axes with the same orientation as the first system, describes also a closed curve C_1, and we need only draw the curve C_1 approximately in order to deduce from it by simple inspection the integer K. In fact, it is only necessary to count the number of revolutions which the radius vector joining the origin of coördinates to the point (X, Y) has turned through in one sense or the other.

We can also write the formula (42) in the form

$$(43) \qquad N - P = \frac{1}{2\,\pi} \int_{(C)} d \arctan\left(\frac{Y}{X}\right) = \frac{1}{2\,\pi} \int_{(C)} \frac{X dY - Y dX}{X^2 + Y^2}.$$

Since the function Y/X takes on the same value after z has described the closed curve C, the definite integral

$$\int_{(C)} \frac{X dY - Y dX}{X^2 + Y^2}$$

is equal to $\pi I(Y/X)$, where the symbol $I(Y/X)$ means the index of the quotient Y/X along the boundary C, that is, the excess of the number of times that that quotient becomes infinite by passing from $+\infty$ to $-\infty$ over the number of times that it becomes infinite by passing from $-\infty$ to $+\infty$ (I, §§ 79, 154, 2d ed.; §§ 77, 154, 1st ed.). We can write the formula (43), then, in the equivalent form

$$(44) \qquad\qquad N - P = \frac{1}{2} I\left(\frac{Y}{X}\right).$$

49. Application to the theory of equations. When the function $f(z)$ is itself analytic within the curve C, and has neither poles nor zeros on the curve, the preceding formulæ contain only the roots of the equation $f(z) = 0$ which lie within the region bounded by C. The formulæ (42), (43), and (44) show the number N of these roots by means of the variation of the angle of $f(z)$ along the curve or by means of the index of Y/X.

If the function $f(z)$ is a polynomial in z, with any coefficients whatever, and when the boundary C is composed of a finite number of segments of unicursal curves, this index can be calculated by elementary operations, that is, by multiplications and divisions of polynomials. In fact, let AB be an arc of the boundary which can be represented by the expressions

$$x = \phi(t), \qquad y = \psi(t),$$

where $\phi(t)$ and $\psi(t)$ are rational functions of a parameter t which varies from α to β as the point (x, y) describes the arc AB in the positive sense. Replacing z by $\phi(t) + i\psi(t)$ in the polynomial $f(z)$, we have

$$f(z) = R(t) + i R_1(t),$$

where $R(t)$ and $R_1(t)$ are rational functions of t with real coefficients. Hence the index of Y/X along the arc AB is equal to the index of the rational function R_1/R as t varies from α to β, which we already know how to calculate (I, § 79, 2d ed.; § 77, 1st ed.). If the boundary C is composed of segments of unicursal curves, we need only calculate the index for each of these segments and take half of their sum, in order to have the number of roots of the equation $f(z) = 0$ within the boundary C.

Note. D'Alembert's theorem is easily deduced from the preceding results. Let us prove first a lemma which we shall have occasion to use several times. Let $F(z)$, $\Phi(z)$ be two functions analytic in the interior of the closed curve C, continuous on the curve itself, and such that along the entire curve C we have $|\Phi(z)| < |F(z)|$; under these conditions *the two equations*

$$F(z) = 0, \qquad F(z) + \Phi(z) = 0$$

have the same number of roots in the interior of C. For we have

$$F(z) + \Phi(z) = F(z)\left[1 + \frac{\Phi(z)}{F(z)}\right].$$

As the point z describes the boundary C, the point $Z = 1 + \Phi(z)/F(z)$ describes a closed curve lying entirely within the circle of unit radius about the point $Z = 1$ as center, since $|Z - 1| < 1$ along the entire curve C. Hence the angle of that factor returns to its initial value after the variable z has described the boundary C, and the variation of the angle of $F(z) + \Phi(z)$ is equal to the variation of the angle of $F(z)$. Consequently the two equations have the same number of roots in the interior of C.

Now let $f(z)$ be a polynomial of degree m with any coefficients whatever, and let us set

$$F(z) = A_0 z^m, \qquad \Phi(z) = A_1 z^{m-1} + \cdots + A_m, \qquad f(z) = F(z) + \Phi(z).$$

Let us choose a positive number R so large that we have

$$\left|\frac{A_1}{A_0}\right|\frac{1}{R} + \left|\frac{A_2}{A_0}\right|\frac{1}{R^2} + \cdots + \left|\frac{A_m}{A_0}\right|\frac{1}{R^m} < 1.$$

Then along the entire circle C, described about the origin as center with a radius greater than R, it is clear that $|\Phi/F| < 1$. Hence the equation $f(z) = 0$ has the same number of roots in the interior of the circle C as the equation $F(z) = 0$, that is, m.

50. Jensen's formula. Let $f(z)$ be an analytic function except for poles in the interior of the circle C with the radius r about the origin as center, and analytic and without zeros on C. Let $a_1, a_2, \cdots, a_n$ be the zeros, and $b_1, b_2, \cdots, b_m$ the poles, of $f(z)$ in the interior of this circle, each being counted according to its degree of multiplicity. We shall suppose, moreover, that the origin is neither a pole nor a zero for $f(z)$. Let us evaluate the definite integral

(45)
$$I = \int_{(C)} \mathrm{Log}\,[f(z)] \frac{dz}{z},$$

taken along C in the positive sense, supposing that the variable z starts, for example, from the point $z = r$ on the real axis, and that a definite determination of the angle of $f(z)$ has been selected in advance. Integrating by parts, we have

(46)
$$I = \{\mathrm{Log}\,(z)\,\mathrm{Log}\,[f(z)]\}_{(C)} - \int_{(C)} \mathrm{Log}\,(z)\, \frac{f'(z)}{f(z)}\, dz,$$

where the first part of the right-hand side denotes the increment of the product $\mathrm{Log}\,(z)\,\mathrm{Log}\,[f(z)]$ when the variable z describes the circle C. If we take zero for the initial value of the angle of z, that increment is equal to

$$(\log r + 2\,\pi i)\,\{\mathrm{Log}\,[f(r)] + 2\,\pi i\,(n - m)\} - \log r\,\mathrm{Log}\,[f(r)]$$
$$= 2\,\pi i\,\mathrm{Log}\,[f(r)] + 2\,\pi i\,(n - m)\log r - 4\,(n - m)\,\pi^2.$$

In order to evaluate the new definite integral, let us consider the closed curve Γ, formed by the circumference C, by the circumference c described about the origin with the infinitesimal radius ρ, and by the two borders ab, $a'b'$ of a cut made along the real axis from the point $z = \rho$ to the point $z = r$ (Fig. 19). We shall suppose for definiteness that $f(z)$ has neither poles nor zeros on that portion of the axis of reals. If it has, we need only make a cut making an infinitesimal angle with the axis of reals. The function $\mathrm{Log}\,z$ is analytic in the interior of Γ, and according to the general formula (40) we have the relation

$$\int_{(ab)} \mathrm{Log}\,(z)\, \frac{f'(z)}{f(z)}\, dz + \int_{(C)} \mathrm{Log}\,(z)\, \frac{f'(z)}{f(z)}\, dz + \int_{(b'a')} \mathrm{Log}\,(z)\, \frac{f'(z)}{f(z)}\, dz$$
$$+ \int_{(C)} \mathrm{Log}\,(z)\, \frac{f'(z)}{f(z)}\, dz = 2\,\pi i\,\mathrm{Log}\left(\frac{a_1 a_2 \cdots a_n}{b_1 b_2 \cdots b_m}\right).$$

The integral along the circle c approaches zero with ρ, for the product $z\,\mathrm{Log}\,z$ is infinitesimal with ρ. On the other hand, if the angle of z is zero along ab, it is equal to $2\,\pi$ along $a'b'$, and the sum of the two corresponding integrals has for limit

$$- \int_0^r 2\,\pi i \frac{f'(z)}{f(z)}\, dz = - 2\,\pi i\,\mathrm{Log}\,[f(r)] + 2\,\pi i\,\mathrm{Log}\,[f(0)].$$

The remaining portion is

$$\int_{(C)} \mathrm{Log}\,(z)\, \frac{f'(z)}{f(z)}\, dz = 2\,\pi i\,\mathrm{Log}\left(\frac{a_1 a_2 \cdots a_n}{b_1 b_1 \cdots b_m}\right) + 2\,\pi i\,\mathrm{Log}\left[\frac{f(r)}{f(0)}\right],$$

and the formula (46) becomes

$$I = 2\,\pi i\,(n - m)\log r + 2\,\pi i\,\mathrm{Log}\,[f(0)] - 2\,\pi i\,\mathrm{Log}\left(\frac{a_1 a_2 \cdots a_n}{b_1 b_1 \cdots b_m}\right) - 4\,(n - m)\,\pi^2.$$

In order to integrate along the circle C, we can put $z = re^{i\phi}$ and let ϕ vary from 0 to $2\,\pi$. It follows that $dz/z = i\,d\phi$. Let $f(z) = Re^{i\Phi}$, where R and Φ are continuous functions of ϕ along C. Equating the coefficients of i in the preceding relation, we obtain Jensen's formula *

$$(47) \qquad \frac{1}{2\pi} \int_0^{2\pi} \log R \, d\phi = \log |f(0)| + \log \left| r^{n-m} \frac{b_1 b_2 \cdots b_m}{a_1 a_2 \cdots a_n} \right|,$$

in which there appear only ordinary Napierian logarithms.

When the function $f(z)$ is analytic in the interior of C, it is clear that the product $b_1 b_2 \cdots b_n$ should be replaced by unity, and the formula becomes

$$(48) \qquad \frac{1}{2\pi} \int_0^{2\pi} \log R \, d\phi = \log |f(0)| + \log \left| \frac{r^n}{a_1 a_2 \cdots a_n} \right|.$$

This relation is interesting in that it contains only the absolute values of the roots of $f(z)$ within the circle C, and the absolute value of $f(z)$ along that circle and for the center of the same circle.

51. Lagrange's formula.
Lagrange's formula, which we have already established by Laplace's method (I, § 195, 2d ed.; § 189, 1st ed.), can be demonstrated also very easily by means of the general theorems of Cauchy. The process which we shall use is due to Hermite.

Let $f(z)$ be an analytic function in a certain region D containing the point a. The equation

$$(49) \qquad F(z) = z - a - \alpha f(z) = 0,$$

where α is a variable parameter, has the root $z = a$, for $\alpha = 0$.[†] Let us suppose that $\alpha \neq 0$, and let C be a circle with the center a and the radius r lying entirely in the region D and such that we have along the entire circumference $|\alpha f(z)| < |z - a|$. By the lemma proved in § 49 the equation $F(z) = 0$ has the same number of roots within the curve C as the equation $z - a = 0$, that is, a single root. Let ζ denote that root, and let $\Pi(z)$ be an analytic function in the circle C.

The function $\Pi(z)/F(z)$ has a single pole in the interior of C, at the point $z = \zeta$, and the corresponding residue is $\Pi(\zeta)/F'(\zeta)$. From the general theorem we have, then,

$$\frac{\Pi(\zeta)}{F'(\zeta)} = \frac{1}{2\pi i} \int_{(C)} \frac{\Pi(z)\,dz}{F(z)} = \frac{1}{2\pi i} \int_{(C)} \frac{\Pi(z)\,dz}{z - a - \alpha f(z)}.$$

In order to develop the integral on the right in powers of α, we shall proceed exactly as we did to derive the Taylor development,

---

* *Acta mathematica*, Vol. XXII.

† It is assumed that $f(a)$ is not zero, for otherwise $F(z)$ would vanish when $z = a$ for *any* value of α and the following developments would not yield any results of interest. — TRANS.

and we shall write

$$\frac{1}{z-a-af(z)} = \frac{1}{z-a} + \frac{af(z)}{(z-a)^2} + \cdots$$
$$+ \frac{[af(z)]^n}{(z-a)^{n+1}} + \frac{1}{z-a-af(z)}\left[\frac{af(z)}{z-a}\right]^{n+1}.$$

Substituting this value in the integral, we find

$$\frac{\Pi(\zeta)}{F'(\zeta)} = J_0 + aJ_1 + \cdots + a^n J_n + R_{n+1},$$

where

$$J_0 = \frac{1}{2\pi i}\int_{(C)}\frac{\Pi(z)\,dz}{z-a}, \qquad \cdots, \qquad J_n = \frac{1}{2\pi i}\int_{(C)}\frac{[f(z)]^n\Pi(z)\,dz}{(z-a)^{n+1}},$$

$$R_{n+1} = \frac{1}{2\pi i}\int_{(C)}\frac{\Pi(z)}{z-a-af(z)}\left[\frac{af(z)}{z-a}\right]^{n+1}dz.$$

Let m be the maximum value of the absolute value of $af(z)$ along the circumference of the circle C; then, by hypothesis, m is less than r. If M is the maximum value of the absolute value of $\Pi(z)$ along C, we have

$$|R_{n+1}| < \frac{1}{2\pi}\left(\frac{m}{r}\right)^{n+1}\frac{2\pi r M}{r-m},$$

which shows that R_{n+1} approaches zero when n increases indefinitely. Moreover, we have, by the definition of the coefficients $J_0, J_1, \cdots, J_n,$ $\cdots$ and the formula (14),

$$J_0 = \Pi(a), \qquad \cdots, \qquad J_n = \frac{1}{n!}\frac{d^n}{da^n}\{[f(a)]^n\Pi(a)\};$$

whence we obtain the following development in series:

$$(50) \qquad \frac{\Pi(\zeta)}{F'(\zeta)} = \Pi(a) + \sum_{n=1}^{+\infty}\frac{a^n}{n!}\frac{d^n}{da^n}\{\Pi(a)[f(a)]^n\}.$$

We can write this expression in a somewhat different form. If we take $\Pi(z) = \Phi(z)[1 - af'(z)]$, where $\Phi(z)$ is an analytic function in the same region, the left-hand side of the equation (50) will no longer contain a and will reduce to $\Phi(\zeta)$. As for the right-hand side, we observe that it contains two terms of degree n in a, whose sum is

$$\frac{a^n}{n!}\frac{d^n}{da^n}\{\Phi(a)[f(a)]^n\} - \frac{a^n}{(n-1)!}\frac{d^{n-1}}{da^{n-1}}\{\Phi(a)[f(a)]^{n-1}f'(a)\}$$
$$= \frac{a^n}{n!}\frac{d^{n-1}}{da^{n-1}}\{\Phi'(a)[f(a)]^n + n\Phi(a)f'(a)[f(a)]^{n-1}$$
$$- n\Phi(a)f'(a)[f(a)]^{n-1}\}$$
$$= \frac{a^n}{n!}\frac{d^{n-1}}{da^{n-1}}\{\Phi'(a)[f(a)]^n\},$$

and we find again Lagrange's formula in its usual form (see I, formula (52), § 195, 2d ed.; § 189, 1st ed.)

$$(51) \quad \Phi(\zeta) = \Phi(a) + \frac{\alpha}{1}\Phi'(a)f(a) + \cdots + \frac{\alpha^n}{n!}\frac{d^{n-1}}{da^{n-1}}\{\Phi'(a)[f(a)]^n\} + \cdots.$$

We have supposed that we have $|\alpha f(z)| < r$ along the circle C, which is true if $|\alpha|$ is small enough. In order to find the maximum value of $|\alpha|$, let us limit ourselves to the case where $f(z)$ is a polynomial or an integral function. Let $\mathcal{M}(r)$ be the maximum value of $|f(z)|$ along the circle C described about the point a as center with the radius r. The proof will apply to this circle, provided $|\alpha|\mathcal{M}(r) < r$. We are thus led to seek the maximum value of the quotient $r/\mathcal{M}(r)$, as r varies from 0 to $+\infty$. This quotient is zero for $r = 0$, for if $\mathcal{M}(r)$ were to approach zero with r, the point $z = a$ would be a zero for $f(z)$, and $F(z)$ would vanish for $z = a$. The same quotient is also zero for $r = \infty$, for otherwise $f(z)$ would be a polynomial of the first degree (§ 36). Aside from these trivial cases, it follows that $r/\mathcal{M}(r)$ passes through a maximum value μ for a value r_1 of r. The reasoning shows that the equation (49) has one and only one root ζ such that $|\zeta - a| < r_1$, provided $|\alpha| < \mu$. Hence the developments (50) and (51) are applicable so long as $|\alpha|$ does not exceed μ, provided the functions $\Pi(z)$ and $\Phi(z)$ are themselves analytic in the circle C_1 of radius r_1.

Example. Let $f(z) = (z^2 - 1)/2$; the equation (49) has the root

$$\zeta = \frac{1 - \sqrt{1 - 2a\alpha + \alpha^2}}{\alpha},$$

which approaches a when α approaches zero. Let us put $\Pi(z) = 1$. Then the formula (50) takes the form

$$(52) \quad \frac{1}{\sqrt{1 - 2a\alpha + \alpha^2}} = 1 + \sum_{1}^{+\infty}\frac{\alpha^n}{n!}\frac{d^n}{da^n}\left[\frac{(a^2 - 1)^n}{2^n}\right] = 1 + \sum_{1}^{+\infty}\alpha^n X_n(a),$$

where X_n is the nth Legendre's polynomial (see I, §§ 90, 189, 2d ed.; §§ 88, 184, 1st ed.). In order to find out between what limits the formula is valid, let us suppose that a is real and greater than unity. On the circle of radius r we have evidently $\mathcal{M}(r) = [(a + r)^2 - 1]/2$, and we are led to seek the maximum value of $2r/[(a + r)^2 - 1]$ as r increases from 0 to $+\infty$. This maximum is found for $r = \sqrt{a^2 - 1}$, and it is equal to $a - \sqrt{a^2 - 1}$. If, however, a lies between -1 and $+1$, we find by a quite elementary calculation that

$$\mathcal{M}(r) = \frac{r^2 + 1 - a^2}{2\sqrt{1 - a^2}}.$$

The maximum of $2r\sqrt{1 - a^2}/(r^2 + 1 - a^2)$ occurs when $r = \sqrt{1 - a^2}$, and it is equal to unity.

It is easy to verify these results. In fact, the radical $\sqrt{1 - 2a\alpha + \alpha^2}$, considered as a function of α, has the two critical points $a \pm \sqrt{a^2 - 1}$. If $a > 1$, the critical point nearest the origin is $a - \sqrt{a^2 - 1}$. When a lies between -1 and $+1$, the absolute value of each of the two critical points $a \pm i\sqrt{1 - a^2}$ is unity.

In the fourth lithographed edition of Hermite's lectures will be found (p. 185) a very complete discussion of Kepler's equation $z - a = \sin z$ by this method. His process leads to the calculation of the root of the transcendental equation $e^r(r - 1) = e^{-r}(r + 1)$ which lies between 1 and 2. Stieltjes has obtained the values

$$r_1 = 1.199678640257734, \qquad \mu = 0.6627434193492.$$

52. Study of functions for infinite values of the variable. In order to study a function $f(z)$ for values of the variable for which the absolute value becomes infinite, we can put $z = 1/z'$ and study the function $f(1/z')$ in the neighborhood of the origin. But it is easy to avoid this auxiliary transformation. We shall suppose first that we can find a positive number R such that *every finite value of z* whose absolute value is greater than R is an ordinary point for $f(z)$. If we describe a circle C about the origin as center with a radius R, the function $f(z)$ will be regular at every point z at a finite distance lying outside of C. We shall call the region of the plane exterior to C *a neighborhood of the point at infinity.*

Let us consider, together with the circle C, a concentric circle C' with a radius $R' > R$. The function $f(z)$, being analytic in the circular ring bounded by C and C', is equal, by Laurent's theorem, to the sum of a series arranged according to integral positive and negative powers of z,

$$(53) \qquad f(z) = \sum_{m=-\infty}^{+\infty} A_{-m} z^m ;$$

the coefficients A_{-m} of this series are independent of the radius R', and, since this radius can be taken as large as we wish, it follows that the formula (53) is valid for the entire neighborhood of the point at infinity, that is, for the whole region exterior to C. We shall now distinguish several cases :

1) When the development of $f(z)$ contains only negative powers of z,

$$(54) \qquad f(z) = A_0 + A_1 \frac{1}{z} + A_2 \frac{1}{z^2} + \cdots + A_m \frac{1}{z^m} + \cdots,$$

the function $f(z)$ approaches A_0 when $|z|$ becomes infinite, and we say that the function $f(z)$ *is regular at the point at infinity*, or, again, that *the point at infinity is an ordinary point for $f(z)$.* If the coefficients A_0, A_1, $\cdots$, A_{m-1} are zero, but A_m is not zero, *the point at infinity is a zero of the mth order for $f(z)$.*

2) When the development of $f(z)$ contains a finite number of positive powers of z,

$$(55) \qquad f(z) = B_m z^m + B_{m-1} z^{m-1} + \cdots$$
$$+ B_1 z + A_0 + A_1 \frac{1}{z} + A_2 \frac{1}{z^2} + \cdots,$$

where the first coefficient B_m is not zero, we shall say that *the point at infinity is a pole of the mth order for $f(z)$*, and the polynomial $B_m z^m + \cdots + B_1 z$ is the *principal part* relative to that pole. When $|z|$ becomes infinite, the same thing is true of $|f(z)|$, whatever may be the manner in which z moves.

3) Finally, when the development of $f(z)$ contains an infinite number of positive powers of z, *the point at infinity is an essentially singular point for $f(z)$.* The series formed by the positive powers of z represents an integral function $G(z)$, which is the *principal part* in the neighborhood of the point at infinity. We see in particular that an integral transcendental function has the point at infinity as an essentially singular point.

The preceding definitions were in a way necessitated by those which have already been adopted for a point at a finite distance. Indeed, if we put $z = 1/z'$, the function $f(z)$ changes to a function of z', $\phi(z') = f(1/z')$, and it is seen at once that we have only carried over to the point at infinity the terms adopted for the point $z' = 0$ with respect to the function $\phi(z')$. Reasoning by analogy, we might be tempted to call the coefficient A_{-1} of z, in the development (53), the *residue*, but this would be unfortunate. In order to preserve the characteristic property, we shall say that the *residue with respect to the point at infinity is the coefficient of $1/z$ with its sign changed*, that is, $-A_1$. This number is equal to

$$\frac{1}{2\pi i} \int f(z)\, dz,$$

where the integral is taken in the positive sense along the boundary of the neighborhood of the point at infinity. But here, the neighborhood of the point at infinity being the part of the plane exterior to C, the corresponding positive sense is that opposite to the usual sense. Indeed, this integral reduces to

$$\frac{1}{2\pi i} \int_{(C)} \frac{A_1\, dz}{z} = \frac{A_1}{2\pi i} (\mathrm{Log}\, z)_{(C)},$$

and, when z describes the circle C in the desired sense, the angle of z diminishes by 2π, which gives $-A_1$ as the value of the integral.

It is essential to observe that it is entirely possible for a function to be regular at the point at infinity without its residue being zero; for example, the function $1 + 1/z$ has this property.

If the point at infinity is a pole or a zero for $f(z)$, we can write, in the neighborhood of that point,

$$f(z) = z^\mu \phi(z),$$

where μ is a positive or negative integer equal to the order of the function with its sign changed, and where $\phi(z)$ is a function which is regular at the point at infinity and which is not zero for $z = \infty$. From the preceding equation we deduce

$$\frac{f'(z)}{f(z)} = \frac{\mu}{z} + \frac{\phi'(z)}{\phi(z)},$$

where the function $\phi'(z)/\phi(z)$ is regular at the point at infinity but has a development commencing with a term of the second or a higher degree in $1/z$. The residue of $f'(z)/f(z)$ is then equal to $-\mu$, that is, to the order of the function $f(z)$ at the point at infinity. The statement is the same as for a pole or a zero at a finite distance.

Let $f(z)$ be a single-valued analytic function having only a finite number of singular points. The convention which has just been made for the point at infinity enables us to state in a very simple form the following general theorem:

The sum of the residues of the function $f(z)$ in the entire plane, the point at infinity included, is zero.

The demonstration is immediate. Describe with the origin as center a circle C containing all the singular points of $f(z)$ (except the point at infinity). The integral $\int f(z)\,dz$, taken along this circle in the ordinary sense, is equal to the product of $2\pi i$ and the sum of the residues with respect to all the singular points of $f(z)$ at a finite distance. On the other hand, the same integral, taken along the same circle in the opposite sense, is equal to the product of $2\pi i$ and the residue relative to the point at infinity. The sum of the two integrals being zero, the same is true of the sum of the residues.

Cauchy applied the term *total residue* (*résidu intégral*) of a function $f(z)$ to the sum of the residues of that function for all the singular points at a finite distance. When there are only a finite number of singular points, we see that the total residue is equal to the residue relative to the point at infinity with its sign changed.

Example. Let

$$f(z) = \frac{P(z)}{\sqrt{Q(z)}},$$

where $P(z)$ and $Q(z)$ are two polynomials, the first of degree p, the second of even degree $2q$. If R is a real number greater than the absolute value of any root of $Q(z)$, the function is single-valued outside of a circle C of radius R, and we can write

$$f(z) = z^{p-q}\phi(z),$$

where $\phi(z)$ is a function which is regular at infinity, and which is not zero for $z = \infty$. The point at infinity is a pole for $f(z)$ if $p > q$, and an ordinary point if $p \leqq q$. The residue will certainly be zero if p is less than $q - 1$.

IV. PERIODS OF DEFINITE INTEGRALS

53. Polar periods. The study of line integrals revealed to us that such integrals possess periods under certain circumstances. Since every integral of a function $f(z)$ of a complex variable z is a sum of line integrals, it is clear that these integrals also may have certain periods. Let us consider first an analytic function $f(z)$ that has only a finite number of isolated singular points, poles, or essentially singular points, within a closed curve C. This case is absolutely analogous to the one which we studied for line integrals (I, § 153), and the reasoning applies here without modification. Any path that can be drawn within the boundary C between the two points z_0, Z of that region, and not passing through any of the singular points of $f(z)$, is equivalent to one fixed path joining these two points, preceded by a succession of loops starting from z_0 and surrounding one or more of the singular points $a_1, a_2, \cdots, a_n$ of $f(z)$. Let $A_1, A_2, \cdots, A_n$ be the corresponding residues of $f(z)$; the integral $\int f(z)\,dz$, taken along the loop surrounding the point a_1, is equal to $\pm\, 2\,\pi i A_1$, and similarly for the others. The different values of the integral $\int_{z_0}^{Z} f(z)\,dz$ are therefore included in the expression

$$(56) \quad \int_{z_0}^{Z} f(z)\,dz = F(Z) + 2\,\pi i (m_1 A_1 + m_2 A_2 + \cdots + m_n A_n),$$

where $F(Z)$ is one of the values of that integral corresponding to the determined path, and $m_1, m_2, \cdots$ are arbitrary positive or negative integers; the periods are

$$2\,\pi i A_1, \quad 2\,\pi i A_2, \quad \cdots, \quad 2\,\pi i A_n.$$

In most cases the points a_1, a_2, $\cdots$, a_n are poles, and the periods result from infinitely small circuits described about these poles; whence the term *polar periods*, which is ordinarily used to distinguish them from periods of another kind mentioned later.

Instead of a region of the plane interior to a closed curve, we may consider a portion of the plane extending to infinity; the function $f(z)$ can then have an infinite number of poles, and the integral an infinite number of periods. If the residue with respect to a singular point a of $f(z)$ is zero, the corresponding period is zero and the point a is also a pole or an essentially singular point for the integral. But if the residue is not zero, the point a is a logarithmic critical point for the integral. If, for example, the point a is a pole of the mth order for $f(z)$, we have in the neighborhood of that point

$$f(z) = \frac{B_m}{(z-a)^m} + \frac{B_{m-1}}{(z-a)^{m-1}} + \cdots + \frac{B_1}{z-a} + A_0 + A_1(z-a) + \cdots,$$

and therefore

$$\int_{z_0}^{z} f(z)\,dz = C - \frac{B_m}{(m-1)(z-a)^{m-1}} + \cdots + B_1 \operatorname{Log}(z-a)$$
$$+ A_0(z-a) + A_1 \frac{(z-a)^2}{2} + \cdots,$$

where C is a constant that depends on the lower limit of integration z_0 and on the path followed by the variable in integration.

When we apply these general considerations to rational functions, many well-known results are at once apparent. Thus, in order that the integral of a rational function may be itself a rational function, it is necessary that that integral shall not have any periods; that is, all its residues must be zero. That condition is, moreover, sufficient. The definite integral

$$\int_{z_0}^{z} \frac{dz}{z-a}$$

has a single critical point $z = a$, and the corresponding period is $2\pi i$; it is, then, in the integral calculus that the true origin of the multiple values of $\operatorname{Log}(z-a)$ is to be found, as we have already pointed out in detail in the case of $\int_1^z dz/z$ (§ 31).

Let us take, in the same way, the definite integral

$$F(z) = \int_0^z \frac{dz}{1+z^2};$$

it has the two logarithmic critical points $+i$ and $-i$, but it has only the single period π. If we limit ourselves to real values of the variable, the different determinations of arc tan x appear as so many distinct functions of the variable x. We see, on the contrary, how Cauchy's work leads us to regard them as so many distinct branches of the same analytic function.

Note. When there are more than three periods, the value of the definite integral at any point z may be entirely indeterminate. Let us recall first the following result, taken from the theory of continued fractions*: Given a real irrational number α, we can always find two integers p and q, positive or negative, such that we have $|p + q\alpha| < \epsilon$, where ϵ is an arbitrarily preassigned positive number.

The numbers p and q having been selected in this way, let us suppose that the sequence of multiples of $p + q\alpha$ is formed. Any real number A is equal to one of these multiples, or lies between two consecutive multiples. We can therefore find two integers m and n such that $|m + n\alpha - A|$ shall be less than ϵ.

With this in mind, let us now consider the function

$$f(z) = \frac{1}{2\pi i}\left(\frac{1}{z-a} + \frac{\alpha}{z-b} + \frac{i}{z-c} + \frac{i\beta}{z-d}\right),$$

where a, b, c, d are four distinct poles and α, β are real irrational numbers. The integral $\int_{z_0}^{z} f(z)\,dz$ has the four periods 1, α, i, $i\beta$. Let $I(z)$ be the value of the integral taken along a particular path from z_0 to z, and let $M + Ni$ denote any complex number whatever. We can always find four integers m, n, m', n' such that the absolute value of the difference

$$I(z) + m + n\alpha + i(m' + n'\beta) - (M + Ni)$$

will be less than any preassigned positive number ϵ. We need only choose these integers so that

$$|m + n\alpha - A| < \frac{\epsilon}{2}, \qquad |m' + n'\beta - B| < \frac{\epsilon}{2},$$

where $M + Ni - I(z) = A + Bi$. Hence we can make the variable describe a path joining the two points given in advance, z_0, z, so that the value of the integral $\int f(z)\,dz$ taken along this path differs as little as we wish from any preassigned number. Thus we see again the decisive influence of the path followed by the variable on the final value of an analytic function.

54. A study of the integral $\int_0^z dz/\sqrt{1-z^2}$. The integral calculus explains the multiple values of the function arc sin z in the simplest manner by the preceding method. They arise from the different determinations of the definite integral

$$(57) \qquad F(z) = \int_0^z \frac{dz}{\sqrt{1-z^2}}$$

according to the path followed by the variable. For definiteness we shall suppose that we start from the origin with the initial value $+1$

---

* A little farther on a direct proof will be found (§ 66).

for the radical, and we shall indicate by I the value of the integral taken along a determined path (or direct path). For example, the path shall be along a straight line if the point z is not situated on the real axis or if it lies upon the real axis within the segment from -1 to $+1$; but when z is real and $|z| > 1$, we shall take for the direct path a path lying above the real axis.

Now, the points $z = +1$, $z = -1$ being the only critical points of $\sqrt{1 - z^2}$, every path leading from the origin to the point z can be replaced by a succession of loops described about the two critical points $+1$ and -1, followed by the direct path. We are then led to study the value of the integral along a loop. Let us consider, for example, the loop $OamaO$, described about the point $z = +1$;

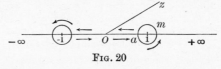

FIG. 20

this loop is composed of the segment Oa passing from the origin to the point $1 - \epsilon$, of the circle ama of radius ϵ described about $z = 1$ as center, and of the segment aO. Hence the integral along the loop is equal to the sum of the integrals

$$\int_0^{1-\epsilon} \frac{dx}{\sqrt{1 - x^2}} + \int_{(ama)} \frac{dz}{\sqrt{1 - z^2}} + \int_{1-\epsilon}^0 \frac{dx}{\sqrt{1 - x^2}}.$$

The integral along the small circle approaches zero with ϵ, for the product $(z - 1) f(z)$ approaches zero. On the other hand, when z has described this small circle, the radical has changed sign and in the integral along the segment aO the negative value should be taken for $\sqrt{1 - x^2}$. The integral along the loop is therefore equal to the limit of $2 \int_0^{1-\epsilon} dx / \sqrt{1 - x^2}$ as ϵ approaches zero, that is, to π. It should be observed that the value of this integral does not depend on the sense in which the loop is described, but we return to the origin with the value -1 for the radical.

If we were to describe the same loop around the point $z = +1$ with -1 as the initial value of the radical, the value of the integral along the loop would be equal to $-\pi$, and we should return to the origin with $+1$ as the value of the radical. In the same way it is seen that a loop described around the critical point $z = -1$ gives $-\pi$ or $+\pi$ for the integral, according as the initial value $+1$ or -1 is taken for the radical on starting from the origin.

If we let the variable describe two loops in succession, we return to the origin with $+1$ for the final value of the radical, and the value of the integral taken along these two loops will be $+2\pi$, 0, or

$- 2\,\pi$, according to the order in which these two loops are described. An even number of loops will give, then, $2\,m\pi$ for the value of the integral, and will bring back the radical to its initial value $+1$. An odd number of loops will give, on the contrary, the value $(2\,m+1)\pi$ to the integral, and the final value of the radical at the origin will be -1. It follows from this that the value of the integral $F(z)$ will be one of the two forms

$$I + 2\,m\pi, \qquad (2\,m+1)\pi - I,$$

according as the path described by the variable can be replaced by the direct path preceded by an *even* number or by an *odd* number of loops.

55. Periods of hyperelliptic integrals. We can study, in a similar manner, the different values of the definite integral

$$(58) \qquad F(z) = \int_{z_0}^{z} \frac{P(z)\,dz}{\sqrt{R(z)}},$$

where $P(z)$ and $R(z)$ are two polynomials, of which the second, $R(z)$, of degree n, vanishes for n distinct values of z:

$$R(z) = A\,(z - e_1)(z - e_2) \cdots (z - e_n).$$

We shall suppose that the point z_0 is distinct from the points $e_1, e_2, \cdots, e_n$; then the equation $u^2 = R(z_0)$ has two distinct roots $+ u_0$ and $- u_0$. We shall select u_0 for the initial value of the radical $R(z)$. If we let the variable z describe a path of any form whatever not passing through any of the critical points $e_1, e_2, \cdots, e_n$, the value of the radical $\sqrt{R(z)}$ at each point of the path will be determined by continuity. Let us suppose that from each of the points $e_1, e_2, \cdots, e_n$ we make an infinite cut in the plane in such a way that these cuts do not cross each other. The integral, taken from z_0 up to any point z along a path that does not cross any of these cuts (which we shall call a direct path), has a completely determined value $I(z)$ for each point of the plane. We have now to study the influence of a loop, described from z_0 around any one of the critical points e_i, on the value of the integral. Let $2\,E_i$ be the value of the integral taken along a closed curve that starts from z_0 and incloses the single critical point e_i, the initial value of the radical being u_0. The value of this integral does not depend on the sense in which the curve is described, but only on the initial value of the radical at the point z_0. In fact, let us call $2\,E_i'$ the value of the integral taken along the same curve in the opposite sense, with the same initial value u_0 of the radical. If we let the variable z describe the curve twice in succession and in the opposite senses, it is clear that the sum of the integrals obtained is zero; but the value of the integral for the first turn is $2 E_i$, and we return to the point z_0 with the value $- u_0$ for the radical. The integral along the curve described in the opposite sense is then equal to $- 2 E_i'$, and consequently $E_i' = E_i$. The closed curve considered may be reduced to a loop formed by the straight line $z_0 a$, the circle c_i of infinitesimal radius about e_i, and the straight line $a z_0$ (Fig. 21); the integral along c_i is infinitesimal, since the product $(z - e_i) P(z)/\sqrt{R(z)}$ approaches zero with the absolute value of $z - e_i$. If we add together the integrals along $z_0 a$ and along $a z_0$, we find

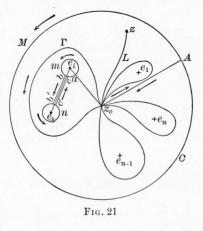

$$E_i = \int_{z_0}^{e_i} \frac{P(z)\,dz}{\sqrt{R(z)}},$$

where the integral is taken along the straight line and the initial value of the radical is u_0.

This being the case, the integral taken along a path which reduces to a succession of two loops described about the points e_α, e_β is equal to $2 E_\alpha - 2 E_\beta$, for we return after the first loop to the point z_0 with the value

FIG. 21

$- u_0$ for the radical, and the integral along the second loop is equal to $- 2 E_\beta$. After having described this new loop we return to the point z_0 with the original initial value u_0. If the path described by the variable z can be reduced to an even number of loops described about the points e_α, e_β, e_γ, e_δ, $\cdots$, e_κ, e_λ successively, followed by the direct path from z_0 to z, where the indices α, β, $\cdots$, κ, λ are taken from among the numbers $1, 2, \cdots, n$, the value of the integral along the path is, by what precedes,

$$F(z) = I + 2(E_\alpha - E_\beta) + 2(E_\gamma - E_\delta) + \cdots + 2(E_\kappa - E_\lambda).$$

If, on the contrary, the path followed by the variable can be reduced to an odd number of loops described successively around the critical points e_α, e_β, $\cdots$, e_κ, e_λ, e_μ, the value of the integral is

$$F(z) = 2(E_\alpha - E_\beta) + \cdots + 2(E_\kappa - E_\lambda) + 2 E_\mu - I.$$

Hence the integral under consideration has as periods all the expressions $2(E_i - E_h)$, but all these periods reduce to $(n-1)$ of them :

$$\omega_1 = 2(E_1 - E_n), \quad \omega_2 = 2(E_2 - E_n), \quad \cdots, \quad \omega_{n-1} = 2(E_{n-1} - E_n),$$

for it is clear that we can write

$$2(E_i - E_h) = 2(E_i - E_n) - 2(E_h - E_n) = \omega_i - \omega_h.$$

Since, on the other hand, $2\,E_\mu = \omega_\mu + 2\,E_n$, we see that all the values of the definite integral $F(z)$ at the point z are given by the two expressions

$$F(z) = I + m_1\omega_1 + \cdots + m_{n-1}\omega_{n-1},$$
$$F(z) = 2\,E_n - I + m_1\omega_1 + \cdots + m_{n-1}\omega_{n-1},$$

where $m_1, m_2, \cdots, m_{n-1}$ are arbitrary integers.

This result gives rise to a certain number of important observations. It is almost self-evident that the periods must be independent of the point z_0 chosen for the starting point, and it is easy to verify this. Consider, for example, the period $2\,E_i - 2\,E_h$; this period is equal to the value of the integral taken along a closed curve Γ passing through the point z_0 and containing only the two critical points $e_i,\ e_h$. If, for definiteness, we suppose that there are no other critical points in the interior of the triangle whose vertices are z_0, e_i, e_h, this closed curve can be replaced by the boundary $bb'nc'cmb$ (Fig. 21); whence, making the radii of the two small circles approach zero, we see that the period is equal to twice the integral

$$\int_{e_i}^{e_h} \frac{P(z)\,dz}{\sqrt{R(z)}}$$

taken along the straight line joining the two critical points $e_i,\ e_h$.

It may happen that the $(n-1)$ periods $\omega_1, \omega_2, \cdots, \omega_{n-1}$ are not independent. This occurs whenever the polynomial $R(z)$ is of *even degree, provided that the degree of $P(z)$ is less than $n/2 - 1$.* With the point z_0 as center let us draw a circle C with a radius so large that the circle contains all the critical points ; and for simplicity let us suppose that the critical points have been numbered from 1 to n in the order in which they are encountered by a radius vector as it turns about z_0 in the positive sense.

The integral

$$\int \frac{P(z)\,dz}{\sqrt{R(z)}},$$

taken along the closed boundary z_0AMAz_0, formed by the radius z_0A, by the circle C, and by the radius Az_0 described in the negative sense, is zero. The integrals along $z_0 A$ and along $A z_0$ cancel, for the circle C contains an *even* number of critical points, and after having described this circle we return to the point A with the same value of the radical. On the other hand, the integral along C approaches zero as the radius becomes infinite, since the product $z P(z)/\sqrt{R(z)}$ approaches zero by the hypothesis made on the degree of the polynomial $P(z)$. Since the value of this integral does not depend on the radius of C, it follows that that value must be zero.

Now the boundary $z_0 A M A z_0$ considered above can be replaced by a succession of loops described around the critical points $e_1, e_2, \cdots, e_n$ in the order of these indices. Hence we have the relation

$$2 E_1 - 2 E_2 + 2 E_3 - 2 E_4 + \cdots + 2 E_{n-1} - 2 E_n = 0,$$

which can be written in the form

$$\omega_1 - \omega_2 + \omega_3 - \omega_4 + \cdots + \omega_{n-1} = 0;$$

and we see that the $n-1$ periods of the integral reduce to $n-2$ periods $\omega_1, \omega_2, \cdots, \omega_{n-2}$.

Consider now the more general form of integral

$$F(z) = \int_{z_0}^{z} \frac{P(z)\, dz}{Q(z)\, \sqrt{R(z)}},$$

where P, Q, R are three polynomials of which the last, $R(z)$, has only simple roots. Among the roots of $Q(z)$ there may be some that belong to $R(z)$; let α_1, $\alpha_2, \cdots, \alpha_s$ be the roots of $Q(z)$ which do not cause $R(z)$ to vanish. The integral $F(z)$ has, as above, the periods $2(E_i - E_h)$, where $2 E_i$ denotes always the integral taken along a closed curve starting from z_0 and inclosing none of the roots of either of the polynomials $Q(z)$ and $R(z)$ except e_i. But $F(z)$ has also a certain number of polar periods arising from the loops described about the poles $\alpha_1, \alpha_2, \cdots, \alpha_s$. The total number of these periods is again diminished by unity if $R(z)$ is of even degree n, and if

$$p < q + \frac{n}{2} - 1,$$

where p and q are the degrees of the polynomials P and Q respectively.

Example. Let $R(z)$ be a polynomial of the fourth degree having a multiple root. Let us find the number of periods of the integral

$$\int_{z_0}^{z} \frac{dz}{\sqrt{R(z)}}.$$

If $R(z)$ has a double root e_1 and two simple roots e_2, e_3, the integral

$$F(z) = \int_{z_0}^{z} \frac{dz}{(z - e_1)\, \sqrt{A(z - e_2)(z - e_3)}}$$

has the period $2\,E_2 - 2\,E_3$, and also a polar period arising from a loop around the pole e_1. By the remark made just above, these two periods are equal. If $R\,(z)$ has two double roots, it is seen immediately that the integral has a single polar period.

If $R\,(z)$ has a triple root, the integral

$$F(z) = \int_{z_0}^z \frac{dz}{(z - e_1)\,\sqrt{(z - e_1)\,(z - e_2)}}$$

has the period $2\,E_1 - 2\,E_2$, but, by the general remark made above, that period is zero. The same thing is true if $R\,(z)$ has a quadruple root. In résumé we have : *If $R\,(z)$ has one or two double roots, the integral has a period; if $R\,(z)$ has a triple or quadruple root, the integral does not have periods.* All these results are easily verified by direct integration.

56. Periods of elliptic integrals of the first kind. The elliptic integral of the first kind,

$$F(z) = \int_{z_0}^z \frac{dz}{\sqrt{R\,(z)}},$$

where $R\,(z)$ is a polynomial of the third or the fourth degree, prime to its derivative, has two periods by the preceding general theory. We shall now show that *the ratio of these two periods is not real.*

We can suppose without loss of generality that $R\,(z)$ is of the third degree. Indeed, if $R_1\,(z)$ is a polynomial of the fourth degree, and if a is a root of this polynomial, we may write (I, § 105, note, 2d ed. ; § 110, 1st ed.)

$$\int \frac{dz}{\sqrt{R_1(z)}} = \int \frac{dy}{\sqrt{R\,(y)}},$$

where $z = a + 1/y$ and where $R\,(y)$ is a polynomial of the third degree. It is evident that the two integrals have the same periods. If $R\,(z)$ is of the third degree, we may suppose that it has the roots 0 and 1, for we need only make a linear substitution $z = \alpha + \beta y$ to reduce any other case to this one. Hence the proof reduces to showing that the integral

(59) $$F(z) = \int_{z_0}^z \frac{dz}{\sqrt{z\,(1 - z)\,(a - z)}},$$

where a is different from zero and from unity, has two periods whose ratio is not real.

If a is real, the property is evident. Thus, if a is greater than unity, for example, the integral has the two periods

$$2 \int_0^1 \frac{dz}{\sqrt{z\,(1 - z)\,(a - z)}}, \qquad 2 \int^a \frac{dz}{\sqrt{z\,(1 - z)\,(a - z)}},$$

of which the first is real, while the second is a pure imaginary. Moreover, none of these periods can be zero.

Suppose now that a is complex, and, for example, that the coefficient of i in a is positive. We can again take for one of the periods

$$\Omega_1 = 2 \int_0^1 \frac{dz}{\sqrt{z(1-z)(a-z)}}.$$

We shall apply Weierstrass's formula (§ 27) to this integral. When z varies from 0 to 1, the factor $1/\sqrt{z(1-z)}$ remains positive, and the point representing $1/\sqrt{a-z}$ describes a curve L whose general nature is easily determined. Let A be the point representing a; when z varies from 0 to 1, the point $a-z$ describes the segment AB parallel to Ox and of unit length (Fig. 22). Let Op and Oq be the bisectors of the angles which the straight lines OA and OB make with Ox, and let Op' and Oq' be straight lines symmetrical to them with respect to Ox. If we select that determination of $\sqrt{a-z}$ whose angle lies between 0 and $\pi/2$, the point $\sqrt{a-z}$ de-

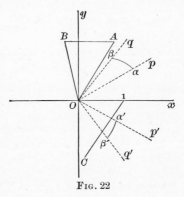

Fig. 22

scribes an arc $\alpha\beta$ from a point α on Op to a point β on Oq; hence the point $1/\sqrt{a-z}$ describes an arc $\alpha'\beta'$ from a point α' on Op' to a point β' of Oq'. It follows that Weierstrass's formula gives

$$\Omega_1 = 2 Z_1 \int_0^1 \frac{dz}{\sqrt{z(1-z)}} = 2\pi Z_1,$$

where Z_1 is the complex number corresponding to a point situated in the interior of every convex closed curve containing the arc $\alpha'\beta'$. It is clear that this point Z_1 is situated in the angle $p'Oq'$, and that it cannot be the origin; hence *the angle of Z_1 lies between $-\pi/2$ and 0.*

We can take for the second period

$$\Omega_2 = 2 \int_{OA} \frac{dz}{\sqrt{z(1-z)(a-z)}} = 2 \int_0^a \frac{dz}{\sqrt{z(1-z)(a-z)}},$$

or, setting $z = at$,

$$\Omega_2 = 2 \int_0^1 \frac{dt}{\sqrt{t(1-t)(1-at)}}.$$

In order to apply Weierstrass's formula to this integral, let us notice that as t increases from 0 to 1 the point at describes the segment OA and the point $1 - at$ describes the equal and parallel segment from $z = 1$ to the point C. Choosing suitably the value of the radical, we see, as before, that we may write

$$\Omega_2 = 2 Z_2 \int_0^1 \frac{dt}{\sqrt{t(1-t)}} = 2\pi Z_2,$$

where Z_2 is a complex number different from zero *whose angle lies between* 0 *and* $\pi/2$. The ratio of the two periods Ω_2/Ω_1 or Z_2/Z_1 is therefore not a real number.

EXERCISES

1. Develop the function

$$y = \frac{1}{2}(x + \sqrt{x^2 - 1})^m + \frac{1}{2}(x - \sqrt{x^2 - 1})^m$$

in powers of x, m being any number.

Find the radius of the circle of convergence.

2. Find the different developments of the function $1/[(z^2 + 1)(z - 2)]$ in positive or negative powers of z, according to the position of the point z in the plane.

3. Calculate the definite integral $\int z^2 \operatorname{Log}[(z + 1)/(z - 1)] \, dz$ taken along a circle of radius 2 about the origin as center, the initial value of the logarithm at the point $z = 2$ being taken as real.

Calculate the definite integral

$$\int \frac{dz}{\sqrt{z^2 + z + 1}}$$

taken over the same boundary.

4. Let $f(z)$ be an analytic function in the interior of a closed curve C containing the origin. Calculate the definite integral $\int_{(C)} f'(z) \operatorname{Log} z \, dz$, taken along the curve C, starting with an initial value z_0.

5. Derive the relation

$$\int_{-\infty}^{+\infty} \frac{dt}{(1 + t^2)^{n+1}} = \frac{1 \cdot 3 \cdot 5 \cdots (2n - 1)}{2 \cdot 4 \cdot 6 \cdots 2n} \pi$$

and deduce from it the definite integrals

$$\int_{-\infty}^{+\infty} \frac{dt}{[(t - \alpha)^2 + \beta^2]^{n+1}}, \qquad \int_{-\infty}^{+\infty} \frac{dt}{(At^2 + 2Bt + C)^{n+1}}.$$

6. Calculate the following definite integrals by means of the theory of residues:

$$\int_0^{+\infty} \frac{\sin mx \, dx}{x(x^2 + a^2)^2}, \qquad m \text{ and } a \text{ being real,}$$

$$\int_{-\infty}^{+\infty} \frac{\cos ax}{1 + x^4} \, dx, \qquad a \text{ being real,}$$

$$\int_{-\infty}^{+\infty} \frac{dx}{(x^2 - 2\beta i x - \beta^2 - \alpha^2)^{n+1}}, \qquad \alpha \text{ and } \beta \text{ being real,}$$

$$\int_{-\infty}^{+\infty} \frac{\cos x\, dx}{(x^2+1)(x^2+4)},$$

$$\int_0^1 \frac{\sqrt[3]{4x^2(1-x)}}{(1+x)^3}\, dx, \qquad\qquad \int_0^{+\infty} \frac{x \log x\, dx}{(1+x^2)^3},$$

$$\int_0^{+\infty} \frac{\cos ax - \cos bx}{x^2}\, dx, \qquad a \text{ and } b \text{ being real and positive.}$$

(To evaluate the last integral, integrate the function $(e^{aiz} - e^{biz})/z^2$ along the boundary indicated by Fig. 17.)

7. The definite integral $\int_0^\pi d\phi/[A + C - (A - C)\cos\phi]$ is equal, when it has any finite value, to $\epsilon\pi/\sqrt{AC}$, where ϵ is equal to ± 1 and is chosen in such a way that the coefficient of i in $\epsilon i \sqrt{AC}/A$ is positive.

8. Let $F(z)$ and $G(z)$ be two analytic functions, and $z = a$ a double root of $G(z) = 0$ that is not a root of $F(z)$. Show that the corresponding residue of $F(z)/G(z)$ is equal to

$$\frac{6\, F'(a)\, G''(a) - 2\, F(a)\, G'''(a)}{3\, [G''(a)]^2}.$$

In a similar manner show that the residue of $F(z)/[G(z)]^2$ for a simple root a of $G(z) = 0$ is equal to

$$\frac{F'(a)\, G'(a) - F(a)\, G''(a)}{[G'(a)]^3}.$$

9. Derive the formula

$$\int_{-1}^{+1} \frac{dx}{(x-a)\sqrt{1-x^2}} = \frac{\pi i}{\sqrt{1-a^2}},$$

the integral being taken along the real axis with the positive value of the radical, and a being a complex number or a real number whose absolute value is greater than unity. Determine the value that should be taken for $\sqrt{1-a^2}$.

10. Consider the integrals $\int_{(S)} dz/\sqrt{1+z^3}$, $\int_{(S_1)} dz/\sqrt{1+z^3}$, where S and S_1 denote two boundaries formed as follows: The boundary S is composed of a straight-line segment OA on Ox (which is made to expand indefinitely), of the circle of radius OA about O as center, and finally of the straight line AO. The boundary S_1 is the succession of three loops which inclose the points a, b, c which represent the roots of the equation $z^3 + 1 = 0$.

Establish the relation that exists between the two integrals

$$\int_0^{+\infty} \frac{dx}{\sqrt{1+x^3}}, \qquad \int_0^1 \frac{dt}{\sqrt{1-t^3}},$$

which arise in the course of the preceding consideration.

11. By integrating the function e^{-z^2} along the boundary of the rectangle formed by the straight lines $y = 0$, $y = b$, $x = +R$, $x = -R$, and then making R become infinite, establish the relation

$$\int_{-\infty}^{+\infty} e^{-x^2} \cos 2bx\, dx = \sqrt{\pi}\, e^{-b^2}.$$

12. Integrate the function $e^{-z}z^{n-1}$, where n is real and positive, along a boundary formed by a radius OA placed along Ox, by an arc of a circle AB of radius OA about O as center, and by a radius BO such that the angle $\alpha = AOB$ lies between 0 and $\pi/2$. Making OA become infinite, deduce from the preceding the values of the definite integrals

$$\int_0^{+\infty} u^{n-1}e^{-au}\cos bu\, du, \qquad \int_0^{+\infty} u^{n-1}e^{-au}\sin bu\, du,$$

where a and b are real and positive. The results obtained are valid for $\alpha = \pi/2$, provided that we have $n < 1$.

13. Let m, m', n be positive integers ($m < n$, $m' < n$). Establish the formula

$$\int_0^{+\infty} \frac{t^{2m} - t^{2m'}}{1 - t^{2n}}\, dt = \frac{\pi}{2n}\left[\operatorname{ctn}\left(\frac{2m+1}{2n}\pi\right) - \operatorname{ctn}\left(\frac{2m'+1}{2n}\pi\right)\right].$$

14. Deduce from the preceding result Euler's formula

$$\int_0^{+\infty} \frac{t^{2m}\, dt}{1 + t^{2n}} = \frac{\pi}{2n\sin\left(\dfrac{2m+1}{2n}\pi\right)}.$$

15. If the real part of a is positive and less than unity, we have

$$\int_{-\infty}^{+\infty} \frac{e^{ax}\, dx}{1 + e^x} = \frac{\pi}{\sin a\pi}.$$

(This can be deduced from the formula (39) (§ 47) or by integrating the function $e^{az}/(1 + e^z)$ along the boundary of the rectangle formed by the straight lines $y = 0$, $y = 2\pi$, $x = +R$, $x = -R$, and then making R become infinite.)

16. Derive in the same way the relation

$$\int_{-\infty}^{+\infty} \frac{e^{ax} - e^{bx}}{1 - e^x}\, dx = \pi(\operatorname{ctn} a\pi - \operatorname{ctn} b\pi),$$

where the real parts of a and b are positive and less than unity.

(Take for the path of integration the rectangle formed by the straight lines $y = 0$, $y = \pi$, $x = R$, $x = -R$, and make use of the preceding exercise.)

17. From the formula

$$\int_{(C)} \frac{(1+z)^n}{z^{k+1}}\, dz = 2\pi i\, \frac{n(n-1)\cdots(n-k+1)}{k!},$$

where n and k are positive integers, and C is a circle having the origin as center, deduce the relations

$$\int_0^{\pi} (2\cos u)^{n+k}\cos(n-k)u\, du = \pi\, \frac{(n+1)(n+2)\cdots(n+k)}{k!},$$

$$\int_{-1}^{+1} \frac{x^{2n}\, dx}{\sqrt{1-x^2}} = \pi\, \frac{1\cdot 3\cdot 5\cdots(2n-1)}{2\cdot 4\cdot 6\cdots 2n}.$$

(Put $z = e^{2iu}$, then $\cos u = x$, and replace n by $n+k$, and k by n.)

18*. The definite integral

$$\Phi(x) = \int_0^{\pi} \frac{d\phi}{1 - \alpha(x + \sqrt{x^2 - 1}\cos\phi)},$$

when it has a finite value, is equal to $\pm\,\pi/\sqrt{1-2\,\alpha x+\alpha^2}$, where the sign depends upon the relative positions of the two points α and x. Deduce from this the expression, due to Jacobi, for the nth Legendre's polynomial,

$$X_n = \frac{1}{\pi}\int_0^\pi (x+\sqrt{x^2-1}\,\cos\phi)^n d\phi.$$

19. Study in the same way the definite integral

$$\int_0^\pi \frac{d\phi}{x-a+\sqrt{x^2-1}\,\cos\phi},$$

and deduce from the result Laplace's formula

$$X_n = \frac{\epsilon}{\pi}\int_0^\pi \frac{d\phi}{(x+\sqrt{x^2-1}\,\cos\phi)^{n+1}},$$

where $\epsilon=\pm 1$, according as the real part of x is positive or negative.

20*. Establish the last result by integrating the function

$$\frac{1}{z^{n+1}\sqrt{1-2\,xz+z^2}}$$

along a circle about the origin as center, whose radius is made to become infinite.

21*. **Gauss's sums.** Let $T_s = e^{2\,\pi i s^2/n}$, where n and s are integers; and let S_n denote the sum $T_0 + T_1 + \cdots + T_{n-1}$. Derive the formula

$$S_n = \frac{(1+i)(1+i^{3n})}{2}\sqrt{n}.$$

(Apply the theorem on residues to the function $\Phi(z) = e^{2\,\pi i z^2/n}/(e^{2\,\pi i z}-1)$, taking for the boundary of integration the sides of the rectangle formed by the straight lines $x=0$, $x=n$, $y=+R$, $y=-R$, and inserting two semicircumferences of radius ϵ about the points $x=0$, $x=n$ as centers, in order to avoid the poles $z=0$ and $z=n$ of the function $\phi(z)$; then let R become infinite.)

22. Let $f(z)$ be an analytic function in the interior of a closed curve Γ containing the points $a, b, c, \cdots, l$. If $\alpha, \beta, \cdots, \lambda$ are positive integers, show that the sum of the residues of the function

$$\phi(z) = \frac{f(z)}{x-z}\Big(\frac{x-a}{z-a}\Big)^\alpha \Big(\frac{x-b}{z-b}\Big)^\beta \cdots \Big(\frac{x-l}{z-l}\Big)^\lambda$$

with respect to the poles $a, b, c, \cdots, l$ is a polynomial $F(x)$ of degree

$$\alpha + \beta + \cdots + \lambda - 1$$

satisfying the relations

$$\begin{array}{llll} F(a)=f(a), & F'(a)=f'(a), & \cdots, & F^{(\alpha-1)}(a)=f^{(\alpha-1)}(a),\\ F(b)=f(b), & F'(b)=f'(b), & \cdots, & F^{(\beta-1)}(b)=f^{(\beta-1)}(b),\\ \cdots\cdots\cdots, & \cdots\cdots\cdots, & \cdots, & \cdots\cdots\cdots\cdots\cdots. \end{array}$$

(Make use of the relation $F(x) = f(x) + [\int_{(\Gamma)} \phi(z)\,dz]/2\,\pi i$.)

23*. Let $f(z)$ be an analytic function in the interior of a circle C with center a. On the other hand, let $a_1, a_2, \cdots, a_n, \cdots$ be an infinite sequence of points within the circle C, the point a_n having the center a for limit as n becomes infinite. For every point z within C there exists a development of the form

$$f(z)=f(a_1)+\cdots+(z-a_1)(z-a_2)\cdots(z-a_{n-1})\sum_{h=1}^n \frac{f(a_h)}{F_n'(a_h)}+\cdots,$$

where
$$F_n(z) = (z - a_1)(z - a_2) \cdots (z - a_n).$$

[LAURENT, *Journal de mathématiques*, 5th series, Vol. VIII, p. 325.]

(Make use of the following formula, which is easily verified,

$$\frac{1}{z - x} = \frac{1}{z - a_1} + \frac{x - a_1}{(z - a_1)(z - a_2)} + \cdots$$
$$+ \frac{(x - a_1) \cdots (x - a_{n-1})}{(z - a_1) \cdots (z - a_{n-1})(z - a_n)} + \frac{1}{z - x} \frac{(x - a_1) \cdots (x - a_n)}{(z - a_1) \cdots (z - a_n)},$$

and follow the method used in establishing Taylor's formula.)

24. Let $z_0 = a + bi$ be a root of the equation $f(z) = X + Yi = 0$ of multiplicity n, where the function $f(z)$ is analytic in its neighborhood. The point $x = a$, $y = b$ is a multiple point of order n for each of the two curves $X = 0$, $Y = 0$. The tangents at this point to each of these curves form a set of lines equally inclined to each other, and each ray of the one bisects the angle between the two adjacent rays of the other.

25. Let $f(z) = X + Yi = A_0 z^m + A_1 z^{m-1} + \cdots + A_m$ be a polynomial of the mth degree whose coefficients are numbers of any kind. All the asymptotes of the two curves $X = 0$, $Y = 0$ pass through the point $- A_1/mA_0$ and are arranged like the tangents in the preceding exercise.

26*. Burman's series. Given two functions $f(x)$, $F(x)$ of a variable x, Burman's formula gives the development of one of them in powers of the other. To make the problem more definite, let us take a simple root a of the equation $F(x) = 0$, and let us suppose that the two functions $f(x)$ and $F(x)$ are analytic in the neighborhood of the point a. In this neighborhood we have

$$F(x) = \frac{x - a}{\phi(x)},$$

the function $\phi(x)$ being regular for $x = a$ if a is a simple root of $F(x) = 0$. Representing $F(x)$ by y, the preceding relation is equivalent to

$$x - a - y\phi(x) = 0,$$

and we are led to develop $f(x)$ in powers of y (Lagrange's formula).

27*. Kepler's equation. The equation $z - a - e \sin z = 0$, where a and e are two positive numbers, $a < \pi$, $e < 1$, has one real root lying between 0 and π, and two roots whose real parts lie between $m\pi$ and $(m + 1)\pi$, where m is any positive even integer or any negative odd integer. If m is positive and odd, or negative and even, there are no roots whose real parts lie between $m\pi$ and $(m + 1)\pi$.

[BRIOT ET BOUQUET, *Théorie des fonctions elliptiques*, 2d ed., p. 199.]

(Study the curve described by the point $u = z - a - e \sin z$ when the variable z describes the four sides of the rectangle formed by the straight lines $x = m\pi$, $x = (m + 1)\pi$, $y = + R$, $y = - R$, where R is very large.)

28*. For very large values of m the two roots of the preceding exercise whose real parts lie between $2m\pi$ and $(2m + 1)\pi$ are approximately equal to $2m\pi + \pi/2 \pm i[\log(2/e) + \log(2m\pi + \pi/2)]$.

[GOURIER, *Annales de l'École Normale*, 2d series, Vol. VII, p. 73.]

CHAPTER III

SINGLE-VALUED ANALYTIC FUNCTIONS

The first part of this chapter is devoted to the demonstration of the general theorems of Weierstrass* and of Mittag-Leffler on integral functions and on single-valued analytic functions with an infinite number of singular points. We shall then make an application of them to elliptic functions.

Since it seemed impossible to develop the theory of elliptic functions with any degree of completeness in a small number of pages, the treatment is limited to a general discussion of the fundamental principles, so as to give the reader some idea of the importance of these functions. For those who wish to make a thorough study of elliptic functions and their applications a simple course in Mathematical Analysis would never suffice; they will always be compelled to turn to special treatises.

I. WEIERSTRASS'S PRIMARY FUNCTIONS. MITTAG-LEFFLER'S THEOREM

57. Expression of an integral function as a product of primary functions. Every polynomial of the mth degree is equal to the product of a constant and m equal or unequal factors of the form $x - a$, and this decomposition displays the roots of the polynomial. Euler was the first to obtain for sin z an analogous development in an infinite product, but the factors of that product, as we shall see farther on, are of the second degree in z. Cauchy had noticed that we are led in certain cases to adjoin a suitable exponential factor to each of the binomial factors such as $x - a$. But Weierstrass was the first to treat the question with complete generality by showing that every integral function having an infinite number of roots can be expressed as the product of an infinite number of factors, each of which vanishes for only a single value of the variable.

---

* The theorems of Weierstrass which are to be presented here were first published in a paper entitled *Zur Theorie der eindeutigen analytischen Functionen* (*Berl. Abhandlungen*, 1876, p. 11 = Werke, Vol. II, p. 77). Picard gave a translation of this paper in the *Annales de l' École Normale supérieure* (1879). The collected researches of Mittag-Leffler are to be found in a memoir in the *Acta mathematica*, Vol. II.

We already know one integral function which does not vanish for any value of z, that is, e^z. The same thing is true of $e^{g(z)}$, where $g(z)$ is a polynomial or an integral transcendental function. Conversely, every integral function which does not vanish for any value of z is expressible in that form. In fact, if the integral function $G(z)$ does not vanish for any value of z, every point $z = a$ is an ordinary point for $G'(z)/G(z)$, which is therefore another integral function $g_1(z)$:

$$\frac{G'(z)}{G(z)} = g_1(z).$$

Integrating both sides between the limits z_0, z, we find

$$\operatorname{Log}\left[\frac{G(z)}{G(z_0)}\right] = \int_{z_0}^{z} g_1(z)\, dz = g(z) - g(z_0),$$

where $g(z)$ is a new integral function of z, and we have

$$G(z) = G(z_0)\, e^{g(z) - g(z_0)} = e^{g(z) - g(z_0) + \operatorname{Log}[G(z_0)]}.$$

The right-hand side is precisely in the desired form.

If an integral function $G(z)$ has only n roots $a_1, a_2, \cdots, a_n$, distinct or not, the function $G(z)$ is evidently of the form

$$G(z) = (z - a_1)(z - a_2) \cdots (z - a_n) e^{g(z)}.$$

Let us consider now the case where the equation $G(z) = 0$ has an infinite number of roots. Since there can be only a finite number of roots whose absolute values are less than or equal to any given number R (§ 41), if we arrange these roots in such a way that their absolute values never diminish as we proceed, each of these roots appears in a definite position in the sequence

(1) $$a_1, a_2, \cdots, a_n, a_{n+1}, \cdots,$$

where $|a_n| \leqq |a_{n+1}|$, and where $|a_n|$ becomes infinite with the index n. We shall suppose that each root appears in this series as often as is required by its degree of multiplicity, and that the root $z = 0$ is omitted from it if $G(0) = 0$. We shall first show how to construct an integral function $G_1(z)$ that has as its roots the numbers in the sequence (1) and no others.

The product $(1 - z/a_n)e^{Q_\nu(z)}$, where $Q_\nu(z)$ denotes a polynomial, is an integral function which does not vanish except for $z = a_n$. We shall take for $Q_\nu(z)$ a polynomial of degree ν determined in the following manner: write the preceding product in the form

$$e^{Q_\nu(z) + \operatorname{Log}\left(1 - \frac{z}{a_n}\right)},$$

and replace $\mathrm{Log}\,(1 - z/a_n)$ by its expansion in a power series; then the development of the exponent will commence with a term of degree $\nu + 1$, provided we take

$$Q_\nu(z) = \frac{z}{a_n} + \frac{z^2}{2\,a_n^2} + \cdots + \frac{z^\nu}{\nu a_n^\nu}.$$

The integer ν is still undetermined. We shall show that this number ν can be chosen as a function of n in such a way that the infinite product

$$(2) \qquad\qquad \prod_{n=1}^{+\infty} \left(1 - \frac{z}{a_n}\right) e^{Q_\nu(z)}$$

will be absolutely and uniformly convergent in every circle C of radius R about the origin as center, however large R may be. The radius R having been chosen, let α be a positive number less than unity. Let us consider separately, in the product (2), those factors corresponding to the roots a_n whose absolute values do not exceed R/α. If there are q roots satisfying this condition, the product of these q factors

$$F_1(z) = \prod_{n=1}^{q} \left(1 - \frac{z}{a_n}\right) e^{Q_\nu(z)}$$

evidently represents an integral function of z. Consider now the product of the factors beginning with the $(q + 1)$th:

$$F_2(z) = \prod_{n=q+1}^{+\infty} \left(1 - \frac{z}{a_n}\right) e^{Q_\nu(z)}.$$

If z remains in the interior of the circle with the radius R, we have $|z| \leqq R$; and since we have $|a_n| > R/\alpha$ when $n > q$, it follows that we also have $|z| < \alpha |a_n|$. A factor of this product can then be written, from the manner in which we have taken $Q_\nu(z)$,

$$\left(1 - \frac{z}{a_n}\right) e^{Q_\nu(z)} = e^{-\frac{1}{\nu+1}\left(\frac{z}{a_n}\right)^{\nu+1} - \frac{1}{\nu+2}\left(\frac{z}{a_n}\right)^{\nu+2} - \cdots};$$

if we denote this factor by $1 + u_n$, we have

$$u_n = e^{-\frac{1}{\nu+1}\left(\frac{z}{a_n}\right)^{\nu+1} - \frac{1}{\nu+2}\left(\frac{z}{a_n}\right)^{\nu+2} - \cdots} - 1.$$

Hence the proof reduces to showing that by a suitable choice of the number ν the series whose general term is $U_n = |u_n|$ is uniformly convergent in the circle of radius R (I, § 176, 2d ed.). In general, if m is any real or complex number, we have

$$|e^m - 1| < e^{|m|} - 1.$$

We have then, a fortiori,

$$U_n < e^{\frac{1}{\nu+1}\left|\frac{z}{a_n}\right|^{\nu+1}\left(1+\frac{\nu+1}{\nu+2}\left|\frac{z}{a_n}\right|+\frac{\nu+1}{\nu+3}\left|\frac{z}{a_n}\right|^2+\cdots\right)} - 1,$$

or, noticing that $|z| < \alpha |a_n|$, when $|z|$ is less than R,

$$U_n < e^{\frac{1}{\nu+1}\left|\frac{z}{a_n}\right|^{\nu+1}\frac{1}{1-\alpha}} - 1.$$

But if x is a real positive number, $e^x - 1$ is less than xe^x; hence we have

$$U_n < \frac{1}{\nu+1}\left|\frac{z}{a_n}\right|^{\nu+1}\frac{1}{1-\alpha}e^{\frac{1}{\nu+1}\left|\frac{z}{a_n}\right|^{\nu+1}\frac{1}{1-\alpha}} < \frac{1}{\nu+1}\left|\frac{z}{a_n}\right|^{\nu+1}\frac{e^{\frac{1}{1-\alpha}}}{1-\alpha}.$$

In order that the series whose general term is U_n shall be uniformly convergent in the circle with the radius R, it is sufficient that the series whose general term is $|z/a_n|^{\nu+1}$ converge uniformly in the same circle. If there exists an integer p such that the series $\Sigma|1/a_n|^p$ converges, we need only take $\nu = p - 1$. If there exists no integer p that has this property,* it is sufficient to take $\nu = n - 1$. For the series whose general term is $|z/a_n|^n$ is uniformly convergent in the circle of radius R, since its terms are smaller than those of the series $\Sigma|R/a_n|^n$, and the nth root of the general term of this last series, or $|R/a_n|$, approaches zero as n increases indefinitely.†

Therefore we can always choose the integer ν so that the infinite product $F_2(z)$ will be absolutely and uniformly convergent in the circle of radius R. Such a product can be replaced by the sum of a uniformly convergent series (§ 176, 2d ed.) whose terms are all analytic. Hence the product $F_2(z)$ is itself an analytic function within this circle (§ 39). Multiplying $F_2(z)$ by the product $F_1(z)$, which contains only a finite number of analytic factors, we see that the infinite product

$$(3) \qquad G_1(z) = \prod_{n=1}^{+\infty}\left(1 - \frac{z}{a_n}\right)e^{Q_\nu(z)}$$

is itself absolutely and uniformly convergent in the interior of the circle C with the radius R, and represents an analytic function within this circle. Since the radius R can be chosen arbitrarily, and since

---

* For example, let $a_n = \log n$ $(n \geqq 2)$. The series whose general term is $(\log n)^{-p}$ is divergent, whatever may be the positive number p, for the sum of the first $(n-1)$ terms is greater than $(n-1)/(\log n)^p$, an expression which becomes infinite with n.

† Borel has pointed out that it is sufficient to take for ν a number such that $\nu+1$ shall be greater than $\log n$. In fact, the series $\Sigma|R/a_n|^{\log n}$ is convergent, for the general term can be written $e^{\log n \log|R/a_n|} = n^{\log|R/a_n|}$. After a sufficiently large value of n, $|a_n|/R$ will be greater than e^2, and the general term less than $1/n^2$.

ν does not depend on R, this product is an integral function $G_1(z)$ which has as its roots precisely all the various numbers of the sequence (1) and no others.

If the integral function $G(z)$ has also the point $z = 0$ as a root of the pth order, the quotient

$$\frac{G(z)}{z^p G_1(z)}$$

is an analytic function which has neither poles nor zeros in the whole plane. Hence this quotient is an integral function of the form $e^{g(z)}$, where $g(z)$ is a polynomial or an integral transcendental function, and we have the following expression for the function $G(z)$:

$$(4) \qquad G(z) = e^{g(z)} z^p \prod_{n=1}^{+\infty} \left(1 - \frac{z}{a_n}\right) e^{Q_\nu(z)}.$$

The integral function $g(z)$ can in its turn be replaced in an infinite variety of ways by the sum of a uniformly convergent series of polynomials

$$g(z) = g_1(z) + g_2(z) + \cdots + g_n(z) + \cdots,$$

and the preceding formula can be written again

$$G(z) = z^p \prod_{n=1}^{+\infty} \left(1 - \frac{z}{a_n}\right) e^{Q_\nu(z) + g_n(z)}.$$

The factors of this product, each of which vanishes only for *one* value of z, are called *primary functions*.

Since the product (4) is absolutely convergent, we can arrange the primary functions in an arbitrary order or group them together in any way that we please. In this product the polynomials $Q_\nu(z)$ depend only on the roots themselves when we have once made a choice of the law which determines the number ν as a function of n. But the exponential factor $e^{g(z)}$ cannot be determined if we know only the roots of the function $G(z)$. Take, for example, the function $\sin \pi z$, which has all the positive and negative integers for simple roots. In this case the series $\Sigma' |1/a_n|^2$ is convergent; hence we can take $\nu = 1$, and the function

$$G(z) = z \prod_{-\infty}^{+\infty} {}' \left(1 - \frac{z}{n}\right) e^{\frac{z}{n}},$$

where the accent placed to the right of Π means that we are not to give the value zero* to the index n, has the same roots as $\sin \pi z$.

---

* When this exception is to be made in a formula, we shall call attention to it by placing an accent (') after the symbol of the product or of the sum.

We have then $\sin \pi z = e^{g(z)} G(z)$, but the reasoning does not tell us anything about the factor $e^{g(z)}$. We shall show later that this factor reduces to the number π.

58. The class of an integral function. Given an infinite sequence $a_1, a_2, \cdots, a_n, \cdots$, where $|a_n|$ becomes infinite with n, we have just seen how to construct an infinite number of integral functions that have all the terms of that sequence for zeros and no others. When there exists an integer p such that the series $\Sigma |a_n|^{-p}$ is convergent, we can take all the polynomials $Q_\nu(z)$ of degree $p-1$.

Given an integral function of the form

$$G(z) = z^r e^{P(z)} \prod_{n=1}^{+\infty} \left(1 - \frac{z}{a_n}\right) e^{\frac{z}{a_n} + \frac{1}{2}\left(\frac{z}{a_n}\right)^2 + \cdots + \frac{1}{p-1}\left(\frac{z}{a_n}\right)^{p-1}},$$

where $P(z)$ is a polynomial of degree not higher than $p-1$, the number $p-1$ is said to be the *class* of that function. Thus, the function

$$\prod_{n=1}^{+\infty} \left(1 - \frac{z}{n^2}\right)$$

is of class *zero*; the function $(\sin \pi z)/\pi$ mentioned above is of class *one*. The study of the class of an integral function has given rise in recent years to a large number of investigations.[*]

59. Single-valued analytic functions with a finite number of singular points. When a single-valued analytic function $F(z)$ has only a finite number of singular points in the whole plane, these singular points are necessarily isolated; hence they are poles or isolated essentially singular points. The point $z = \infty$ is itself an ordinary point or an isolated singular point (§ 52). Conversely, *if a single-valued analytic function has only isolated singular points in the entire plane (including the point at infinity), there can be only a finite number of them.* In fact, the point at infinity is an ordinary point for the function or an isolated singular point. In either case we can describe a circle C with a radius so large that the function will have no other singular point outside this circle than the point at infinity itself. Within the circle C the function can have only a finite number of singular points, for if it had an infinite number of them there would be at least one limit point (§ 41), and this limit point would not be an isolated singular point. Thus *a single-valued analytic*

---

[*] See BOREL, *Leçons sur les fonctions entières* (1900), and the recent work of BLUMENTHAL, *Sur les fonctions entières de genre infini* (1910).

function which has only poles has necessarily only a finite number of them, for a pole is an isolated singular point.

Every single-valued analytic function which is regular for every finite value of z, and for $z = \infty$, is a constant. In fact, if the function were not a constant, since it is regular for every finite value of z, it would be a polynomial or an integral function, and the point at infinity would be a pole or an essentially singular point.

Now let $F(z)$ be a single-valued analytic function with n distinct singular points $a_1, a_2, \cdots, a_n$ in the finite portion of the plane, and let $G_i[1/(z - a_i)]$ be the principal part of the development of $F(z)$ in the neighborhood of the point a_i; then G_i is a polynomial or an integral transcendental function in $1/(z - a_i)$. In either case this principal part is regular for every value of z (including $z = \infty$) except $z = a_i$. Similarly, let $P(z)$ be the principal part of the development of $F(z)$ in the neighborhood of the point at infinity. $P(z)$ is zero if the point at infinity is an ordinary point for $F(z)$. The difference

$$D = F(z) - P(z) - \sum_{i=1}^{n} G_i\left(\frac{1}{z - a_i}\right)$$

is evidently regular for every value of z including $z = \infty$; it is therefore a constant C, and we have the equality*

$$(5) \qquad F(z) = P(z) + \sum_{i=1}^{n} G_i\left(\frac{1}{z - a_i}\right) + C,$$

which shows that the function $F(z)$ is completely determined, except for an additive constant, when the principal part in the neighborhood of each of the singular points is known. These principal parts, as well as the singular points, may be assigned arbitrarily.

When all the singular points are poles, the principal parts G_i are polynomials; $P(z)$ is also a polynomial, if it is not zero, and the right-hand side of (5) reduces to a rational fraction. Since, on the other hand, a single-valued analytic function which has only poles for its singular points can have only a finite number of them, we conclude from this *that a single-valued analytic function, all of whose singular points are poles, is a rational fraction.*

---

* We might obtain the same formula by equating to zero the sum of the residues of the function

$$F(x)\left(\frac{1}{x - z} - \frac{1}{x - z_0}\right),$$

where z and z_0 are considered as constants and x as the variable (see § 52).

60. Single-valued analytic functions with an infinite number of singular points. If a single-valued analytic function has an infinite number of singular points in a finite region, it must have at least one limit point within or on the boundary of the region. For example, the function $1/\sin(1/z)$ has as poles all the roots of the equation $\sin(1/z) = 0$, that is, all the points $z = 1/k\pi$, where k is any integer whatever. The origin is a limit point of these poles. Similarly, the function

$$\cfrac{1}{\sin\left(\cfrac{1}{\sin\dfrac{1}{z}}\right)}$$

has for singular points all the roots of the equation $\sin(1/z) = 1/(k\pi)$, among which are all the points

$$z = \cfrac{1}{2\,k'\pi + \text{arc}\sin\left(\dfrac{1}{k\pi}\right)},$$

where k and k' are two arbitrary integers. All the points $1/(2\,k'\pi)$ are limit points, for if, k' remaining fixed, k increases indefinitely, the preceding expression has $1/(2\,k'\pi)$ for its limit. It would be easy to construct more and more complicated examples of the same kind by increasing the number of sin symbols. There also exist, as we shall see a little farther on, functions for which every point of a certain curve is a singular point.

It may happen that a single-valued analytic function has only a finite number of singular points in every finite portion of the plane, although it has an infinite number of them in the entire plane. Then outside of any circle C, however great its radius may be, there are always an infinite number of singular points, and we shall say that the point at infinity is a limit point of these singular points. In the following paragraphs we shall examine single-valued analytic functions with an infinite number of isolated singular points which have the point at infinity as their only limit point.

61. Mittag-Leffler's theorem. If there are only a finite number of singular points in every finite portion of the plane, we can, as we have already noticed for the zeros of an integral function, arrange these singular points in a sequence

$$(6) \qquad a_1, \qquad a_2, \qquad \cdots, \qquad a_n, \qquad \cdots$$

in such a way that we have $|a_n| \leqq |a_{n+1}|$ and that $|a_n|$ becomes infinite with n. We may suppose also that all the terms of this sequence are different. To each term a_i of the sequence (6) let us assign a polynomial or an integral function in $1/(z - a_i)$, $G_i[1/(z - a_i)]$, taken in an entirely arbitrary manner. Mittag-Leffler's theorem may be stated thus :

There exists a single-valued analytic function which is regular for every finite value of z that does not occur in the sequence (6), *and for which the principal part in the neighborhood of the point $z = a_i$ is* $G_i[1/(z - a_i)]$.

We shall prove this by showing that it is possible to assign to each function $G_i[1/(z - a_i)]$ a polynomial $P_i(z)$ such that the series

$$\sum_{i=1}^{+\infty} \left[G_i\left(\frac{1}{z - a_i}\right) + P_i(z) \right]$$

defines an analytic function that has these properties.

If the point $z = 0$ occurs in the sequence (6), we shall take the corresponding polynomial equal to zero. Let us assign a positive number ϵ_i to each of the other points a_i so that the series $\Sigma \epsilon_i$ shall be convergent, and let us denote by α a positive number less than unity. Let C_i be the circle about the origin as center passing through the point a_i, and C_i' the circle concentric to the preceding with a radius equal to $\alpha |a_i|$. Since the function $G_i[1/(z - a_i)]$ is analytic in the circle C_i, we have for every point within C_i

$$G_i\left(\frac{1}{z - a_i}\right) = \alpha_{i0} + \alpha_{i1} z + \cdots + \alpha_{in} z^n + \cdots.$$

The power series on the right is uniformly convergent in the circle C_i'; hence we can find an integer ν so large that we have, in the interior of the circle C_i',

$$(7) \qquad \left| G_i\left(\frac{1}{z - a_i}\right) - \alpha_{i0} - \alpha_{i1} z - \cdots - \alpha_{i\nu} z^\nu \right| < \epsilon_i.$$

Having determined the number ν in this manner, we shall take for $P_i(z)$ the polynomial $- \alpha_{i0} - \alpha_{i1} z - \cdots - \alpha_{i\nu} z^\nu$.

Now let C be a circle of radius R about the point $z = 0$ as center. Let us consider separately the singular points a_i in the sequence (6) whose absolute values do not exceed R/α. If there are q of them, we shall set

$$F_1(z) = \sum_{i=1}^{q} \left[G_i\left(\frac{1}{z - a_i}\right) + P_i(z) \right].$$

The remaining infinite series,

$$F_2(z) = \sum_{i=q+1}^{+\infty} \left[G_i\left(\frac{1}{z - a_i}\right) + P_i(z) \right],$$

is absolutely and uniformly convergent in the circle C, since for every point in this circle $|z| < R < a|a_i|$ if the index i is greater than q. From the inequality (7), and from the manner in which we have taken the polynomials $P_i(z)$, the absolute value of the general term of the second series is less than ϵ_i when z is within the circle C. Hence the function $F_2(z)$ is an analytic function within this circle, and it is clear that if we add $F_1(z)$ to it, the sum

$$(8) \qquad F(z) = \sum_{i=1}^{+\infty} \left[G_i\left(\frac{1}{z - a_i}\right) + P_i(z) \right]$$

will have the same singular points in the circle C, with the same principal parts, as $F_1(z)$. These singular points are precisely the terms of the sequence (6) whose absolute values are less than R, and the principal part in the neighborhood of the point a_i is $G_i[1/(z - a_i)]$. Since the radius R may be of any magnitude, it follows that the function $F(z)$ satisfies all the conditions of the theorem stated above.

It is clear that if we add to $F(z)$ a polynomial or any integral function whatever $G(z)$, the sum $F(z) + G(z)$ will have the same singular points, with the same principal parts, as the function $F(z)$. Conversely, we have thus the general expression for single-valued analytic functions having given singular points with corresponding given principal parts; for the difference of two such functions, being regular for every finite value of z, is a polynomial or a transcendental integral function. Since it is possible to represent the function $G(z)$ in turn by the sum of a series of polynomials, the function $F(z) + G(z)$ can itself be represented by the sum of a series of which each term is obtained by adding a suitable polynomial to the principal part $G_i[1/(z - a_i)]$.

If all the principal parts G_i are polynomials, the function is analytic except for poles in the whole finite region of the plane, and conversely. We see, then, that every function analytic except for poles can be represented by the sum of a series each of whose terms is a rational fraction which becomes infinite only for a single finite value of the variable. This representation is analogous to the decomposition of a rational fraction into simple elements.

Every function $\Phi(z)$ that is analytic except for poles can also be represented by the quotient of two integral functions. For suppose that the poles of $\Phi(z)$ are the terms of the sequence (6), each being counted according to its degree of multiplicity. Let $G(z)$ be an integral function having these zeros; then the product $\Phi(z)\ G(z)$ has no poles. It is therefore an integral function $G_1(z)$, and we have the equality

$$\Phi(z) = \frac{G_1(z)}{G(z)}.$$

62. Certain special cases. The preceding demonstration of the general theorem does not always give the simplest method of constructing a single-valued analytic function satisfying the desired conditions. Suppose, for example, it is required to construct a function $\Phi(z)$ having as poles of the first order all the points of the sequence (6), each residue being equal to unity; we shall suppose that $z = 0$ is not a pole. The principal part relative to the pole a_i is $1/(z - a_i)$, and we can write

$$\frac{1}{z - a_i} = -\frac{1}{a_i} - \frac{z}{a_i^2} - \cdots - \frac{z^{\nu-1}}{a_i^\nu} + \frac{1}{z - a_i}\left(\frac{z}{a_i}\right)^\nu.$$

If we take

$$P_i(z) = \frac{1}{a_i} + \frac{z}{a_i^2} + \cdots + \frac{z^{\nu-1}}{a_i^\nu},$$

the proof reduces to determining the integer ν as a function of the index i in such a way that the series

$$\sum_{i=1}^{+\infty} \frac{1}{z - a_i}\left(\frac{z}{a_i}\right)^\nu = -\sum_{i=1}^{+\infty} \frac{z^\nu}{\left(1 - \dfrac{z}{a_i}\right)} \frac{1}{a_i^{\nu+1}}$$

shall be absolutely and uniformly convergent in every circle described about the origin as center, neglecting a sufficient number of terms at the beginning. For this it is sufficient that the series $\Sigma(z/a_i)^{\nu+1}$ be itself absolutely and uniformly convergent in the same region. If there exists a number p such that the series $\Sigma|1/a_i|^p$ is convergent, we need only take $\nu = p - 1$. If there exists no such integer, we will take as above (§ 57) $\nu = i - 1$, or $\nu + 1 > \log i$. The number ν having been thus chosen, the function

$$(9) \qquad \Phi(z) = \sum_{i=1}^{+\infty}\left[\frac{1}{z - a_i} + \frac{1}{a_i} + \frac{z}{a_i^2} + \cdots + \frac{z^{\nu-1}}{a_i^\nu}\right],$$

which is analytic except for poles, has all the points of the sequence (6) as poles of the first order with each residue equal to unity.

It is easy to deduce from this a new proof of Weierstrass's theorem on the decomposition of an integral function into primary functions. In fact, we can integrate the series (9) term by term along any path whatever not passing through any of the poles; for if the path lies in a circle C having its center at the origin, the series (9) can be replaced by a series which is uniformly convergent in this circle, together with the sum of a *finite* number of functions analytic except for poles. This results from the demonstration of formula (9). If we integrate, taking the point $z = 0$ for the lower limit, we find

$$\int_0^z \Phi(z)\,dz = \sum_{i=1} \left[\mathrm{Log}\left(1 - \frac{z}{a_i}\right) + \frac{z}{a_i} + \frac{z^2}{2\,a_i^2} + \cdots + \frac{z^\nu}{\nu a_i^\nu}\right],$$

and consequently

(10) $$e^{\int_0^z \Phi(z)\,dz} = \prod_{i=1}^{+\infty}\left(1 - \frac{z}{a_i}\right) e^{\frac{z}{a_i} + \frac{z^2}{2\,a_i^2} + \cdots + \frac{z^\nu}{\nu a_i^\nu}}.$$

It is easy to verify the fact that the left-hand side of the equation (10) is an integral function of z. In the neighborhood of a value a of z that does not occur in the sequence (6) the integral $\int_0^z \Phi(z)\,dz$ is analytic; hence the function

$$e^{\int_0^z \Phi(z)\,dz}$$

is also analytic and different from zero for $z = a$. In the neighborhood of the point a_i we have

$$\Phi(z) = \frac{1}{z - a_i} + P(z - a_i),$$

$$\int_0^z \Phi(z)\,dz = \mathrm{Log}(z - a_i) + Q(z - a_i),$$

$$e^{\int_0^z \Phi(z)\,dz} = (z - a_i)\,e^{Q(z - a_i)},$$

where the functions P and Q are analytic. It is seen that this integral function has the terms of the sequence (6) for its roots, and the formula (10) is identical with the formula (3) established above.

The same demonstration would apply also to integral functions having multiple roots. If a_i is a multiple root of order r, it would suffice to suppose that $\Phi(z)$ has the pole $z = a_i$ with a residue equal to r.

Let us try again to form a function analytic except for poles of the second order at all the points of the sequence (6), the principal part in the neighborhood of the point a_i being $1/(z - a_i)^2$. We shall suppose that $z = 0$ is an ordinary point, and that the series $\Sigma|1/a_i|^3$ is convergent; it is clear that the series $\Sigma|1/a_i|^4$ will also be convergent. Limiting the development of $1/(z - a_2)^2$ in powers of z to its first term, we can write

$$\frac{1}{(z - a_i)^2} - \frac{1}{a_i^2} = \frac{2\,a_i z - z^2}{a_i^2 (z - a_i)^2} = \frac{2\,a_i z - z^2}{a_i^4 \left(1 - \dfrac{z}{a_i}\right)^2},$$

and the series

(11) $$\Phi(z) = \sum_{i=1}^{+\infty} \left[\frac{1}{(z - a_i)^2} - \frac{1}{a_i^2}\right] = \sum_{i=1}^{+\infty} \frac{2\,a_i z - z^2}{a_i^4 \left(1 - \dfrac{z}{a_i}\right)^2}$$

satisfies all the conditions, provided it is uniformly convergent in every circle C described about the origin as center, neglecting a sufficient number of terms at the beginning. Now if we take only those terms of the series coming from the poles a_i for which we have $|a_i| > R/\alpha$, R being the radius of the circle C and α a positive number less than unity, the absolute value of $(1 - z/a_i)^{-2}$ will remain less than an upper bound, and the series whose general term is $2\,z/a_i^3 - z^2/a_i^4$ is absolutely and uniformly convergent in the circle C, by the hypotheses made concerning the poles a_i.

63. Cauchy's method. If $F(z)$ is a function analytic except for poles, Mittag-Leffler's theorem enables us to form a series of rational terms whose sum $F_1(z)$ has the same poles and the same principal parts as $F(z)$. But it still remains to find the integral function which is equal to the difference $F(z) - F_1(z)$. Long before Weierstrass's work, Cauchy had deduced from the theory of residues a method by which a function analytic except for poles may, under very general conditions on the function, be decomposed into a sum of an infinite number of rational terms. It is, moreover, easy to generalize his method.

Let $F(z)$ be a function analytic except for poles and regular in the neighborhood of the origin; and let $C_1, C_2, \cdots, C_n, \cdots$ be an infinite succession of closed curves surrounding the point $z = 0$, not passing through any of the poles, and such that, beginning with a value of n sufficiently large, the distance from the origin to any point whatever of C_n remains greater than any given number. It is clear that any pole whatever of $F(z)$ will finally be interior to all the curves $C_n, C_{n+1}, \cdots$, provided the index n is taken large enough. The definite integral

$$\frac{1}{2\,\pi i} \int_{(C_n)} \frac{F(z)}{z - x}\,dz,$$

where x is any point within C_n different from the poles, is equal to $F(x)$ increased by the sum of the residues of $F(z)/(z - x)$ with respect to the different poles of $F(z)$ within C_n. Let a_k be one of these poles. Then the corresponding principal part $G_k[1/(z - a_k)]$ is a rational function, and we have in the neighborhood of the point a_k

$$F(z) = \frac{A_m}{(z - a_k)^m} + \frac{A_{m-1}}{(z - a_k)^{m-1}} + \cdots + \frac{A_1}{z - a_k} + B_0 + B_1(z - a_k) + \cdots.$$

In the neighborhood of this point we can also write

$$\frac{1}{z - x} = -\frac{1}{x - a_k - (z - a_k)} = -\frac{1}{x - a_k} - \frac{z - a_k}{(x - a_k)^2} - \frac{(z - a_k)^2}{(x - a_k)^3} - \cdots.$$

Writing out the product we see that the residue of $F(z)/(z - x)$ with respect to the pole a_k is equal to

$$-\frac{A_1}{x - a_k} - \cdots - \frac{A_{m-1}}{(x - a_k)^{m-1}} - \frac{A_m}{(x - a_k)^m} = -G_k\left(\frac{1}{x - a_k}\right).$$

We have, then, the relation

$$(12) \qquad F(x) = \sum_{C_n} G_k\left(\frac{1}{x - a_k}\right) + \frac{1}{2\pi i}\int_{(C_n)} \frac{F(z)\,dz}{z - x},$$

where the symbol $\sum_{C_n}$ indicates a summation extended to all the poles a_k within the curve C_n. On the other hand, we can replace $1/(z - x)$ by

$$\frac{1}{z} + \frac{x}{z^2} + \cdots + \frac{x^p}{z^{p+1}} + \frac{1}{z - x}\left(\frac{x}{z}\right)^{p+1}.$$

and write the preceding formula in the form

$$(13) \qquad \begin{cases} F(x) = \sum_{C_n} G_k\left(\frac{1}{x - a_k}\right) + \frac{1}{2\pi i}\int_{(C_n)} \frac{F(z)\,dz}{z} + \cdots \\[2mm] \qquad + \frac{x^p}{2\pi i}\int_{(C_n)} \frac{F(z)}{z^{p+1}}\,dz + \frac{1}{2\pi i}\int_{(C_n)} \frac{F(z)}{z - x}\left(\frac{x}{z}\right)^{p+1}\,dz. \end{cases}$$

The integral

$$\frac{1}{2\pi i}\int_{(C_n)} \frac{F(z)\,dz}{z}$$

is equal to $F(0)$ increased by the sum of the residues of $F(z)/z$ with respect to the poles of $F(z)$ within C_n. More generally, the definite integral

$$\frac{1}{2\pi i}\int_{(C_n)} \frac{F(z)\,dz}{z^r}$$

is equal to

$$\frac{F^{(r-1)}(0)}{(r - 1)!}$$

plus the sum of the residues of $z^{-r}F(z)$ with respect to the poles of $F(z)$ within C_n. If we represent by $s_k^{(r-1)}$ the residue of $z^{-r}F(z)$

relative to the pole a_k, we can write the equation (13) in the form

$$(14) \quad \begin{cases} F(x) = F(0) + \dfrac{x}{1} F'(0) + \cdots + \dfrac{x^p}{p!} F^{(p)}(0) \\[2mm] \quad + \sum_{C_n} \left[G_k \left(\dfrac{1}{x - a_k} \right) + s_k^{(0)} + s_k^{(1)} x + \cdots + s_k^{(p)} x^p \right] \\[2mm] \quad + \dfrac{1}{2\pi i} \int_{(C_n)} \dfrac{F(z)}{z - x} \left(\dfrac{x}{z} \right)^{p+1} dz. \end{cases}$$

In order to obtain an upper bound for the last term, let us write it in the form

$$R_n = \frac{x^{p+1}}{2\pi i} \int_{(C_n)} \frac{F(z)}{z^p} \frac{dz}{z(z - x)}.$$

Let us suppose that along C_n the absolute value of $z^{-p} F(z)$ remains less than M, and that the absolute value of z is greater than δ. Since the number n is to become infinite, we may suppose that we have already taken it so large that δ may be taken greater than $|x|$; hence along C_n we shall have

$$\left| \frac{1}{z - x} \right| < \frac{1}{\delta - |x|}.$$

If S_n is the length of the curve C_n, we have then

$$|R_n| < \frac{|x|^{p+1}}{2\pi} M \frac{S_n}{\delta(\delta - |x|)}.$$

We shall have proved that this term R_n approaches zero as n becomes infinite if we can find a sequence of closed curves $C_1, C_2, \cdots, C_n, \cdots$ and a positive integer p satisfying the following conditions:

1) The absolute value of $z^{-p} F(z)$ remains less than a fixed number M along each of these curves.

2) The ratio S_n/δ of the length of the curve C_n to the minimum distance δ of the origin to a point of C_n remains less than an upper bound L as n becomes infinite.

If these conditions are satisfied, $|R_n|$ is less than a fixed number divided by a number $\delta - |x|$ which becomes infinite with n. The term R_n therefore approaches zero, and we have in the limit

$$(15) \quad \begin{cases} F(x) = F(0) + x F'(0) + \cdots + \dfrac{x^p}{p!} F^{(p)}(0) \\[2mm] \quad + \lim_{n = \infty} \sum_{C_n} \left[G_k \left(\dfrac{1}{x - a_k} \right) + s_k^{(0)} + s_k^{(1)} x + \cdots + s_k^{(p)} x^p \right]. \end{cases}$$

Thus we have found a development of the function $F(x)$ as a sum of an infinite series of rational terms. The order in which they occur in the series is determined by the arrangement of the curves $C_1, C_2, \cdots, C_n, \cdots$ in their sequence. If the series obtained is absolutely convergent, we can write the terms in an arbitrary order.

Note. If the point $z = 0$ were a pole for $F(z)$ with the principal part $G(1/z)$, it would suffice to apply the preceding method to the function $F(z) - G(1/z)$.

64. Expansion of ctn x and of sin x. Let us apply this method to the function $F(z) = \mathrm{ctn}\, z - 1/z$, which has only poles of the first order at the points $z = k\pi$, where k is any integer different from zero, the residue at each pole being equal to unity. We shall take for the curve C_n a square, such as $BCB'C'$, having the origin for center and having sides of length $2\, n\pi + \pi$ parallel to the axes; none of the poles are on this boundary, and the ratio of the length S_n to the minimum distance δ from the origin to a point of the boundary is constant and equal to 8. The square of the absolute value of ctn $(x + yi)$ is equal to

$$\frac{e^{2y} + e^{-2y} + 2\cos 2x}{e^{2y} + e^{-2y} - 2\cos 2x}.$$

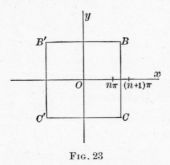

Fig. 23

On the sides BC and $B'C'$ we have $\cos 2x = -1$, and the absolute value is less than 1. On the sides BB' and CC' the square of this absolute value is less than

$$\frac{e^{2y} + e^{-2y} + 2}{e^{2y} + e^{-2y} - 2} = \left(\frac{1 + e^{-2y}}{1 - e^{-2y}}\right)^2.$$

We must replace $2\, y$ in this formula by $\pm (2\, n + 1)\, \pi$, and the expression thus obtained approaches unity when n becomes infinite. Since the absolute value of $1/z$ along C_n approaches zero when n becomes infinite, it follows that the absolute value of the function ctn $z - 1/z$ on the boundary C_n remains less than a fixed number M, whatever n may be. Hence we can apply to this function the formula (15), taking $p = 0$. We have here

$$F(0) = \lim_{x = 0}\left(\frac{x \cos x - \sin x}{x \sin x}\right) = 0,$$

and s_k^0, which represents the residue of $(\mathrm{ctn}\, z - 1/z)/z$ for the pole $k\pi$, is equal to $1/k\pi$. We have, then,

$$(16) \qquad \mathrm{ctn}\, x - \frac{1}{x} = \lim_{n = \infty} \sum_{-n}^{n}{}' \left(\frac{1}{x - k\pi} + \frac{1}{k\pi}\right),$$

where the value $k = 0$ is excluded from the summation. The infinite series obtained by letting n become infinite is absolutely convergent, for the general term can be written in the form

$$\frac{1}{x - k\pi} + \frac{1}{k\pi} = \frac{x}{k\pi(k\pi - x)} = \frac{1}{k^2\pi^2} \frac{x}{\left(1 - \dfrac{x}{k\pi}\right)}$$

and the absolute value of the factor $x/(1 - x/k\pi)$ remains less than a certain upper bound, provided x is not a multiple of π. We have, then, precisely

$$(17) \qquad \operatorname{ctn} x = \frac{1}{x} + \sum_{-\infty}^{+\infty}{}' \left(\frac{1}{x - k\pi} + \frac{1}{k\pi}\right).$$

Integrating the two members of this relation along a path starting from the origin and not passing through any of the poles, we find

$$\int_0^x \left(\operatorname{ctn} x - \frac{1}{x}\right) dx = \operatorname{Log}\left(\frac{\sin x}{x}\right) = \sum_{-\infty}^{+\infty}{}' \operatorname{Log}\left(1 - \frac{x}{k\pi}\right) + \frac{x}{k\pi},$$

from which we derive

$$(18) \qquad \sin x = x \prod_{-\infty}^{+\infty}{}' \left(1 - \frac{x}{k\pi}\right) e^{\frac{x}{k\pi}}.$$

The factor $e^{g(x)}$ is here equal to unity. If in the series (17) we combine the two terms which come from opposite values of k, we obtain the formula

$$(17') \qquad \operatorname{ctn} x = \frac{1}{x} + 2x \sum_{1}^{+\infty}{}' \frac{1}{x^2 - k^2\pi^2}.$$

Combining the two factors of the product (18) which correspond to opposite values of k, we have the new formula*

$$(18') \qquad \sin x = x \prod_{1}^{+\infty} \left(1 - \frac{x^2}{k^2\pi^2}\right),$$

or, substituting πx for x,

$$\frac{\sin \pi x}{\pi} = x \prod_{1}^{+\infty} \left(1 - \frac{x^2}{k^2}\right).$$

Note 1. The last formulæ show plainly the periodicity of $\sin x$, which does not appear from the power series development. We see, in fact, that $(\sin \pi x)/\pi$ is the limit as n becomes infinite of the polynomial

$$\phi_n(x) = \left(1 - \frac{x}{n}\right)\left(1 - \frac{x}{n-1}\right) \cdots (1 - x)\,x\,(1 + x) \cdots \left(1 + \frac{x}{n}\right).$$

---

* This decomposition of sin x into an infinite product is due to Euler, who obtained it in an elementary manner (*Introductio in Analysin infinitorum*).

Replacing x by $x + 1$, this formula may be written in the form

$$\phi_n(x + 1) = -\,\phi_n(x)\,\frac{n + 1 + x}{n - x}\,;$$

whence, letting n become infinite, we find $\sin(\pi x + \pi) = -\sin \pi x$, or

$$\sin(z + \pi) = -\sin z,$$

and therefore $\sin(z + 2\pi) = \sin z$.

Note 2. In this particular example it is easy to justify the necessity of associating with each binomial factor of the form $1 - x/a_k$ a suitable exponential factor if we wish to obtain an absolutely convergent product. For definiteness let us suppose x real and positive. The series $\Sigma x/n$ being divergent, the product

$$P_m = x\left(1 + \frac{x}{1}\right)\cdots\left(1 + \frac{x}{m}\right)$$

becomes infinite with m, while the product

$$Q_n = (1 - x)\left(1 - \frac{x}{2}\right)\cdots\left(1 - \frac{x}{n}\right)$$

approaches zero as n becomes infinite (I, § 177, 2d ed.). If we take $m = n$, the product $P_m Q_m$ has $(\sin \pi x)/\pi$ for its limit; but if we make m and n become infinite independently of each other, the limit of this product is completely indeterminate. This is easily verified by means of Weierstrass's primary functions, whatever may be the value of x. Let us note first that the two infinite products

$$F_1(x) = x\prod_{n=1}^{+\infty}\left(1 + \frac{x}{n}\right)e^{-\frac{x}{n}},\qquad F_2(x) = \prod_{n=1}^{+\infty}\left(1 - \frac{x}{n}\right)e^{\frac{x}{n}}$$

are both absolutely convergent, and their product $F_1(x)F_2(x)$ is equal to $(\sin \pi x)/\pi$. With these facts in mind, let us write the product $P_m Q_n$ in the form

$$P_m Q_n = x\prod_{\nu=1}^{m}\left(1 + \frac{x}{\nu}\right)e^{-\frac{x}{\nu}}\prod_{\nu=1}^{n}\left(1 - \frac{x}{\nu}\right)\frac{x}{e^{\nu}}\,e^{x\left(1 + \frac{1}{2} + \cdots + \frac{1}{m} - 1 - \frac{1}{2} - \cdots - \frac{1}{n}\right)}.$$

When the two numbers m and n become infinite, the product of all the factors on the right-hand side, omitting the last, has $F_1(x)F_2(x) = (\sin \pi x)/\pi$ for its limit. As for the last factor, we have seen that the expression

$$1 + \frac{1}{2} + \cdots + \frac{1}{m} - 1 - \frac{1}{2} - \cdots - \frac{1}{n}$$

has for its limit $\log \omega$, where ω denotes the limit of the quotient m/n (I, § 161). The product $P_m Q_n$ has, therefore,

$$\frac{\sin \pi x}{\pi}\,e^{x \log \omega}$$

for its limit. Hence we see the manner in which that limit depends upon the law according to which the two numbers m and n become infinite.

Note 3. We can make exactly analogous observations on the expansion of $\operatorname{ctn} x$. We shall show only how the periodicity of this function can be deduced from the series (17). Let us notice first of all that the series whose general term is

$$\frac{1}{k\pi} - \frac{1}{(k - 1)\pi} = -\frac{1}{k(k - 1)\pi},$$

where the index k takes on all the integral values from $-\infty$ to $+\infty$, excepting $k = 0$, $k = 1$, is absolutely convergent; and its sum is $-2/\pi$, as is seen on making k vary first from 2 to $+\infty$, then from -1 to $-\infty$. We can therefore write the development of $\operatorname{ctn} x$ in the form

$$\operatorname{ctn} x = \frac{1}{x} + \frac{1}{x-\pi} - \frac{1}{\pi} + \sum_{-\infty}^{+\infty}{}'' \left[\frac{1}{x-k\pi} + \frac{1}{(k-1)\pi} \right],$$

where the values $k = 0$, $k = 1$ are excluded from the summation. This results from subtracting from each term of the series (17) the corresponding term of the convergent series formed by the preceding series together with the additional term $2/\pi$. Substituting $x + \pi$ for x, we find

$$\operatorname{ctn}(x + \pi) = \frac{1}{x} + \frac{1}{x+\pi} - \frac{1}{\pi} + \sum_{-\infty}^{+\infty}{}'' \left[\frac{1}{x-(k-1)\pi} + \frac{1}{(k-1)\pi} \right],$$

or, again,

$$\operatorname{ctn}(x + \pi) = \frac{1}{x} + \sum_{-\infty}^{+\infty}{}' \left[\frac{1}{x-(k-1)\pi} + \frac{1}{(k-1)\pi} \right],$$

where $k-1$ takes on all integral values except 0. The right-hand side is identical with $\operatorname{ctn} x$.

II. DOUBLY PERIODIC FUNCTIONS. ELLIPTIC FUNCTIONS

65. Periodic functions. Expansion in series. A single-valued analytic function $f(z)$ is said to be *periodic* if there exists a real or complex number ω such that we have, whatever may be z, $f(z + \omega) = f(z)$; this number ω is called a *period*. Let us mark in the plane the point representing ω, and let us lay off on the unlimited straight line passing through the origin and the point ω a length equal to $|\omega|$ any number of times in both directions. We obtain thus the points ω, $2\,\omega$, $3\,\omega$, $\cdots$, $n\omega$, $\cdots$ and the points $-\omega$, $-2\,\omega$, $\cdots$, $-n\omega$, $\cdots$. Through these different points

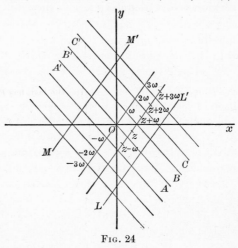

Fig. 24

and through the origin let us draw parallels to any direction different from $O\omega$; the plane is thus divided into an infinite number of cross strips of equal breadth (Fig. 24).

If through any point z we draw a parallel to the direction $O\omega$, we shall obtain all the points of that straight line by allowing the real parameter λ in the expression $z + \lambda\omega$ to vary from $-\infty$ to $+\infty$. In particular, if the point z describes the first strip $AA'BB'$, the corresponding point $z + \omega$ will describe the contiguous strip $BB'CC'$, the point $z + 2\omega$ will describe the third strip, and so on in this manner. All the values of the function $f(z)$ in the first strip will be duplicated at the corresponding points in each of the other strips.

Let LL' and MM' be two unlimited straight lines parallel to the direction $O\omega$. Let us put $u = e^{2i\pi z/\omega}$, and let us examine the region of the u-plane described by the variable u when the point z remains in the unlimited cross strip contained between the two parallels LL' and MM'. If $\alpha + \beta i$ is a point of LL', we shall obtain all the other points of that straight line by putting $z = \alpha + \beta i + \lambda\omega$ and making λ vary from $-\infty$ to $+\infty$. Thus, we have

$$u = e^{\frac{2i\pi}{\omega}(\alpha + \beta i + \lambda\omega)} = e^{2\pi i\lambda} e^{2\pi i \frac{\alpha + \beta i}{\omega}};$$

hence, as λ varies from $-\infty$ to $+\infty$, u describes a circle C_1 having the origin for center. Similarly, we see that as z describes the straight line MM', u remains on a circle C_2 concentric with the first; as the point z describes the unlimited strip contained between the two straight lines LL', MM', the point u describes the ring-shaped region contained between the two circles C_1, C_2. But while to any value of z there corresponds only one value of u, to a value of u there correspond an infinite number of values of z which form an arithmetic progression, with the common difference ω, extending forever in both directions.

A periodic function $f(z)$, with the period ω, that is analytic in the infinite cross strip between the two straight lines LL', MM', is equal to a function $\phi(u)$ of the new variable u which is analytic in the ring-shaped region between the two circles C_1 and C_2. For although to a value of u there correspond an infinite number of values of z, all these values of z give the same value to $f(z)$ on account of its periodicity. Moreover, if u_0 is a particular value of u, and z_0 any corresponding value of z, that determination of z which approaches z_0 as u approaches u_0 is an analytic function of u in the neighborhood of u_0; hence the same thing is true of $\phi(u)$. We can therefore apply Laurent's theorem to this function $\phi(u)$. In the ring-shaped region contained between the two circles C_1, C_2 this function is equal to the sum of a series of the following form:

$$\phi(u) = \sum_{m=-\infty}^{+\infty} A_m u^m.$$

Returning to the variable z, we conclude from this that in the interior of the cross strip considered above the periodic function $f(z)$ is equal to the sum of the series

$$(19) \qquad f(z) = \sum_{-\infty}^{+\infty} A_m e^{\frac{2 m i \pi z}{\omega}} .$$

If the function $f(z)$ is analytic in the whole plane, we can suppose that the two straight lines LL', MM', which bound the strip, recede indefinitely in opposite directions. *Every periodic integral function is therefore developable in a series of positive and negative powers of $e^{2 \pi i z / \omega}$ convergent for every finite value of z.*

66. Impossibility of a single-valued analytic function with three periods. By a famous theorem due to Jacobi, a single-valued analytic function cannot have more than two independent periods. To prove this we shall show that a single-valued analytic function cannot have *three* independent periods.* Let us first prove the following lemma :

Let a, b, c be any three real or complex quantities, and m, n, p three arbitrary integers, positive or negative, *of which one at least is different from zero*. If we give to the integers m, n, p all systems of possible values, except

$$m = n = p = 0,$$

the lower limit of $|ma + nb + pc|$ *is equal to zero.*

Consider the set (E) of points of the plane which represent quantities of the form $ma + nb + pc$. If two points corresponding to two different systems of integers coincide, we have, for example,

$$ma + nb + pc = m_1 a + n_1 b + p_1 c,$$

and therefore

$$(m - m_1) a + (n - n_1) b + (p - p_1) c = 0,$$

where at least one of the numbers $m - m_1$, $n - n_1$, $p - p_1$ is not zero. In this case the truth of the lemma is evident. If all the points of the set (E) are distinct, let 2δ be the lower limit of $|ma + nb + pc|$; this number 2δ is also the lower limit of the distance between any two points whatever of the set (E). In fact, the distance between the two points $ma + nb + pc$ and $m_1 a + n_1 b + p_1 c$ is equal to $|(m - m_1) a + (n - n_1) b + (p - p_1) c|$. We are going to show that we are led to an absurd conclusion by supposing $\delta > 0$.

Let N be a positive integer ; let us give to each of the integers m, n, p one of the values of the sequence $- N$, $-(N-1)$, $\cdots$, 0, $\cdots$, $N - 1$, N, and let us combine these values of m, n, p, in all possible manners. We obtain thus $(2 N + 1)^3$ points of the set (E), and these points are all distinct by hypothesis. Let us suppose $|a| \geqq |b| \geqq |c|$; then the distance from the origin to any one of the points of (E) just selected is at most equal to $3 N |a|$. These points therefore lie in the interior of a circle C of radius $3 N |a|$ about the origin as center or on the circle itself. If from each of these points as center we describe a

---

* Three periods a, b, c are said to be *dependent* if there exist three integers m, n, p (not all zero) for which $ma + nb + pc = 0$.— TRANS.

circle of radius δ, all these circles will be interior to a circle C_1 of radius equal to $3\,N\,|\,a\,| + \delta$ about the origin as center, and no two of them will overlap, since the distance between the centers of two of them cannot be smaller than $2\,\delta$. The sum of the areas of all these small circles is therefore less than the area of the circle C_1, and we have

$$(3\,N\,|\,a\,| + \delta)^2 > (2\,N + 1)^3 \delta^2,$$

or

$$\delta < \frac{3\,N\,|\,a\,|}{(2\,N + 1)^{\frac{3}{2}} - 1}.$$

The right-hand side approaches zero as N becomes infinite ; hence this inequality cannot be satisfied for all values of N by any positive number δ. Consequently the lower limit of $|\,ma + nb + pc\,|$ cannot be a positive number ; hence that lower limit is zero, and the truth of the lemma is established.

We see, then, that when no systems of integers m, n, p (except $m = n = p = 0$) exist such that $ma + nb + pc = 0$, we can always find integral values for these numbers such that $|\,ma + nb + pc\,|$ will be less than an arbitrary positive number ϵ. In this case a single-valued analytic function $f(z)$ cannot have the three independent periods a, b, c. For, let z_0 be an ordinary point for $f(z)$, and let us describe a circle of radius ϵ about the point z_0 as center, where ϵ is so small that the equation $f(z) = f(z_0)$ has no other root than $z = z_0$ inside of this circle (§ 40). If a, b, c are the periods of $f(z)$, it is clear that $ma + nb + pc$ is also a period for all values of the integers m, n, p ; hence we have

$$f(z_0 + ma + nb + pc) = f(z_0).$$

If we choose m, n, p in such a manner that $|\,ma + nb + pc\,|$ is less than ϵ, the equation $f(z) = f(z_0)$ would have a root z_1 different from z_0, where $|\,z_1 - z_0\,| < \epsilon$, which is impossible.

When there exists between a, b, c a relation of the form

(20) $$ma + nb + pc = 0,$$

without all the numbers m, n, p being zero, a single-valued analytic function $f(z)$ may have the periods a, b, c, but these periods reduce to two periods or to a single period. We may suppose that the three integers have no common divisor other than unity. Let D be the greatest common divisor of the two numbers m, n; $m = Dm'$, $n = Dn'$. Since the two numbers m', n' are prime to each other, we can find two other integers m'', n'' such that $m'n'' - m''n' = 1$. Let us put

$$m'a + n'b = a', \qquad m''a + n''b = b';$$

then we shall have, conversely, $a = n''a' - n'b'$, $b = m'b' - m''a'$. If a and b are periods of $f(z)$, a' and b' are also, and conversely. Hence we can replace the system of two periods a and b by the system of two periods a' and b'. The relation (20) becomes $Da' + pc = 0$; D and p being prime to each other, let us take two other integers D' and p' such that $Dp' - D'p = 1$, and let us put $D'a' + p'c = c'$. We obtain from the preceding relations $a' = -pc'$, $c = Dc'$, whence it is obvious that the three periods a, b, c are linear combinations of the two periods b' and c'.

Note. As a corollary of the preceding lemma we see that if α and β are two real quantities and m, n two arbitrary integers (of which at least one is not zero), the lower limit of $|\,m\alpha + n\beta\,|$ is equal to zero. For if we put $a = \alpha$, $b = \beta$, $c = i$, the absolute value of $m\alpha + n\beta + pi$ can be less than a number $\epsilon < 1$ only if we have $p = 0$, $|m\alpha + n\beta| < \epsilon$. From this it follows that a single-valued analytic function $f(z)$ cannot have two real independent periods α and β. If the quotient β/α is irrational, it is possible to find two numbers m and n such that $|m\alpha + n\beta|$ is less than ϵ, and it will be possible to carry through the reasoning just as before. If the quotient β/α is rational and equal to the irreducible fraction m/n, let us choose two integers m' and n' such that $mn' - m'n = 1$, and let us put $m'\alpha - n'\beta = \gamma$. The number γ is also a period, and from the two relations $m\alpha - n\beta = 0$, $m'\alpha - n'\beta = \gamma$ we derive $\alpha = -n\gamma$, $\beta = -m\gamma$, so that α and β are multiples of the single period γ. More generally, a single-valued analytic function $f(z)$ cannot have two independent periods a and b *whose ratio is real*, for the function $f(az)$ would have the two real periods 1 and b/a.*

67. Doubly periodic functions. A doubly periodic function is a single-valued analytic function having two periods whose ratio is not real. To conform to Weierstrass's notation, we shall indicate the independent variable by u, the two periods by 2ω and $2\omega'$, and we shall suppose that the coefficient of i in ω'/ω is positive. Let us mark in the plane the points 2ω, 4ω, 6ω, $\cdots$ and the points $2\omega'$, $4\omega'$, $6\omega'$, $\cdots$. Through the points $2m\omega$ let us draw parallels to the

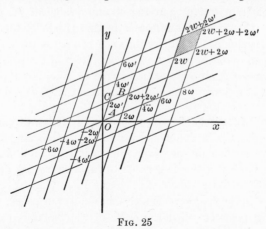

Fig. 25

direction $O\omega'$, and through the points $2m'\omega'$ parallels to the direction $O\omega$. The plane is divided in this manner into a net of congruent parallelograms (Fig. 25). Let $f(u)$ be a single-valued analytic function with the two periods 2ω, $2\omega'$; from the two relations $f(u + 2\omega) = f(u)$, $f(u + 2\omega') = f(u)$ we deduce at once

---

* It is now easy to prove that there exists for any periodic single-valued function at least one pair of periods in terms of which any other period can be expressed as an integral linear combination; such a pair is called a *primitive pair of periods.* — TRANS.

$f(u + 2\,m\omega + 2\,m'\omega') = f(u)$, so that $2\,m\omega + 2\,m'\omega'$ is also a period for all values of the integers m and m'. We shall represent this general period by $2\,w$.

The points that represent the various periods are precisely the vertices of the preceding net of parallelograms. When the point u describes the parallelogram $OABC$ whose vertices are $O, 2\,\omega, 2\,\omega + 2\,\omega'$, $2\,\omega'$, the point $u + 2\,w$ describes the parallelogram whose vertices are the points $2\,w, 2\,w + 2\,\omega, 2\,w + 2\,\omega + 2\,\omega', 2\,w + 2\,\omega'$, and the function $f(u)$ takes on the same value at any pair of corresponding points of the two parallelograms. Every parallelogram whose vertices are four points of the type $u_0, u_0 + 2\,w, u_0 + 2\,\omega', u_0 + 2\,\omega + 2\,\omega'$ is called a *parallelogram of periods ;* in general we consider the parallelogram $OABC$, but we could substitute any point in the plane for the origin. The period $2\,\omega + 2\,\omega'$ will be designated for brevity by $2\,\omega''$; the center of the parallelogram $OABC$ is the point ω'', while the points ω and ω' are the middle points of the sides OA and OC.

Every integral doubly periodic function is a constant. In fact, let $f(u)$ be a doubly periodic function ; if it is integral, it is analytic in the parallelogram $OABC$, and the absolute value of $f(u)$ remains always less than a fixed number M in this parallelogram. But on account of the double periodicity the value of $f(u)$ at any point of the plane is equal to the value of $f(u)$ at some point of the parallelogram $OABC$. Hence the absolute value of $f(u)$ remains less than a fixed number M. It follows by Liouville's theorem that $f(u)$ is a constant.

68. Elliptic functions. General properties. It follows from the preceding theorem that a doubly periodic function has singular points in the finite portion of the plane, unless it reduces to a constant. The term *elliptic function* is applied to functions which are doubly periodic and analytic except for poles. In any parallelogram of periods an elliptic function has a certain number of poles ; the number of these poles is called the *order* of the function, each being counted according to its degree of multiplicity *. It should be noticed that if an elliptic function $f(u)$ has a pole u_0 on the side OC, the point $u_0 + 2\,\omega$, situated on the opposite side AB, is also a pole ; but we should count only one of these poles in evaluating the number of poles contained in $OABC$. Similarly, if the origin is a pole, all the

---

* It is to be understood that the parallelogram is so chosen that the order is as small as possible. Otherwise, the number of poles in a parallelogram could be taken to be any multiple of this least number, since a multiple of a period is a period. — TRANS. (See also the footnote, p. 149.)

vertices of the net are also poles of $f(u)$, but we should count only one of them in each parallelogram. If, for example, we move that vertex of the net which lies at the origin to a suitable point as near as we please to the origin, the given function $f(u)$ no longer has any poles on the boundary of the parallelogram. When we have occasion to integrate an elliptic function $f(u)$ along the boundary of the parallelogram of periods, we shall always suppose, if it is necessary, that the parallelogram has been displaced in such a way that $f(u)$ has no longer any poles on its boundary. The application of the general theorems of the theory of analytic functions leads quite easily to the fundamental propositions:

1) *The sum of the residues of an elliptic function with respect to the poles situated in a parallelogram of periods is zero.*

Let us suppose for definiteness that $f(u)$ has no poles on the boundary $OABCO$. The sum of the residues with respect to the poles situated within the boundary is equal to

$$\frac{1}{2\pi i}\int f(u)\,du,$$

the integral being taken along $OABCO$. But this integral is zero, for the sum of the integrals taken along two opposite sides of the parallelogram is zero. Thus we have

$$\int_{(OA)} f(u)\,du = \int_0^{2\omega} f(u)\,du, \qquad \int_{(BC)} f(u)\,du = \int_{2\omega+2\omega'}^{2\omega'} f(u)\,du,$$

and if we substitute $u + 2\,\omega'$ for u in the last integral, we have

$$\int_{(BC)} f(u)\,du = \int_{2\omega}^0 f(u+2\,\omega')\,du = \int_{2\omega}^0 f(u)\,du = -\int_{(OA)} f(u)\,du.$$

Similarly, the sum of the integrals along AB and along CO is zero. In fact, this property is almost self-evident from the figure (Fig. 26). For let us consider two corresponding elements of the two integrals along OA and along BC. At the points m and m' the values of $f(u)$ are the same, while the values of du have opposite signs.

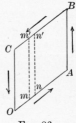

Fig. 26

The preceding theorem proves that an elliptic function $f(u)$ cannot have only a single pole of the first order in a parallelogram of periods. *An elliptic function is at least of the second order.*

2) *The number of zeros of an elliptic function in a parallelogram of periods is equal to the order of that function* (each of the zeros being counted according to its degree of multiplicity).

Let $f(u)$ be an elliptic function; the quotient $f'(u)/f(u) = \phi(u)$ is also an elliptic function, and the sum of the residues of $\phi(u)$ in a parallelogram is equal to the number of zeros of $f(u)$ diminished by the number of the poles (§ 48). Applying the preceding theorem to the function $\phi(u)$, we see the truth of the proposition just stated. In general, the number of roots of the equation $f(u) = C$ in a parallelogram of periods is equal to the order of the function, for the function $f(u) - C$ has the same poles as $f(u)$, whatever may be the constant C.

3) *The difference between the sum of the zeros and the sum of the poles of an elliptic function in a parallelogram of periods is equal to a period.*

Consider the integral

$$\frac{1}{2\pi i} \int u \frac{f'(u)}{f(u)} \, du$$

along the boundary of the parallelogram $OABC$. This integral is equal, as we have already seen (§ 48), to the sum of the zeros of $f(u)$ within the boundary, diminished by the sum of the poles of $f(u)$ within the same boundary. Let us evaluate the sum of the integrals resulting from the two opposite sides OA and BC:

$$\int_0^{2\omega} u \frac{f'(u)}{f(u)} \, du + \int_{2\omega+2\omega'}^{2\omega'} u \frac{f'(u)}{f(u)} \, du.$$

If we substitute $u + 2\omega'$ for u in the last integral, this sum is equal to

$$\int_0^{2\omega} u \frac{f'(u)}{f(u)} \, du + \int_{2\omega}^{0} (u + 2\omega') \frac{f'(u + 2\omega')}{f(u + 2\omega')} \, du,$$

or, on account of the periodicity of $f(u)$, to

$$-\int_0^{2\omega} 2\omega' \frac{f'(u)}{f(u)} \, du.$$

The integral

$$\int_0^{2\omega} \frac{f'(u)}{f(u)} \, du$$

is equal to the variation of $\text{Log}[f(u)]$ when u describes the side OA; but since $f(u)$ returns to its initial value, the variation of $\text{Log}[f(u)]$ is equal to $- 2m_2\pi i$, where m_2 is an integer. The sum of the integrals along the opposite sides OA and BC is therefore equal to

$(4\,m_2\pi i\omega')/2\,\pi i = 2\,m_2\omega'$. Similarly, the sum of the integrals along AB and along CO is of the form $2\,m_1\omega$. The difference considered above is therefore equal to $2\,m_1\omega + 2\,m_2\omega'$; that is, to a period.

By a similar argument it can be shown that the proposition is also applicable to the roots of the equation $f(u) = C$, contained in a parallelogram of periods, for any value of the constant C.

4) *Between any two elliptic functions with the same periods there exists an algebraic relation.*

Let $f(u)$, $f_1(u)$ be two elliptic functions with the same periods $2\,\omega$, $2\,\omega'$. In a parallelogram of periods let us take the points a_1, $a_2, \cdots,\ a_m$ which are poles for either of the two functions $f(u)$, $f_1(u)$ or for both of them; let μ_i be the higher order of multiplicity of the point a_i with respect to the two functions, and let $\mu_1 + \mu_2 + \cdots + \mu_m = N$. Now let $F(x, y)$ be a polynomial of degree n with constant coefficients. If we replace x and y by $f(u)$ and $f_1(u)$, respectively, in this polynomial, there will result a new elliptic function $\Phi(u)$ which can have no other poles than the points $a_1, a_2, \cdots, a_m$ and those which are deducible from them by the addition of a period. In order that this function $\Phi(u)$ may reduce to a constant, it is necessary and sufficient that the principal parts disappear in the neighborhood of each of the points $a_1, a_2, \cdots, a_m$. Now the point a_i is a pole for $\Phi(u)$ of an order at most equal to $n\mu_i$. Writing the conditions that all the principal parts shall be zero, we shall have then, in all, at most

$$n(\mu_1 + \mu_2 + \cdots + \mu_m) = Nn$$

linear homogeneous equations between the coefficients of the polynomial $F(x, y)$ in which the constant term does not appear. There are $n(n + 3)/2$ of these coefficients; if we choose n so large that $n(n + 3) > 2\,Nn$, or $n + 3 > 2\,N$, we obtain a system of linear homogeneous equations in which the number of unknowns is greater than that of the equations. Such equations have always a system of solutions not all zero. If $F(x, y)$ is a polynomial determined by these equations, the elliptic functions $f(u), f_1(u)$ satisfy the algebraic relation

$$F[f(u), f_1(u)] = C,$$

where C denotes a constant.

Notes. Before leaving these general theorems, let us make some further observations which we shall need later.

A single-valued analytic function $f(u)$ is said to be *even* if we have $f(-u) = f(u)$; it is said to be *odd* if we have $f(-u) = -f(u)$.

The derivative of an even function is an odd function, and the derivative of an odd function is an even function. In general, the derivatives of even order of an even function are themselves even functions, and the derivatives of odd order are odd functions. On the contrary, the derivatives of even order of an odd function are odd functions, and the derivatives of odd order are even functions.

Let $f(u)$ be an odd elliptic function; if w is a half-period, we must have at the same time $f(w) = -f(-w)$ and $f(w) = f(-w)$, since $w = -w + 2w$. It is necessary, then, that $f(w)$ shall be zero or infinite, that is, that w must be a zero or a pole for $f(u)$. The order of multiplicity of the zero or of the pole is necessarily odd; if w were a zero of even order $2n$ for $f(u)$, the derivative $f^{(2n)}(u)$, which is odd, would be analytic and different from zero for $u = w$. If w were a pole of even order for $f(u)$, it would be a zero of even order for $1/f(u)$. Hence we may say that *every half-period is a zero or a pole of an odd order for any odd elliptic function.*

If an even elliptic function $f(u)$ has a half-period w for a pole or for a zero, *the order of multiplicity of the pole or of the zero is an even number.* If, for example, w were a zero of odd order $2n + 1$, it would be a zero of even order for the derivative $f'(u)$, which is an odd function. The proof is exactly similar for poles. Since twice a period is also a period, all that we have just said about half-periods applies also to the periods themselves.

69. The function $p(u)$. We have already seen that every elliptic function has at least two simple poles, or one pole of the second order, in a parallelogram of periods. In Jacobi's notation we take functions having two simple poles for our elements; in Weierstrass's notation, on the contrary, we take for our element an elliptic function having a single pole of the second order in a parallelogram. Since the residue must be zero, the principal part in the neighborhood of the pole a must be of the form $A/(u-a)^2$. In order to make the problem completely definite, it suffices to take $A = 1$ and to suppose that the poles of the function are the origin $u = 0$ and all the vertices of the network $2w = 2m\omega + 2m'\omega'$. We are thus led first to solve the following problem:

To form an elliptic function having as poles of the second order all the points $2w = 2m\omega + 2m'\omega'$, where m and m' are any two integers whatever, and having no other poles, so that the principal part in the neighborhood of the point $2w$ shall be $1/(u - 2w)^2$.

Before applying to this problem the general method of § 62, we shall first prove that the double series

(21)
$$\sum{}' \frac{1}{|m\omega + m'\omega'|^\mu},$$

where m and m' take on all the integral values from $-\infty$ to $+\infty$ (the combination $m = m' = 0$ being excepted), is convergent, *provided that the exponent μ is a positive number greater than 2.* Consider the triangle having the three points $u = 0$, $u = m\omega$, $u = m\omega + m'\omega'$ for its vertices; the lengths of the three sides of the triangle are respectively $|m\omega|$, $|m'\omega'|$, $|m\omega + m'\omega'|$. We have, then, the relation

$$|m\omega + m'\omega'|^2 = m^2|\omega|^2 + m'^2|\omega'|^2 + 2\,mm'|\omega\omega'|\cos\theta,$$

where θ is the angle between the two directions $O\omega$, $O\omega'(0 < \theta < \pi)$. For brevity let $|\omega| = a$, $|\omega'| = b$, and let us suppose $a \leqq b$. The preceding relation can then be written in the form

$$|m\omega + m'\omega'|^2 = m^2a^2 + m'^2b^2 \pm 2\,mm'ab\cos\Theta,$$

where the angle Θ is equal to θ if $\theta \leqq \pi/2$, and to $\pi - \theta$ if $\theta > \pi/2$. The angle Θ cannot be zero, since the three points O, ω, ω' are not in a straight line, and we have $0 \leqq \cos\Theta < 1$. We have, then, also

$$|m\omega + m'\omega'|^2 = (1 - \cos\Theta)(m^2a^2 + m'^2b^2) + \cos\Theta(ma \pm m'b)^2,$$

and consequently

$$|m\omega + m'\omega'|^2 \geqq (1 - \cos\Theta)(m^2a^2 + m'^2b^2) \geqq (1 - \cos\Theta)a^2(m^2 + m'^2).$$

From this it follows that the terms of the series (21) are respectively less than or equal to those of the series $\Sigma'1/(m^2 + m'^2)^{\mu/2}$ multiplied by a constant factor, and we know that the last series is convergent if the exponent $\mu/2$ is greater than unity (I, § 172). Hence the series (21) is convergent if we put $\mu = 3$ or $\mu = 4$. According to a result derived in § 62, the series

$$\phi(u) = \frac{1}{u^2} + \sum{}' \left[\frac{1}{(u - 2\,w)^2} - \frac{1}{4\,w^2} \right], \qquad (w = m\omega + m'\omega'),$$

represents a function that is analytic except for poles, and that has the same poles, with the same principal parts, as the elliptic function sought. We shall show that this function $\phi(u)$ has precisely the two periods $2\,\omega$ and $2\,\omega'$. Consider first the series

$$\sum{}'' \left[\frac{1}{(2\,w + 2\,\omega)^2} - \frac{1}{(2\,w)^2} \right],$$

where $2\,w = 2\,m\omega + 2\,m'\omega'$, the summation being extended to all the integral values of m and m', except the combinations $m = m' = 0$

and $m = -1$, $m' = 0$. This series is absolutely convergent, for it results from the series $\phi(u)$ when we substitute -2ω for u and omit two terms. It is easily seen that the sum of this series is zero by considering it as a double series and evaluating separately each of the rows of the rectangular double array. Subtracting this series from $\phi(u)$, we can then write

$$\phi(u) = \frac{1}{u^2} + \frac{1}{(u + 2\omega)^2} - \frac{1}{4\omega^2} + \sum'' \left[\frac{1}{(u - 2w)^2} - \frac{1}{(2w + 2\omega)^2} \right],$$

the combinations $(m = m' = 0)$, $(m = -1, m' = 0)$ being always excluded from the summation. Let us now change u to $u - 2\omega$; then we have

$$\phi(u - 2\omega) = \frac{1}{u^2} + \sum' \left[\frac{1}{(u - 2\omega - 2w)^2} - \frac{1}{(2w + 2\omega)^2} \right],$$

the combination $m = -1$, $m' = 0$ being the only one excluded from the summation. But the right-hand side of this equality is identical with $\phi(u)$. This function has therefore the period 2ω, and in like manner we can prove that it has the period $2\omega'$. This is the function which Weierstrass represents by the notation $p(u)$, and which is thus defined by the equation

$$(22) \quad p(u) = \frac{1}{u^2} + \sum' \left[\frac{1}{(u - 2w)^2} - \frac{1}{4w^2} \right], \qquad (w = m\omega + m'\omega').$$

If we put $u = 0$ in the difference $p(u) - 1/u^2$, all the terms of the double sum are zero, and that difference is itself zero. The function $p(u)$ possesses, then, the following properties:

1) It is doubly periodic and has for poles all the points $2w$ and only those.

2) The principal part in the neighborhood of the origin is $1/u^2$.

3) The difference $p(u) - 1/u^2$ is zero for $u = 0$.

These properties characterize the function $p(u)$. In fact, any analytic function $f(u)$ possessing the first two properties differs from $p(u)$ only by a constant, since the difference is a doubly periodic function without any poles. If we have also $f(u) - 1/u^2 = 0$ for $u = 0$, $f(u) - p(u)$ is also zero for $u = 0$; we have, therefore, $f(u) = p(u)$.

The function $p(-u)$ evidently possesses these three properties; we have, then, $p(-u) = p(u)$, and the function $p(u)$ is even, which is also easily seen from the formula (22).

Let us consider the period of $p(u)$ whose absolute value is smallest, and let δ be its absolute value. Within the circle C_δ with the radius δ, described about the origin as center, the difference $p(u) - 1/u^2$ is analytic and can be developed in positive powers of u. The general term of the series (22), developed in powers of u, gives

$$\frac{1}{(u-2w)^2} - \frac{1}{4w^2} = \frac{2u}{(2w)^3} + \frac{3u^2}{(2w)^4} + \cdots + \frac{(n+1)u^n}{(2w)^{n+2}} + \cdots,$$

and it is easy to prove that the function

$$\frac{5}{16|w|^3} \frac{u}{1 - \dfrac{u}{|w|}}$$

dominates this series in a circle of radius $\delta/2$, and, a fortiori, the expression obtained from it by replacing $1 - u/|w|$ by $1 - 2u/\delta$ dominates the series. Since the series $\Sigma' 1/|w|^3$ is convergent, we have the right to add the resulting series term by term (§ 9). The coefficients of the odd powers of u are zero, for the terms resulting from periods symmetrical with respect to the origin cancel, and we can write the development of $p(u)$ in the form

$$(23) \qquad p(u) = \frac{1}{u^2} + c_2 u^2 + c_3 u^4 + \cdots + c_\lambda u^{2\lambda-2} + \cdots,$$

where

$$(24) \qquad \begin{cases} c_2 = 3\sum' \dfrac{1}{(2w)^4}, \qquad c_3 = 5\sum' \dfrac{1}{(2w)^6}, \qquad \cdots, \\[2mm] \quad c_\lambda = (2\lambda - 1)\sum' \dfrac{1}{(2w)^{2\lambda}}, \qquad \cdots. \end{cases}$$

Whereas the formula (22) is applicable to the whole plane, the new development (23) is valid only in the interior of the circle C_δ having its center at the origin and passing through the nearest vertex of the periodic network.

The derivative $p'(u)$ is itself an elliptic function having all the points $2w$ for poles of the third order. It is represented in the whole plane by the series

$$(25) \qquad p'(u) = -\frac{2}{u^3} - 2\sum' \frac{1}{(u-2w)^3}.$$

In general, the nth derivative $p^{(n)}(u)$ is an elliptic function having all the points $2w$ for poles of order $n+2$, and it is represented by the series

$$(26) \quad p^{(n)}(u) = (-1)^n \frac{(n+1)!}{u^{n+2}} + (-1)^n (n+1)! \sum' \frac{1}{(u-2w)^{n+2}}.$$

We leave to the reader the verification of the correctness of these developments, which does not present any difficulty in view of the properties established above (§§ 39 and 61).

70. The algebraic relation between $p(u)$ and $p'(u)$. By the general theorem of § 68 there exists an algebraic relation between $p(u)$ and $p'(u)$. It is easily obtained as follows: In the neighborhood of the origin we have, from the formula (23),

$$p'(u) = -\frac{2}{u^3} + 2\,c_2 u + 4\,c_3 u^3 + \cdots,$$

$$[p'(u)]^2 = \frac{4}{u^6} - \frac{8\,c_2}{u^2} - 16\,c_3 + \cdots,$$

$$[p(u)]^3 = \frac{1}{u^6} + \frac{3\,c_2}{u^2} + 3\,c_3 + \cdots,$$

where the terms of the series not written are zero for $u = 0$. The difference $p'^2(u) - 4\,p^3(u)$ has therefore the origin as a pole of the second order, and in the neighborhood of this point we have

$$p'^2(u) - 4\,p^3(u) = -\frac{20\,c_2}{u^2} - 28\,c_3 + \cdots,$$

where the terms not written are zero for $u = 0$.

Hence the elliptic function $-20\,c_2 p(u) - 28\,c_3$ has the same poles, with the same principal parts, as the elliptic function $p'^2 - 4\,p^3$, and their difference is zero when $u = 0$. These two elliptic functions are therefore identical, and we have the desired relation, which we shall write in the form

$$(27) \qquad [p'(u)]^2 = 4\,p^3(u) - g_2 p(u) - g_3,$$

where

$$g_2 = 20\,c_2 = 60 \sum{}' \left(\frac{1}{2\,w}\right)^4, \qquad g_3 = 28\,c_3 = 140 \sum{}' \left(\frac{1}{2\,w}\right)^6.$$

The relation (27) is fundamental in the theory of elliptic functions; the quantities g_2 and g_3 are called the *invariants*.

All the coefficients c_λ of the development (23) are polynomials in terms of the invariants g_2 and g_3. In fact, taking the derivative of the relation (27) and dividing the result by $2\,p'(u)$, we derive the formula

$$(28) \qquad p''(u) = 6\,p^2(u) - \frac{g_2}{2}.$$

On the other hand, we have in the neighborhood of the origin

$$p''(u) = \frac{6}{u^4} + 2\,c_2 + 12\,c_3 u^2 + \cdots + (2\lambda - 2)(2\lambda - 3)c_\lambda u^{2\lambda - 4} + \cdots.$$

Replacing $p(u)$ and $p''(u)$ by their developments in the relation (28), and remembering that (28) is satisfied identically, we obtain the recurrent relation

$$c_\lambda = \frac{3}{(2\,\lambda + 1)(\lambda - 3)} \sum_\nu c_\nu c_{\lambda - \nu}, \qquad [\nu = 2, 3, \cdots, (\lambda - 2)],$$

which enables us to calculate step by step all the coefficients c_λ in terms of c_2 and c_3, and consequently in terms of g_2 and g_3; we find thus

$$c_4 = \frac{g_2^2}{2^4 \cdot 3 \cdot 5^2}, \qquad c_5 = \frac{3\,g_2 g_3}{2^4 \cdot 5 \cdot 7 \cdot 11}, \qquad \cdots.$$

This computation brings out the remarkable algebraic fact that all the sums $\Sigma' 1/(2\,w)^{2n}$ are expressible as polynomials in terms of the first two.

We know a priori the roots of $p'(u)$. This function, being of the third order, has three roots in each parallelogram of periods. Since it is odd, it has the roots $u = \omega$, $u = \omega'$, $u = \omega'' = \omega + \omega'$ (§ 68, notes). By (27) the roots of the equation $4\,p^3 - g_2 p - g_3 = 0$ are precisely the values of $p(u)$ for $u = \omega$, ω', ω''. These three roots are ordinarily represented by e_1, e_2, e_3:

$$e_1 = p(\omega), \qquad e_2 = p(\omega'), \qquad e_3 = p(\omega'').$$

These three roots are all different; for if we had, for example, $e_1 = e_2$, the equation $p(u) = e_1$ would have two double roots ω and ω' in the interior of a parallelogram of periods, which is impossible, since $p(u)$ is of the second order. Moreover, we have

$$4\,p^3(u) - g_2 p(u) - g_3 = 4[p(u) - e_1][p(u) - e_2][p(u) - e_3],$$

and between the invariants g_2, g_3 and the roots e_1, e_2, e_3 we have the relations

$$e_1 + e_2 + e_3 = 0, \qquad e_1 e_2 + e_1 e_3 + e_2 e_3 = -\frac{g_2}{4}, \qquad e_1 e_2 e_3 = \frac{g_3}{4}.$$

The discriminant $(g_2^3 - 27\,g_3^2)/16$ is necessarily different from zero.

71. The function $\zeta(u)$. If we integrate the function $p(u) - 1/u^2$ along any path whatever starting from the origin and not passing through any pole, we have the relation

$$\int_0^u \left[p(u) - \frac{1}{u^2} \right] du = -\sum' \left[\frac{1}{u - 2\,w} + \frac{1}{2\,w} + \frac{u}{(2\,w)^2} \right].$$

The series on the right represents a function which is analytic except for poles, having all the points $u = 2\,w$, except $u = 0$, for poles of the first order. Changing the sign and adding the fraction $1/u$, we shall put

$$(29) \qquad \zeta(u) = \frac{1}{u} + \sum' \left[\frac{1}{u - 2w} + \frac{1}{2w} + \frac{u}{(2w)^2} \right].$$

The preceding relation can be written

$$(30) \qquad \int_0^u \left[p(u) - \frac{1}{u^2} \right] du = -\zeta(u) + \frac{1}{u},$$

and, taking the derivatives of the two sides, we find

$$(31) \qquad \zeta'(u) = -p(u).$$

It is easily seen from either one of these formulæ that the function $\zeta(u)$ is odd. In the neighborhood of the origin we have by (23) and (30),

$$\zeta(u) = \frac{1}{u} - \frac{c_2}{3} u^3 - \frac{c_3}{5} u^5 - \cdots.$$

The function $\zeta(u)$ cannot have the periods 2ω and $2\omega'$, for it would have only one pole of the first order in a parallelogram of periods. But since the two functions $\zeta(u + 2w)$ and $\zeta(u)$ have the same derivative $-p(u)$, these two functions differ only by a constant; hence the function $\zeta(u)$ increases by a constant quantity when the argument u increases by a period. It is easy to obtain an expression for this constant. Let us write, for greater clearness, the formula (30) in the form

$$\int_0^u \left[p(v) - \frac{1}{v^2} \right] dv = \frac{1}{u} - \zeta(u).$$

Changing u to $u + 2\omega$ and subtracting the two formulæ, we find

$$\zeta(u + 2\omega) - \zeta(u) = -\int_u^{u+2\omega} p(v)\, dv.$$

We shall put

$$2\eta = -\int_u^{u+2\omega} p(v)\, dv, \qquad 2\eta' = -\int_u^{u+2\omega'} p(v)\, dv.$$

Then η and η' are constants independent of the lower limit u and of the path of integration. This last point is evident a priori, since all the residues of $p(v)$ are zero. The function $\zeta(u)$ satisfies, then, the two relations

$$\zeta(u + 2\omega) = \zeta(u) + 2\eta, \qquad \zeta(u + 2\omega') = \zeta(u) + 2\eta'.$$

If we put in these formulæ $u = -\omega$ and $u = -\omega'$ respectively, we find $\eta = \zeta(\omega)$, $\eta' = \zeta(\omega')$.

There exists a very simple relation between the four quantities ω, ω', η, η'. To establish it we have only to evaluate in two ways the integral $\int \zeta(u)\,du$, taken along the parallelogram whose vertices are u_0, $u_0 + 2\,\omega$, $u_0 + 2\,\omega + 2\,\omega'$, $u_0 + 2\,\omega'$. We shall suppose that $\zeta(u)$ has no poles on the boundary, and that the coefficient of i in ω'/ω is positive, so that the vertices will be encountered in the order in which they are written when the boundary of the parallelogram is described in the positive sense. There is a single pole of $\zeta(u)$ in the interior of this boundary, with a residue equal to $+1$; hence the integral under consideration is equal to $2\,\pi i$. On the other hand, by § 68 the sum of the integrals taken along the side joining the vertices u_0, $u_0 + 2\,\omega$ and along the opposite side is equal to the expression

$$\int_{u_0}^{u_0+2\omega} [\zeta(u) - \zeta(u + 2\,\omega')]\,du = -\,4\,\omega\eta'.$$

Similarly, the sum of the integrals coming from the other two sides is equal to $4\,\omega'\eta$. We have, then,

$$(32) \qquad \omega'\eta - \omega\eta' = \frac{\pi}{2}\,i,$$

which is the relation mentioned above.

Let us again calculate the definite integral

$$F(u) = \int_u^{u+2\omega} \zeta(v)\,dv,$$

taken along any path whatever not passing through any of the poles. We have

$$F'(u) = \zeta(u + 2\,\omega) - \zeta(u) = 2\,\eta,$$

so that $F(u)$ is of the form $F(u) = 2\,\eta u + K$, the constant K being determined except for a multiple of $2\,\pi i$, for we can always modify the path of integration without changing the extremities in such a way as to increase the integral by any multiple whatever of $2\,\pi i$. To find this constant K let us calculate the definite integral

$$\int_{-\omega}^{+\omega} \left[\zeta(v) - \frac{1}{v}\right] dv$$

along a path very close to the segment of a straight line which joins the two points ω and $-\omega$. This integral is zero, for we can replace the path of integration by the rectilinear path, and the elements of the new integral cancel in pairs. But, on replacing u by $-\omega$ in the expression which gives $F(u)$, we have

$$\int_{-\omega}^{+\omega} \zeta(v)\,dv = -\,2\,\eta\omega + K,$$

and since we have also

$$\int_{-\omega}^{+\omega} \frac{dv}{v} = \pm \pi i,$$

we can take $K = 2\eta\omega \pm \pi i$. Hence, without making any supposition as to the path of integration, we have, in general,

$$(33) \qquad \int_{u}^{u+2\omega} \zeta(v)dv = 2\eta(u + \omega) + (2m + 1)\pi i,$$

where m is an integer, and we have an analogous formula for the integral $\int_{u}^{u+2\omega'} \zeta(v) dv$.

72. The function $\sigma(u)$. Integrating the function $\zeta(u) - 1/u$ along any path starting from the origin and not passing through any pole, we have

$$\int_{0}^{u} \left[\zeta(u) - \frac{1}{u}\right] du = \sum' \left[\mathrm{Log}\left(1 - \frac{u}{2w}\right) + \frac{u}{2w} + \frac{u^2}{8w^2}\right]$$

and consequently

$$(34) \qquad ue^{\int_{0}^{u}\left[\zeta(u) - \frac{1}{u}\right]du} = u\prod'\left(1 - \frac{u}{2w}\right)e^{\frac{u}{2w} + \frac{u^2}{8w^2}}.$$

The integral function on the right is the simplest of the integral functions which have all the periods $2w$ for simple roots; it is the function $\sigma(u)$:

$$(35) \qquad \sigma(u) = u\prod'\left(1 - \frac{u}{2w}\right)e^{\frac{u}{2w} + \frac{u^2}{8w^2}}.$$

The equality (34) can be written

$$(34') \qquad \sigma(u) = ue^{\int_{0}^{u}\left[\zeta(u) - \frac{1}{u}\right]du};$$

whence, taking the logarithmic derivative of both sides, we obtain

$$(36) \qquad \frac{\sigma'(u)}{\sigma(u)} = \frac{1}{u} + \zeta(u) - \frac{1}{u} = \zeta(u).$$

The function $\sigma(u)$, being an integral function, cannot be doubly periodic. When its argument increases by a period, it is multiplied by an exponential factor, which can be determined as follows :
From the formula (34') we have

$$\frac{\sigma(u + 2\omega)}{\sigma(u)} = \frac{u + 2\omega}{u} e^{\int_{u}^{u+2\omega}\left[\zeta(u) - \frac{1}{u}\right]du} = e^{\int_{u}^{u+2\omega} \zeta(u)du}.$$

This factor was calculated in § 71, whence we find

$$(37) \qquad \sigma(u + 2\omega) = e^{2\eta(u+\omega) + (2m+1)\pi i}\sigma(u) = -e^{2\eta(u+\omega)}\sigma(u).$$

It is easy to establish in a similar manner the relation

$$(38) \qquad \sigma(u + 2\,\omega') = - e^{2\,\eta'(u+\omega')}\sigma(u).$$

From either of the formulæ (35) or (34') it follows that $\sigma(u)$ is an *odd* function.

If we expand this function $\sigma(u)$ in powers of u, the expansion obtained will be valid for the whole plane. It is easy to show that all the coefficients are polynomials in g_2 and g_3. For we have

$$\int_0^u \left[\zeta(u) - \frac{1}{u} \right] du = - \frac{c_2}{3 \cdot 4} u^4 - \frac{c_3}{5 \cdot 6} u^6 - \cdots - \frac{c_\lambda}{2\,\lambda(2\,\lambda - 1)} u^{2\lambda} - \cdots$$

$$\sigma(u) = u e^{-\frac{c_2}{3 \cdot 4} u^4 - \frac{c_3}{5 \cdot 6} u^6 - \cdots}.$$

We see that there is no term in u^3 and that any coefficient is a polynomial in the c_λ's and therefore in the invariants g_2 and g_3; the first five terms are as follows:

$$(39) \quad \sigma(u) = u - \frac{g_2 u^5}{2^4 \cdot 3 \cdot 5} - \frac{g_3 u^7}{2^3 \cdot 3 \cdot 5 \cdot 7} - \frac{g_2^2 u^9}{2^9 \cdot 3^2 \cdot 5 \cdot 7} - \frac{g_2 g_3 u^{11}}{2^7 \cdot 3^2 \cdot 5^2 \cdot 7 \cdot 11} - \cdots.$$

The three functions $p(u)$, $\zeta(u)$, $\sigma(u)$ are the essential elements of the theory of elliptic functions. The first two can be derived from $\sigma(u)$ by means of the two relations $\zeta(u) = \sigma'(u)/\sigma(u)$, $p(u) = -\zeta'(u)$.

73. General expressions for elliptic functions. Every elliptic function $f(u)$ can be expressed in terms of the single function $\sigma(u)$, or again in terms of the function $\zeta(u)$ and of its derivatives, or finally in terms of the two functions $p(u)$ and $p'(u)$. We shall present concisely the three methods.

Method 1. *Expression of $f(u)$ in terms of the function $\sigma(u)$.* Let $a_1, a_2, \cdots, a_n$ be the zeros of the function $f(u)$ in a parallelogram of periods, and $b_1, b_2, \cdots, b_n$ the poles of $f(u)$ in the same parallelogram, each of the zeros and each of the poles being counted as often as is required by its degree of multiplicity. Between these zeros and poles we have the relation

$$(40) \qquad a_1 + a_2 + \cdots + a_n = b_1 + b_2 + \cdots + b_n + 2\,\Omega,$$

where $2\,\Omega$ is a period.

Let us now consider the function

$$\phi(u) = \frac{\sigma(u - a_1) \cdots \sigma(u - a_n)}{\sigma(u - b_1) \cdots \sigma(u - b_n - 2\,\Omega)}.$$

This function has the same poles and the same zeros as the function $f(u)$, for the only zeros of the factor $\sigma(u - a_i)$ are $u = a_i$ and the values of u which differ from a_i only by a period. On the other hand, this function $\phi(u)$ is doubly periodic, for if we change u to $u + 2\omega$, for example, the relation (37) shows that the numerator and the denominator of $\phi(u)$ are multiplied respectively by the two factors

$$(-1)^n e^{2\eta(nu + n\omega - a_1 - a_2 - \cdots - a_n)}, \qquad (-1)^n e^{2\eta(nu + n\omega - b_1 - b_2 - \cdots - b_n - 2\Omega)},$$

and these two factors are equal, by (40). Similarly, we find that $\phi(u + 2\omega') = \phi(u)$. The quotient $f(u)/\phi(u)$ is therefore a doubly periodic function of u having no infinite values; that is, it is a constant, and we can write

$$(41) \qquad f(u) = C \, \frac{\sigma(u - a_1)\sigma(u - a_2) \cdots \sigma(u - a_n)}{\sigma(u - b_1)\sigma(u - b_2) \cdots \sigma(u - b_n - 2\Omega)}.$$

To determine the constant C it is sufficient to give to the variable u any value which is neither a pole nor a zero.

More generally, to express an elliptic function $f(u)$ in terms of the function $\sigma(u)$, when we know its poles and its zeros, it will suffice to choose n zeros $(a'_1, a'_2, \cdots, a'_n)$ and n poles $(b'_1, b'_2, \cdots, b'_n)$ in such a way that $\Sigma a'_i = \Sigma b'_i$ and that each root of $f(u)$ can be obtained by adding a period to one of the quantities a'_i, and each pole by adding a period to one of the quantities b'_i. These poles and zeros may be situated in any way in the plane, provided the preceding conditions are satisfied.

Method 2. Expression of $f(u)$ in terms of the function ζ and of its derivatives. Let us consider k poles $a_1, a_2, \cdots, a_k$ of the function $f(u)$ such that every other pole is obtained by adding a period to one of them. We could take, for example, the poles lying in the same parallelogram, but that is not necessary. Let

$$\frac{A_1^{(i)}}{u - a_i} + \frac{A_2^{(i)}}{(u - a_i)^2} + \cdots + \frac{A_{n_i}^{(i)}}{(u - a_i)^{n_i}}$$

be the principal part of $f(u)$ in the neighborhood of the point a_i. The difference

$$f(u) - \sum_{i=1}^{k} \left[A_1^{(i)} \zeta(u - a_i) - A_2^{(i)} \zeta'(u - a_i) \cdots \right.$$
$$\left. + \frac{(-1)^{n_i - 1} A_{n_i}^{(i)}}{(n_i - 1)!} \zeta^{(n_i - 1)}(u - a_i) \right]$$

is an analytic function in the whole plane. Moreover, it is a doubly periodic function, for when we change u to $u + 2\omega$, this function is increased by $-2\eta \Sigma A_1^{(i)}$, which is zero, since $\Sigma A_1^{(i)}$ represents the sum of the residues in a parallelogram. That difference is therefore a constant, and we have

$$(42) \quad \begin{cases} f(u) = C + \sum_{i=1}^{k} \Big[A_1^{(i)} \zeta(u - a_i) - A_2^{(i)} \zeta'(u - a_i) \cdots \\ \qquad\qquad + (-1)^{n_i - 1} \dfrac{A_{n_i}^{(i)}}{(n_i - 1)!} \zeta^{(n_i - 1)}(u - a_i) \Big]. \end{cases}$$

The preceding formula is due to Hermite. In order to apply it we must know the poles of the elliptic function $f(u)$ and the corresponding principal parts. Just as formula (41) is the analogon of the formula which expresses a rational function as a quotient of two polynomials decomposed into their linear factors, the formula (42) is the analogon of the formula for the decomposition of a rational fraction into simple elements. Here the function $\zeta(u - a)$ plays the part of the simple element.

Method 3. *Expression of $f(u)$ in terms of $p(u)$ and of $p'(u)$.* Let us consider first an even elliptic function $f(u)$. The zeros of this function, *which are not periods*, are symmetric in pairs. We can therefore find n zeros $(a_1, a_2, \cdots, a_n)$ such that all the zeros except the periods are included in the expressions

$$\pm a_1 + 2w, \quad \pm a_2 + 2w, \quad \cdots, \quad \pm a_n + 2w.$$

We shall take, for example, the parallelogram whose vertices are $\omega + \omega'$, $\omega' - \omega$, $-\omega - \omega'$, $\omega - \omega'$ and the zeros in this parallelogram lying on the same side of a straight line passing through the origin, carefully excluding half the boundary in a suitable manner. If a zero a_i is not a half-period, it will be made to appear in the sequence $a_1, a_2, \cdots, a_n$ as often as there are units in its degree of multiplicity. If the zero a_1, for example, is a half-period, it will be a zero of even order $2r$ (§ 68, notes). We shall make this zero appear only r times in the sequence $a_1, a_2, \cdots, a_n$. With this understanding, the product

$$[p(u) - p(a_1)][p(u) - p(a_2)] \cdots [p(u) - p(a_n)]$$

has the same zeros, with the same orders, as $f(u)$, excepting the case of $f(0) = 0$. Similarly, we shall form another product,

$$[p(u) - p(b_1)][p(u) - p(b_2)] \cdots [p(u) - p(b_m)],$$

having the poles of $f(u)$ for its zeros and with the same orders, again not considering the end points of any period. Let us put

$$\phi(u) = \frac{[p(u) - p(a_1)][p(u) - p(a_2)] \cdots [p(u) - p(a_n)]}{[p(u) - p(b_1)][p(u) - p(b_2)] \cdots [p(u) - p(b_m)]};$$

the quotient $f(u)/\phi(u)$ is an elliptic function which has a finite value *different from zero* for every value of u which is not a period. This elliptic function reduces to a constant, for it could only have periods for poles; and if it did, its reciprocal would not have any poles. We have, then,

$$f(u) = C\,\frac{[p(u) - p(a_1)][p(u) - p(a_2)] \cdots [p(u) - p(a_n)]}{[p(u) - p(b_1)][p(u) - p(b_2)] \cdots [p(u) - p(b_m)]}.$$

If $f_1(u)$ is an odd elliptic function, $f_1(u)/p'(u)$ is an even function, and therefore this quotient is a rational function of $p(u)$. Finally, any elliptic function $F(u)$ is the sum of an even function and an odd function:

$$F(u) = \frac{F(u) + F(-u)}{2} + \frac{F(u) - F(-u)}{2}.$$

Applying the preceding results, we see that every elliptic function can be expressed in the form

(43) $$F(u) = R[p(u)] + p'(u)\,R_1[p(u)],$$

where R and R_1 are rational functions.

74. Addition formulæ. The addition formula for the function $\sin x$ enables us to express $\sin(a + b)$ in terms of the values of that function and of its derivative for $x = a$ and $x = b$. There exists an analogous formula for the function $p(u)$, except that the expression for $p(u + v)$ in terms of $p(u)$, $p(v)$, $p'(u)$, $p'(v)$ is somewhat more complicated on account of the presence of a denominator.

Let us first apply the general formula (41), in which the function $\sigma(u)$ appears, to the elliptic function $p(u) - p(v)$. We see at once that $\sigma(u + v)\,\sigma(u - v)/\sigma^2(u)$ is an elliptic function with the same zeros and the same poles as $p(u) - p(v)$. We have, then,

$$p(u) - p(v) = C\,\frac{\sigma(u + v)\,\sigma(u - v)}{\sigma^2(u)};$$

in order to determine the constant C it suffices to multiply the two sides by $\sigma^2(u)$ and to let u approach zero. We thus find the relation $1 = -\,C\sigma^2(v)$, whence we derive

(44) $$p(u) - p(v) = -\,\frac{\sigma(u + v)\,\sigma(u - v)}{\sigma^2(u)\,\sigma^2(v)}.$$

If we take the logarithmic derivative on both sides, regarding v as a constant and u as the independent variable, we find

$$\frac{p'(u)}{p(u) - p(v)} = \zeta(u + v) + \zeta(u - v) - 2\,\zeta(u),$$

or, interchanging u and v in this result,.

$$\frac{-\mathrm{p}'(v)}{\mathrm{p}(u)-\mathrm{p}(v)} = \zeta(u+v) - \zeta(u-v) - 2\zeta(v).$$

Finally, adding these two results, we obtain the relation

$$(45) \qquad \zeta(u+v) - \zeta(u) - \zeta(v) = \frac{1}{2}\frac{\mathrm{p}'(u)-\mathrm{p}'(v)}{\mathrm{p}(u)-\mathrm{p}(v)},$$

which constitutes the addition formula for the function $\zeta(u)$.

Differentiating the two sides with respect to u, we should obtain the expression for $\mathrm{p}(u+v)$; the right-hand side would contain the second derivative $\mathrm{p}''(u)$, which would have to be replaced by $6\,\mathrm{p}^2(u) - g_2/2$. This calculation is somewhat long, and we can obtain the result in a more elegant way by proving first the relation

$$(46) \quad \mathrm{p}(u+v) + \mathrm{p}(u) + \mathrm{p}(v) = [\zeta(u+v) - \zeta(u) - \zeta(v)]^2.$$

Let us always regard u as the independent variable; the two sides are elliptic functions having for poles of the second order $u = 0$, $u = -v$, and all the points deducible from them by the addition of a period. In the neighborhood of the origin we have

$$\zeta(u+v) - \zeta(u) - \zeta(v) = \zeta(v) + u\zeta'(v) + \cdots - \zeta(u) - \zeta(v)$$
$$= -\frac{1}{u} + u\zeta'(v) + \alpha u^2 + \cdots$$

and consequently

$$[\zeta(u+v) - \zeta(u) - \zeta(v)]^2 = \frac{1}{u^2} - 2\zeta'(v) - 2\alpha u + \cdots.$$

The principal part is $1/u^2$, as also for the left-hand side. Let us compare similarly the principal parts in the neighborhood of the pole $u = -v$. Putting $u = -v + h$, we have

$$\zeta(h) - \zeta(-v+h) - \zeta(v) = \frac{1}{h} - h\zeta'(v) + \beta h^2 + \cdots,$$

$$[\zeta(h) - \zeta(h-v) - \zeta(v)]^2 = \frac{1}{h^2} - 2\zeta'(v) + \cdots.$$

The principal part of the right-hand side of (46) in the neighborhood of the point $u = -v$ is, then, $1/(u+v)^2$, just as for the left-hand side. Hence the difference between the two sides of (46) is a constant. To find this constant, let us compare, for instance, the developments in the neighborhood of the origin. We have in this neighborhood

$$\mathrm{p}(u+v) + \mathrm{p}(u) + \mathrm{p}(v) = \frac{1}{u^2} + 2\,\mathrm{p}(v) + u\mathrm{p}'(v) + \cdots.$$

Comparing this development with that of $[\zeta(u+v) - \zeta(u) - \zeta(v)]^2$, we see that the difference is zero for $u = 0$. The relation (46) is therefore established. Combining the two equalities (45) and (46), we obtain the addition formula for the function $p(u)$:

$$(47) \qquad p(u+v) + p(u) + p(v) = \frac{1}{4}\left[\frac{p'(u) - p'(v)}{p(u) - p(v)}\right]^2.$$

75. Integration of elliptic functions. Hermite's decomposition formula (42) lends itself immediately to the integration of an elliptic function. Applying it, we find

$$(48) \quad \begin{cases} \displaystyle \int f(u)\,du = Cu + \sum_{i=1}^{k} \Big\{ A_1^{(i)} \operatorname{Log}[\sigma(u - a_i)] - A_2^{(i)} \zeta(u - a_i) + \cdots \\ \displaystyle \qquad\qquad\qquad + (-1)^{n_i - 1} \frac{A_{n_i}^{(i)}}{(n_i - 1)!} \zeta^{(n_i - 2)}(u - a_i) \Big\}. \end{cases}$$

We see that the integral of an elliptic function is expressible in terms of the same transcendentals σ, ζ, p as the functions themselves, but the function $\sigma(u)$ may appear in the result as the argument of a logarithm. In order that the integral of an elliptic function may be itself an elliptic function, it is necessary first that the integral shall not present any logarithmic critical points; that is, all the residues $A_1^{(i)}$ must be zero. If this is so, the integral is a function analytic except for poles. In order that it be elliptic, it will suffice that it is not changed by the addition of a period to u, that is, that

$$2C\omega - 2\eta\sum_i A_2^{(i)} = 0, \qquad 2C\omega' - 2\eta'\sum_i A_2^{(i)} = 0;$$

whence we derive $C = 0$, $\Sigma A_2^{(i)} = 0$. If these conditions are satisfied, the integral will appear in the form indicated by Hermite's theorem.

When the elliptic function which is to be integrated is expressed in terms of $p(u)$ and $p'(u)$, it is often advantageous to start from that form instead of employing the general method. Suppose that we wish to integrate the elliptic function $R[p(u)] + p'(u)R_1[p(u)]$, R and R_1 being rational functions. We have only to notice in regard to the integral $\int R_1[p(u)]p'(u)\,du$ that the change of variable $p(u) = t$ reduces it to the integral of a rational function. As for the integral $\int R[p(u)]\,du$, we could reduce it to a certain number of type forms by means of rational operations combined with suitably chosen integrations by parts; but it turns out that this would amount to making in another form the same reductions that were made in Volume I (§ 105, 2d ed.; § 110, 1st ed.). For, if we make the change of variable $p(u) = t$, which gives

$$p'(u)\,du = dt, \qquad \text{or} \qquad du = \frac{dt}{p'(u)} = \frac{dt}{\sqrt{4t^3 - g_2 t - g_3}},$$

the integral $\int R\left[\mathrm{p}\left(u\right)\right] du$ takes the form

$$\int \frac{R\left(t\right) dt}{\sqrt{4\,t^3 - g_2 t - g_3}}.$$

We have seen how this integral decomposes into a rational function of t and of the radical $\sqrt{4\,t^3 - g_2 t - g_3}$, a sum of a certain number of integrals of the form $\int t^n dt / \sqrt{4\,t^3 - g_2 t - g_3}$, and finally a certain number of integrals of the form

$$\int \frac{Q\left(t\right)}{P\left(t\right)} \frac{dt}{\sqrt{4\,t^3 - g_2 t - g_3}},$$

where $P\left(t\right)$ is a polynomial prime to its derivative and also to $4\,t^3 - g_2 t - g_3$, and where $Q\left(t\right)$ is a polynomial prime to $P\left(t\right)$ and of lower degree than $P\left(t\right)$.

Returning to the variable u, we see that the integral $\int R\left[\mathrm{p}\left(u\right)\right] du$ is equal to a rational function of $\mathrm{p}\left(u\right)$ and $\mathrm{p}'\left(u\right)$, plus a certain number of integrals such as $\int \left[\mathrm{p}\left(u\right)\right]^n du$ and a certain number of other integrals of the form

$$(49) \qquad \int \frac{Q\left[\mathrm{p}\left(u\right)\right] du}{P\left[\mathrm{p}\left(u\right)\right]};$$

and this reduction can be accomplished by rational operations (multiplications and divisions of polynomials) combined with certain integrations by parts.

We can easily obtain a recurrent formula for the calculation of the integrals $I_n = \int \left[\mathrm{p}\left(u\right)\right]^n du$. If, in the relation

$$\frac{d}{du}\left\{\left[\mathrm{p}\left(u\right)\right]^{n-1} \mathrm{p}'\left(u\right)\right\} = (n-1)\left[\mathrm{p}\left(u\right)\right]^{n-2} \mathrm{p}'^2\left(u\right) + \left[\mathrm{p}\left(u\right)\right]^{n-1} \mathrm{p}''\left(u\right),$$

we replace $\mathrm{p}'^2\left(u\right)$ and $\mathrm{p}''\left(u\right)$ by $4\,\mathrm{p}^3\left(u\right) - g_2 \mathrm{p}\left(u\right) - g_3$ and $6\,\mathrm{p}^2\left(u\right) - g_2/2$ respectively, there results, after arranging with respect to $\mathrm{p}\left(u\right)$,

$$\frac{d}{du}\left\{\left[\mathrm{p}\left(u\right)\right]^{n-1}\mathrm{p}'\left(u\right)\right\}$$
$$= (4\,n + 2)\left[\mathrm{p}\left(u\right)\right]^{n+1} - \left(n - \frac{1}{2}\right) g_2 \left[\mathrm{p}\left(u\right)\right]^{n-1} - (n-1) g_3 \left[\mathrm{p}\left(u\right)\right]^{n-2},$$

and from this we derive, by integrating the two sides,

$$(50) \quad \left[\mathrm{p}\left(u\right)\right]^{n-1}\mathrm{p}'\left(u\right) = (4\,n + 2) I_{n+1} - \left(n - \frac{1}{2}\right) g_2 I_{n-1} - (n-1) g_3 I_{n-2}.$$

By putting successively $n = 1, 2, 3, \cdots$ in this formula, all the integrals I_n can be calculated successively from the first two, $I_0 = u$, $I_1 = -\zeta\left(u\right)$.

To reduce further the integrals of the form (49), it will be necessary to know the roots of the polynomial $P\left(t\right)$. If we know these roots, we can reduce the calculation to that of a certain number of integrals of the form

$$\int \frac{du}{\mathrm{p}\left(u\right) - \mathrm{p}\left(v\right)},$$

where $\mathrm{p}\left(v\right)$ is different from e_1, e_2, e_3, since the polynomial $P\left(t\right)$ is prime to $4\,t^3 - g_2 t - g_3$. The value of v is therefore not a half-period, and $\mathrm{p}'\left(v\right)$ is not zero. The formula

$$\frac{-\mathrm{p}'\left(v\right)}{\mathrm{p}\left(u\right) - \mathrm{p}\left(v\right)} = \zeta\left(u + v\right) - \zeta\left(u - v\right) - 2\,\zeta\left(v\right),$$

established in § 74, then gives

$$(51) \quad \int \frac{du}{\mathrm{p}\left(u\right) - \mathrm{p}\left(v\right)} = \frac{-1}{\mathrm{p}'\left(v\right)}\left[\mathrm{Log}\,\sigma\left(u + v\right) - \mathrm{Log}\,\sigma\left(u - v\right) - 2\,u\zeta\left(v\right)\right] + \mathrm{C}.$$

76. The function θ. The series by means of which we have defined the functions $p(u)$, $\zeta(u)$, $\sigma(u)$ do not easily lend themselves to numerical computation, including even the power series development of $\sigma(u)$, which is valid for the whole plane. The founders of the theory of elliptic functions, Abel and Jacobi, had introduced another remarkable transcendental, which had previously been encountered by Fourier in his work on the theory of heat, and which can be developed in a very rapidly convergent series; it is called the θ function. We shall establish briefly the principal properties of this function, and show how the Weierstrass $\sigma(u)$ function can be easily deduced from it.

Let $\tau = r + si$ be a complex quantity in which the coefficient s of i is *positive*. If v denotes a complex variable, the function $\theta(v)$ is defined by the series

$$(52) \qquad \theta(v) = \frac{1}{i} \sum_{-\infty}^{+\infty} (-1)^n q^{\left(n+\frac{1}{2}\right)^2} e^{(2n+1)\pi i v}, \qquad q = e^{\pi i \tau},$$

which may be regarded as a Laurent series in which $e^{\pi i v}$ has been substituted for z. This series is absolutely convergent, for the absolute value U_n of the general term is given by

$$U_n = e^{-\pi s \left(n+\frac{1}{2}\right)^2 - (2n+1)\pi \beta}$$

if $v = \alpha + \beta i$; hence $\sqrt[n]{U_n}$ approaches zero when n becomes infinite through positive values, and the same is true of $\sqrt[n]{U_{-n}}$. It follows that the function $\theta(v)$ is an integral transcendental function of the variable v. It is also an odd function, for if we unite the terms of the series which correspond to the values n and $-n-1$ of the index (where n varies from 0 to $+\infty$), the development (52) can be replaced by the following formula:

$$(53) \qquad \theta(v) = 2 \sum_{0}^{+\infty} (-1)^n q^{\left(n+\frac{1}{2}\right)^2} \sin(2n+1)\pi v,$$

which shows that we have

$$\theta(-v) = -\theta(v), \qquad \theta(0) = 0.$$

When v is increased by unity, the general term of the series (52) is multiplied by $e^{(2n+1)\pi i} = -1$. We have, then, $\theta(v+1) = -\theta(v)$. If we change v to $v + \tau$, no simple relation between the two series is immediately seen; but if we write

$$\theta(v+\tau) = \frac{1}{i} \sum_{-\infty}^{+\infty} (-1)^n q^{\left(n+\frac{1}{2}\right)^2 + 2n + 1} e^{(2n+1)\pi i v},$$

and then change n to $n-1$ in this series, the general term of the new series

$$(-1)^{n-1} q^{\left(n-\frac{1}{2}\right)^2 + 2n - 1} e^{(2n+1)\pi i v} e^{-2\pi i v}$$

is equal to the general term of the series (52) multiplied by $-q^{-1} e^{-2\pi i v}$. Hence the function $\theta(v)$ satisfies the two relations

$$(54) \qquad \theta(v+1) = -\theta(v), \qquad \theta(v+\tau) = -q^{-1} e^{-2\pi i v} \theta(v).$$

Since the origin is a root of $\theta(v)$, these relations show that $\theta(v)$ has for zeros all the points $m_1 + m_2 \tau$, where m_1 and m_2 are arbitrary positive or negative integers.

These are the only roots of the equation $\theta(v) = 0$. For, let us consider a parallelogram whose vertices are the four points v_0, $v_0 + 1$, $v_0 + 1 + \tau$, $v_0 + \tau$, the first vertex v_0 being taken in such a way that no root of $\theta(v)$ lies on the boundary. We shall show that the equation $\theta(v) = 0$ has a single root in this parallelogram. For this purpose it is sufficient to calculate the integral

$$\int \frac{\theta'(v)}{\theta(v)} \, dv$$

along its boundary in the positive sense. By the hypothesis made upon τ, we encounter the vertices in the order in which they are written.

From the relations (54) we derive

$$\frac{\theta'(v+1)}{\theta(v+1)} = \frac{\theta'(v)}{\theta(v)}, \qquad \frac{\theta'(v+\tau)}{\theta(v+\tau)} = \frac{\theta'(v)}{\theta(v)} - 2\pi i.$$

The first of these relations shows that at the corresponding points n and n' (Fig. 27) of the sides AD, BC, the function $\theta'(v)/\theta(v)$ takes on the same value. Since these two sides are described in contrary senses, the sum of the corresponding integrals is zero. On the contrary, if we take two corresponding points m, m' on the sides AB, DC, the value of $\theta'(v)/\theta(v)$ at the point m' is equal to the value of the same function at the point m, diminished by $2\pi i$. The sum of the two integrals coming from these two sides is therefore equal to

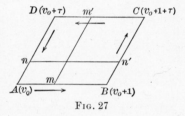

FIG. 27

$\int_{(CD)} -2\pi i\,dv$, that is, to $2\pi i$. As there is evidently one and only one point in the parallelogram $ABCD$ which is represented by a quantity of the form $m_1 + m_2\tau$, it follows that the function $\theta(v)$ has no other roots than those found above.

Summing up, the function $\theta(v)$ is an odd integral function; it has all the points $m_1 + m_2\tau$ for simple zeros; it has no other zeros; and it satisfies the relations (54). Let now 2ω, $2\omega'$ be two periods such that the coefficient of i in ω'/ω is positive. In $\theta(v)$ let us replace the variable v by $u/2\omega$ and τ by ω'/ω, and let $\phi(u)$ be the function

$$(55) \qquad \phi(u) = \theta\left(\frac{u}{2\omega}\right).$$

Then $\phi(u)$ is an odd integral function having all the periods $2w = 2m\omega + 2m'\omega'$ for zeros of the first order, and the relations (54) are replaced by the following:

$$(56) \qquad \phi(u+2\omega) = -\phi(u), \qquad \phi(u+2\omega') = -e^{-\pi i\left(\frac{u+\omega'}{\omega}\right)}\phi(u).$$

These properties are very nearly those of the function $\sigma(u)$. In order to reduce it to $\sigma(u)$, it suffices to multiply $\phi(u)$ by an exponential factor. Let us put

$$(57) \qquad \psi(u) = \frac{2\omega}{\theta'(0)} e^{\frac{\eta}{2\omega}u^2} \phi(u),$$

where η is the function of ω and ω' defined as in § 71. This new function $\psi(u)$ is an odd integral function having the same zeros as $\phi(u)$. The first of the relations (56) becomes

$$(58) \qquad \psi(u + 2\,\omega) = -\frac{2\,\omega}{\theta'(0)}\, e^{\frac{\eta}{2\,\omega}(u+2\,\omega)^2}\, \phi(u) = -\, e^{2\,\eta(u+\omega)}\, \psi(u).$$

We have next

$$\psi(u + 2\,\omega') = -\frac{2\,\omega}{\theta'(0)}\, e^{\frac{\eta}{2\,\omega}(u+2\,\omega')^2}\, e^{-\frac{\pi i}{\omega}(u+\omega')}\, \phi(u),$$

or, since $\eta\omega' - \eta'\omega = \pi i/2$,

$$(59) \qquad\qquad \psi(u + 2\,\omega') = -\, e^{2\,\eta'(u+\omega')}\, \psi(u).$$

The relations (58) and (59) are identical with the relations established above for the function $\sigma(u)$. Hence the quotient $\psi(u)/\sigma(u)$ has the two periods $2\,\omega$ and $2\,\omega'$, for the two terms of this ratio are multiplied by the same factor when u increases by a period. Since the two functions have the same zeros, this quotient is constant; moreover, the coefficient of u in each of the two developments is equal to unity. We have, then, $\sigma(u) = \psi(u)$, or

$$(60) \qquad\qquad \sigma(u) = \frac{2\,\omega}{\theta'(0)}\, e^{\frac{\eta}{2\,\omega}u^2}\, \theta\!\left(\frac{u}{2\,\omega}\right),$$

and the function $\sigma(u)$ is expressed in terms of the function θ, as we proposed. If we give the argument v real values, the absolute value of q being less than unity, the series (53) is rapidly convergent. We shall not further elaborate these indications, which suffice to suggest the fundamental part taken by the θ function in the applications of elliptic functions.

III. INVERSE FUNCTIONS. CURVES OF DEFICIENCY ONE

77. Relations between the periods and the invariants. To every system of two complex numbers ω, ω', whose ratio ω'/ω is not real, corresponds a completely determined elliptic function $p(u)$, which has the two periods $2\,\omega$, $2\,\omega'$, and which is regular for all the values of u that are not of the form $2\,m\omega + 2\,m'\omega'$, all of which are poles of the second order. The functions $\zeta(u)$ and $\sigma(u)$, which are deducible from $p(u)$ by one or by two integrations, respectively, are likewise determined by the system of periods $(2\,\omega, 2\,\omega')$. When there is any reason for indicating the periods, we shall make use of the notation $p(u\,|\,\omega,\,\omega')$, $\zeta(u\,|\,\omega,\,\omega')$, $\sigma(u\,|\,\omega,\,\omega')$ to denote the three fundamental functions.

But it is to be noticed that we can replace the system $(\omega,\,\omega')$ by an infinite number of other systems $(\Omega,\,\Omega')$ without changing the function $p(u)$. For let m, m', n, n' be any four positive or negative integers such that we have $mn' - m'n = \pm 1$. If we put

$$\Omega = m\omega + n\omega', \qquad \Omega' = m'\omega + n'\omega',$$

we shall have, conversely,

$$\omega = \pm\,(n'\Omega - n\Omega'), \qquad \omega' = \pm\,(m\Omega' - m'\Omega),$$

and it is clear that all the periods of the elliptic function $p(u)$ are combinations of the two periods $2\,\Omega,\ 2\,\Omega'$, as well as of the two periods $2\,\omega,\ 2\,\omega'$. The two systems of periods $(2\,\omega,\ 2\,\omega')$ and $(2\,\Omega,\ 2\,\Omega')$ are said to be equivalent. The function $p(u\,|\,\Omega,\ \Omega')$ has the same periods and the same poles, with the same principal parts, as the function $p(u\,|\,\omega,\ \omega')$, and their difference is zero for $u = 0$. They are therefore identical. This fact results also from the development (22), for the set of quantities $2\,m\omega + 2\,m'\omega'$ is identical with the set of quantities $2\,m\Omega + 2\,m'\Omega'$. For the same reason, we have $\zeta(u\,|\,\Omega,\ \Omega') = \zeta(u\,|\,\omega,\ \omega')$ and $\sigma(u\,|\,\Omega,\ \Omega') = \sigma(u\,|\,\omega,\ \omega')$.

Similarly, the three functions $p(u),\ \zeta(u),\ \sigma(u)$ are completely determined by the invariants $g_2,\ g_3$. For we have seen that the function $\sigma(u)$ is represented by a power-series development all of whose coefficients are polynomials in $g_2,\ g_3$. We have, then, $\zeta(u) = \sigma'(u)/\sigma(u)$, and finally $p(u) = -\,\zeta'(u)$. In order to indicate the functions which correspond to the invariants g_2 and g_3, we shall use the notation

$$p(u\,;\,g_2,\,g_3),\qquad \zeta(u\,;\,g_2,\,g_3),\qquad \sigma(u\,;\,g_2,\,g_3).$$

Just here an essential question presents itself. While it is evident, from the very definition of the function $p(u)$, that to a system $(\omega,\ \omega')$ corresponds an elliptic function $p(u)$, provided the ratio ω'/ω is not real, there is nothing to prove a priori that to *every* system of values for the invariants $g_2,\ g_3$ corresponds an elliptic function. We know, indeed, that the expression $g_2^3 - 27\,g_3^2$ must be different from zero, but it is not certain that this condition is sufficient. The problem which must be treated here amounts in the end to solving the transcendental equations established above,

$$(61)\quad g_2 = 60\sum{}'\frac{1}{(2\,m\omega + 2\,m'\omega')^4},\qquad g_3 = 140\sum{}'\frac{1}{(2\,m\omega + 2\,m'\omega')^6},$$

for the unknowns $\omega,\ \omega'$, or at least to determining whether or not these equations have a system of solutions such that ω'/ω is not real whenever $g_2^3 - 27\,g_3^2$ is not zero. If there exists a single system of solutions, there exist an infinite number of systems, but there appears to be no way of approach for a direct study of the preceding equations. We can arrive at the solution of this problem in an indirect way by studying the inversion of the elliptic integral of the first kind.

Note. Let $\omega,\ \omega'$ be two complex numbers such that ω'/ω is not real. The corresponding function $p(u\,|\,\omega,\ \omega')$ satisfies the differential equation

$$\left[\frac{dp(u)}{du}\right]^2 = 4\,p^3 - g_2\,p - g_3,$$

where g_2 and g_3 are defined by the equations (61). For $u = \omega$, $p(\omega)$ is equal to one of the roots e_1 of the equation $4p^3 - g_2 p - g_3 = 0$. When u varies from 0 to ω, $p(u)$ describes a curve L going from infinity to the point e_1. From the relation $du = dp/\sqrt{4p^3 - g_2 p - g_3}$ we conclude that the half-period ω is equal to the definite integral

$$\omega = \int_{\infty}^{e_1} \frac{dp}{\sqrt{4p^3 - g_2 p - g_3}}$$

taken along the curve L. An analogous expression for ω' can be obtained by replacing e_1 by e_2 in the preceding integral.

We have thus the two half-periods expressed in terms of the invariants g_2, g_3. In order to be able to deduce from this result the solution of the problem before us, it would be necessary to show that the new system is *equivalent* to the system (61), that is, that it defines g_2 and g_3 as single-valued functions of ω, ω'.

78. The inverse function to the elliptic integral of the first kind. Let $R(z)$ be a polynomial of the third or of the fourth degree which is prime to its derivative. We shall write this polynomial in the form

$$R(z) = A(z - a_1)(z - a_2)(z - a_3)(z - a_4),$$

where a_1, a_2, a_3, a_4 denote four different roots if $R(z)$ is of the fourth degree. On the other hand, if $R(z)$ is of the third degree, we shall denote its three roots by a_1, a_2, a_3, and we shall also set $a_4 = \infty$, agreeing to replace $z - \infty$ by unity in the expression $R(z)$.

The elliptic integral of the first kind is of the form

$$(62) \qquad u = \int_{z_0}^{z} \frac{dz}{\sqrt{R(z)}},$$

where the lower limit z_0 is supposed, for definiteness, to be different from any of the roots of $R(z)$ and to be finite, and where the radical has an assigned initial value. If $R(z)$ is of the fourth degree, the radical $\sqrt{R(z)}$ has four critical points a_1, a_2, a_3, a_4, and each of the determinations of $\sqrt{R(z)}$ has the point $z = \infty$ for a pole of the second order. If $R(z)$ is of the third degree, the radical $\sqrt{R(z)}$ has only three critical points in the finite plane a_1, a_2 a_3; but if the variable z describes a circle containing the three points a_1, a_2, a_3, the two values of the radical are permuted. The point $z = \infty$ is therefore a branch point for the function $\sqrt{R(z)}$.

Let us recall the properties of the elliptic integral u proved in § 55. If $\overline{u(z)}$ denotes one of the values of that integral when we go from the point z_0 to the point z by a determined path, the same integral can take on at the same point z an infinite number of determinations which are included in the expressions

$$(63) \quad u = \overline{u(z)} + 2m\omega + 2m'\omega', \quad u = I - \overline{u(z)} + 2m\omega + 2m'\omega',$$

if the path is varied. In these formulæ m and m' are two entirely arbitrary integers, $2\,\omega$ and $2\omega'$ two periods whose ratio is not real, and I a constant which we may take equal, for example, to the integral over the loop described about the point a_1.

Let $p(u\,|\,\omega,\,\omega')$ be the elliptic function constructed with the periods $2\,\omega$, $2\,\omega'$ of the elliptic integral (62). Let us substitute in that function for the variable u the integral (62) itself diminished by $I/2$, and let $\Phi(z)$ be the function thus obtained:

$$(64) \qquad \Phi(z) = p\left[\int_{z_0}^{z} \frac{dz}{\sqrt{R(z)}} - \frac{I}{2}\,\bigg|\,\omega,\,\omega'\right] = p\left(u - \frac{I}{2}\,\bigg|\,\omega,\,\omega'\right).$$

This function $\Phi(z)$ *is a single-valued function of z.* In fact, if we replace u by any one of the determinations (63), we find always, whatever m and m' may be,

$$\Phi(z) = p\left[\overline{u(z)} - \frac{I}{2}\,\bigg|\,\omega,\,\omega'\right], \quad \text{or} \quad \Phi(z) = p\left[\frac{I}{2} - \overline{u(z)}\,\big|\,\omega,\,\omega'\right],$$

which shows that $\Phi(z)$ is single-valued.

Let us see what points can be singular points for this function $\Phi(z)$. First let z_1 be any finite value of z different from a branch point. Let us suppose that we go from the point z_0 to the point z_1 by a definite path. We arrive at z_1 with a certain value for the radical and a value u_1 for the integral. In the neighborhood of the point z_1, $1/\sqrt{R(z)}$ is an analytic function of z, and we have a development of the form

$$\frac{1}{\sqrt{R(z)}} = \alpha_0 + \alpha_1(z - z_1) + \alpha_2(z - z_1)^2 + \cdots, \qquad \alpha_0 \neq 0,$$

whence we derive

$$(65) \qquad u = u_1 + \alpha_0(z - z_1) + \frac{\alpha_1}{1\,.\,2}(z - z_1)^2 + \cdots.$$

If $u_1 - I/2$ is not equal to a period, the function $p(u - I/2)$ is analytic in the neighborhood of the point u_1, and consequently $\Phi(z)$ is analytic in the neighborhood of the point z_1. If $u_1 - I/2$ is a period, the point u_1 is a pole of the second order for $p(u - I/2)$, and therefore z_1 is a pole of the second order for $\Phi(z)$, for in the neighborhood of the point u_1

$$p\left(u - \frac{I}{2}\right) = \frac{P(u - u_1)}{(u - u_1)^2},$$

where P is an analytic function.

Suppose next that z approaches a critical point a_i. In the neighborhood of the point a_i we have

$$[R(z)]^{-\frac{1}{2}} = (z - a_i)^{-\frac{1}{2}} P_i(z - a_i),$$

where P_i is analytic for $z = a_i$, or

$$\frac{1}{\sqrt{R(z)}} = \frac{1}{\sqrt{z - a_i}} [\alpha_0 + \alpha_1(z - a_i) + \alpha_2(z - a_i)^2 + \cdots], \qquad \alpha_0 \neq 0;$$

whence, integrating term by term, we find

$$(66) \qquad u = u_i + \sqrt{z - a_i}\Big[2\,\alpha_0 + \frac{2}{3}\,\alpha_1(z - a_i) + \cdots\Big].$$

If $u_i - I/2$ is not a period, $p(u - I/2)$ is an analytic function of u in the neighborhood of the point u_i. Substituting in the development of this function in powers of $u - u_i$ the value of the difference $u - u_i$ obtained from the formula (66), the fractional powers of $(z - a_i)$ must disappear, since we know that the left-hand side is a single-valued function of z; hence the function $\Phi(z)$ is analytic in the neighborhood of the point a_i. Let us notice in passing that this shows that $u_i - I/2$ must be a half-period. Similarly, if $u_i - I/2$ is equal to a period, the point a_i is a pole of the first order for $\Phi(z)$.

Finally, let us study the function $\Phi(z)$ for infinite values of z. We have to distinguish two cases according as $R(z)$ is of the fourth degree or of the third degree. If the polynomial $R(z)$ is of the fourth degree, exterior to a circle C described about the origin as center and containing the four roots, each of the determinations of $1/\sqrt{R(z)}$ is an analytic function of $1/z$. For example, we have for one of them

$$\frac{1}{\sqrt{R(z)}} = \frac{\alpha_0}{z^2} + \frac{\alpha_1}{z^3} + \frac{\alpha_2}{z^4} + \cdots, \qquad \alpha_0 \neq 0,$$

and it would suffice to change all the signs to obtain the development of the second determination. If the absolute value of z becomes infinite, the radical $1/\sqrt{R(z)}$ having the value which we have just written, the integral approaches a finite value u_∞, and we have in the neighborhood of the point at infinity

$$(67) \qquad u = u_\infty - \frac{\alpha_0}{z} - \frac{\alpha_1}{2\,z^2} - \frac{\alpha_2}{3\,z^3} - \cdots.$$

If $u_\infty - I/2$ is not a period, the function $p(u - I/2)$ is regular for the point u_∞, and consequently the point $z = \infty$ is an ordinary point for $\Phi(z)$. If $u_\infty - I/2$ is a period, the point u_∞ is a pole of the second order for $\mathrm{p}\,(u - I/2)$, and since we can write, in the neighborhood of the point $z = \infty$,

$$\frac{1}{u - u_\infty} = z\Big(\beta_0 + \frac{\beta_1}{z} + \frac{\beta_2}{z^2} + \cdots\Big),$$

the point $z = \infty$ is also a pole of the second order for the function $\Phi(z)$.

If $R(z)$ is of the third degree, we have a development of the form

$$\frac{1}{\sqrt{R(z)}} = \frac{1}{z^{\frac{3}{2}}}\Big(\alpha_0 + \frac{\alpha_1}{z} + \frac{\alpha_2}{z^2} + \cdots\Big), \qquad \alpha_0 \neq 0,$$

which holds exterior to a circle having the origin for center and containing the three critical points a_1, a_2, a_3. It follows that

$$(68) \qquad u = u_\infty - \frac{1}{\sqrt{z}}\Big(2\,\alpha_0 + \frac{2\,\alpha_1}{3}\frac{1}{z} + \cdots\Big).$$

Reasoning as above, we see that the point at infinity is an ordinary point or a pole of the first order for $\Phi(z)$. The function $\Phi(z)$ has certainly only poles for singular points; *it is therefore a rational function of z*, and the elliptic integral of the first kind (62) satisfies a relation of the form

$$(69) \qquad \mathrm{p}\Big(u - \frac{I}{2}\Big) = \Phi(z),$$

where $\Phi(z)$ is a rational function. We do not know as yet the degree of this function, but we shall show that it is equal to *unity*. For that purpose we shall study the inverse function. In other words, we shall now consider u as the independent variable, and we shall examine the properties of the upper limit z of the integral (62), considered as a function of that integral u. We shall divide the study, which requires considerable care, into several parts:

1) *To every finite value of u correspond m values of z if m is the degree of the rational function $\Phi(z)$.*

For let u_1 be a finite value of u. The equation $\Phi(z) = \mathrm{p}\,(u_1 - I/2)$ determines m values for z, which are in general distinct and finite, though it is possible for some of the roots to coincide or become infinite for particular values of u_1. Let z_1 be one of these values of z. The values of the elliptic integral u which correspond to this value of z satisfy the equation

$$\mathrm{p}\Big(u - \frac{I}{2}\Big) = \Phi(z_1) = \mathrm{p}\Big(u_1 - \frac{I}{2}\Big);$$

we have, then, one of the two relations

$$u = u_1 + 2\,m_1\omega + 2\,m_2\omega', \qquad u = I - u_1 + 2\,m_1\omega + 2\,m_2\omega'.$$

In either case we can make the variable z describe a path from z_0 to z_1 such that the value of the integral taken over this path shall be precisely u_1. If the function $\Phi(z)$ is of degree m, there are then m values of z for which the integral (62) takes a given value u.

2) Let u_1 be a finite value of u to which corresponds a finite value z_1 of z; *that determination of z which approaches z_1 when u approaches u_1 is an analytic function of u in the neighborhood of the point u_1.*

For if z_1 is not a critical point, the values of u and z which approach respectively u_1 and z_1 are connected by the relation (65), where the coefficient α_0 is not zero. By the general theorem on implicit functions (I, § 193, 2d ed.; § 187, 1st ed.) we deduce from it a development for $z - z_1$ in positive integral powers of $u - u_1$.

If, for the particular value u_i, z were equal to the critical value a_i, we could in the same way consider the right-hand side of (66) as a development in powers of $\sqrt{z - a_i}$. Since α_0 is not zero, we can solve (66) for $\sqrt{z - a_i}$, and therefore for $z - a_i$, expressing each of them as a power series in $u - u_i$.

3) Let u_∞ be one of the values which the integral u takes on when $|z|$ becomes infinite; *the point u_∞ is a pole for that determination of z whose absolute value becomes infinite.*

In fact, the value of the integral u which approaches u_∞ is represented in the neighborhood of the point at infinity by one of the developments (67) and (68). In the first case we obtain for $1/z$ a development in a series of positive powers of $u - u_\infty$.

$$\frac{1}{z} = \beta_1(u - u_\infty) + \beta_2(u - u_\infty)^2 + \cdots, \qquad \beta_1 \neq 0;$$

in the second case we have a similar development for $1/\sqrt{z}$, and therefore

$$\frac{1}{z} = (u - u_\infty)^2 [\beta_1 + \beta_2(u - u_\infty) + \cdots]^2.$$

The point u_∞ is therefore a pole of the first or second order for z, according as the polynomial $R(z)$ is of the fourth or of the third degree.

4) We are going to show finally that *to a value of u there can correspond only one value of z.* For let us suppose that as the variable z describes two paths going from z_0 to two different points z_1, z_2, the two values of the integral taken over these two paths are equal. It would then be possible to find a path L joining these two points z_1, z_2 such that the integral

$$\int_L \frac{dz}{\sqrt{R(z)}}$$

would be zero. If we represent the integral $u = X + Yi$ by the point with the coördinates (X, Y) in the system of rectangular axes OX, OY, we see that the point u would describe a closed curve Γ when the point z describes the open curve L. We shall show that this is not consistent with the properties which we have just demonstrated.

To each value of u there correspond, by means of the relation $p\,(u - I/2) = \Phi(z)$, a *finite* number of values of z, each of which varies in a continuous manner with u, provided the path described by u does not pass through any of the points corresponding to the value $z = \infty$.* According to our supposition, when the variable u describes in its plane the closed curve Γ starting from the point $A\,(u_0)$ and returning to that point, z describes an open arc of a continuous curve passing from the point z_1 to the point z_2. Let us take two points M and P (Fig. 28) on the curve Γ.

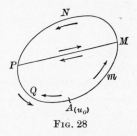

Let the initial value of z at A be z_1, and let z', z'' be the values obtained when we reach the points M and P respectively, after u has described the paths AM and $AMNP$. Again, let z_1'' be the value with which we arrive at the point P after u has described the arc AQP. It results from the hypothesis that z'' and z_1'' are different. Let us join the two

FIG. 28

points M and P by a transversal MP interior to the curve Γ, and let us suppose that the variable u describes the arc AmM and then the transversal MP; let z_2'' be the value with which we arrive at the point P. This value z_2'' will be different from z'' or else from z_1''. If it is different from z_1'', the two paths $AmMP$ and AQP do not lead to the same value of z at the point P. If z'' and z_2'' are different, the two paths $AmMP$ and $AmMNP$ do not lead to the same value at P; therefore, if we start from the point M with the value z' for z, we obtain different values for z according as we proceed from M to P along the path MP or along the path MNP. In either case we see that we can replace the closed boundary Γ by a smaller closed boundary Γ_1, partly interior to Γ, such that, when u describes this closed boundary, z describes an open arc. Repeating this same operation on the boundary Γ_1, and continuing thus indefinitely, we should obtain an unlimited sequence of closed boundaries Γ, Γ_1, Γ_2, $\cdots$ having the same property as the closed boundary Γ. Since we evidently can

---

* We assume the properties of implicit functions which will be established later (Chapter V).

make the dimensions of these successive boundaries approach zero, we may conclude that the boundary Γ_n approaches a limit point λ. From the way in which this point has been defined, there will always exist in the interior of a circle of radius ϵ described about λ as a center a closed path not leading the variable z back to its original value, however small ϵ may be. Now that is impossible, for the point λ is an ordinary point or a pole for each of the different determinations of z; in both cases z is a single-valued function of u in the neighborhood of λ. We are thus led to a contradiction in supposing that the integral $\int dz / \sqrt{R(z)}$, taken over an open path L, can be zero, or, what amounts to the same thing, by supposing that to a value of u correspond two values of z.

We have noticed above that, if for two different values of z we have $\Phi(z_1) = \Phi(z_2)$, we can find a path L from z_1 to z_2 such that the integral

$$\int_L \frac{dz}{\sqrt{R(z)}}$$

will be zero. Hence the rational function $\Phi(z)$ cannot take on the same value for two different values of z; that is, the function $\Phi(z)$ must be of the first degree: $\Phi(z) = (az + b)/(cz + d)$. It follows, from the relation (69), that

$$(70) \qquad z = \frac{b - d\mathrm{p}\left(u - \dfrac{I}{2}\right)}{c\mathrm{p}\left(u - \dfrac{I}{2}\right) - a},$$

and we may state the following important proposition: *The upper limit z of an elliptic integral of the first kind, considered as a function of that integral, is an elliptic function of the second order.*

Elliptic integrals had been studied in a thorough manner by Legendre, but it was by reversing the problem that Abel and Jacobi were led to the discovery of elliptic functions.

The actual determination of the elliptic function $z = f(u)$ constitutes the *problem of inversion*. By the relation (62) we have

$$\frac{dz}{du} = \sqrt{R(z)},$$

and therefore $\sqrt{R(z)} = f'(u)$. It is clear that the radical $\sqrt{R(z)}$ is itself an elliptic function of u. We can restate all the preceding results in geometric language as follows:

Let $R(z)$ be a polynomial of the third or fourth degree, prime to its derivative; the coördinates of any point of the curve C,

(71) $$y^2 = R(x),$$

can be expressed in terms of elliptic functions of the integral of the first kind,

$$u = \int_{x_0}^{x} \frac{dx}{y} = \int_{x_0}^{x} \frac{dx}{\sqrt{R(x)}},$$

in such a way that to a point (x, y) of that curve corresponds only one value of u, any period being disregarded.

To prove the last part of the proposition, we need only remark that all the values of u which correspond to a given value of x are included in the two expressions

$$u_0 + 2\,m_1\omega + 2\,m_2\omega', \qquad I - u_0 + 2\,m_1\omega + 2\,m_2\omega'.$$

All the values of u included in the first expression come from an even number of loops described about critical points, followed by the direct path from x_0 to x, with the same initial value of the radical $\sqrt{R(x)}$. The values of u included in the second expression come from an odd number of loops described about the critical points, followed by the direct path from x_0 to x, where the corresponding initial value of the radical $\sqrt{R(x)}$ is the negative of the former. If we are given both x and y at the same time, the corresponding values are then included in a single one of the two formulæ.

From the investigation above, it follows that the elliptic function $x = f(u)$ has a pole of the second order in a parallelogram if $R(x)$ is of the third degree, and two simple poles if $R(x)$ is of the fourth degree; hence $y = f'(u)$ is of the third or of the fourth order, according to the degree of the polynomial $R(x)$.

Note. Suppose that, by any means whatever, the coördinates (x, y) of a point of the curve $y^2 = R(x)$ have been expressed as elliptic functions of a parameter v, say $x = \phi(v)$, $y = \phi_1(v)$. The integral of the first kind u becomes, then,

$$u = \int \frac{dx}{y} = \int \frac{\phi'(v)\,dv}{\phi_1(v)}.$$

The elliptic function $\phi'(v)/\phi_1(v)$ cannot have a pole, since u must always have a finite value for every finite value of v; it reduces, then, to a constant k, and we have $u = kv + l$. The constant l evidently depends on the value chosen for the lower limit of the integral u. The coefficient k can be determined by giving to v a particular value.

79. A new definition of $p(u)$ by means of the invariants. It is now quite easy to answer the question proposed in § 77. Given two numbers g_2, g_3 such that $g_2^3 - 27\,g_3^2$ is not zero, *there always exists an elliptic function* $p(u)$ *for which* g_2 *and* g_3 *are the invariants.*

For the polynomial

$$R(z) = 4\,z^3 - g_2 z - g_3$$

is prime to its derivative, and the elliptic integral $\int dz/\sqrt{R(z)}$ has two periods, $2\,\omega$, $2\,\omega'$, whose ratio is imaginary. Let $p(u\,|\,\omega,\,\omega')$ be the corresponding elliptic function. We shall substitute for the argument u in this function the integral

$$(72) \qquad u = \int_{z_0}^{z} \frac{dz}{\sqrt{R(z)}} - H,$$

where H is a constant chosen in such a way that one of the values of u shall be equal to zero for $z = \infty$. We shall take H, for example, equal to the value of the integral $\int_{z_0}^{\infty} dz/\sqrt{R(z)}$ taken over a ray L starting at z_0. We shall show first that the function thus obtained is a single-valued analytic function of z. Let z be any point of the plane, and let us denote by v and v' the values of the integrals

$$v = \int_{(z_0 m z)} \frac{dz}{\sqrt{R(z)}},$$

$$v' = \int_{(z_0 n z)} \frac{dz}{\sqrt{R(z)}},$$

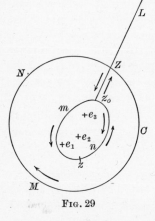

Fig. 29

starting with the same initial value for $\sqrt{R(z)}$ and taken over the two paths $z_0 m z$, $z_0 n z$, which together form a closed curve containing the three critical points e_1, e_2, e_3 of the radical. Consider the closed curve $z_0 m z n z_0 Z M N Z z_0$ formed by the curve $z_0 m z n z_0$, the segment $z_0 Z$, the circle C of very large radius, and the segment $Z z_0$. The function $1/\sqrt{R(z)}$ is analytic in the interior of this boundary, and we have the relation

$$v + v' - \int_{z_0}^{Z} \frac{dz}{\sqrt{R(z)}} + \int_{(C)} \frac{dz}{\sqrt{R(z)}} - \int_{z_0}^{Z} \frac{dz}{\sqrt{R(z)}} = 0,$$

which becomes, as the radius of the circle C becomes infinite,

$$v + v' - 2\,H = 0.$$

The values of u resulting from the two paths $z_0 mz$, $z_0 nz$ therefore satisfy the relation $u + u' = 0$. From this we conclude that the function

$$\mathrm{p}(u\,|\,\omega,\ \omega') = \mathrm{p}\left(\int_{z_0}^{z} \frac{dz}{\sqrt{R(z)}} - H \,|\, \omega,\ \omega' \right)$$

is a single-valued function of z. We have seen that it is a linear function of the form $(az + b)/(cz + d)$. To determine a, b, c, d it will suffice to study the development of this function in the neighborhood of the point at infinity. We have in this neighborhood

$$\frac{1}{\sqrt{R(z)}} = \frac{1}{2 z^{\frac{3}{2}}} \left(1 - \frac{g_2}{4 z^2} - \frac{g_3}{4 z^3} \right)^{-\frac{1}{2}} = \frac{1}{2 z^{\frac{3}{2}}} + \frac{g_2}{16 z^{\frac{7}{2}}} + \cdots;$$

hence the value of u, which is zero for z infinite, is represented by the series

$$u = -\frac{1}{z^{\frac{1}{2}}} \left(1 + \frac{g_2}{40 z^2} + \cdots \right);$$

whence

$$\frac{1}{u^2} = z \left(1 + \frac{g_2}{40 z^2} + \cdots \right)^{-2} = z - \frac{g_2}{20 z} + \cdots.$$

It follows that the difference $\mathrm{p}(u) - z$ is zero for $z = \infty$. But the difference $(az + b)/(cz + d) - z$ can be zero for $z = \infty$ only if we have $c = 0$, $b = 0$, $a = d$; and the function $\mathrm{p}(u\,|\,\omega,\ \omega')$ reduces to z when we substitute for u the integral (72). Taking the point at infinity itself for the lower limit, this integral can also be written in the form

(72') $$u = \int_{\infty}^{z} \frac{dz}{\sqrt{R(z)}},$$

and this relation makes $\mathrm{p}(u) = z$, where the function $\mathrm{p}(u)$ is constructed with the periods $2\,\omega$, $2\,\omega'$ of the integral $\int dz/\sqrt{R(z)}$.

Comparing the values of du/dz deduced from these relations, we have $\mathrm{p}'(u) = \sqrt{R(z)}$, or, after squaring both sides,

(73) $$\mathrm{p}'^2(u) = R(z) = 4\,\mathrm{p}^3(u) - g_2\mathrm{p}(u) - g_3.$$

The numbers g_2, g_3, therefore, are the invariants of the elliptic function $\mathrm{p}(u)$, constructed with the periods $2\,\omega$, $2\,\omega'$. This result answers the question proposed above in § 77. If $g_2^3 - 27\,g_3^2$ is not zero, the equations (61) are satisfied by an infinite number of systems of values for ω, ω'. If e_1, e_2, e_3 are the three roots of the equation

$$R(z) = 4\,z^3 - g_2 z - g_3 = 0,$$

one system of solutions is given, for example, by the formulæ

$$(74) \qquad \omega = \int_{e_1}^{\infty} \frac{dz}{\sqrt{R(z)}}, \qquad \omega' = \int_{e_2}^{\infty} \frac{dz}{\sqrt{R(z)}},$$

from which all other systems will be deducible, as has been explained.

In the applications of analysis in which elliptic functions occur, the function $p(u)$ is usually defined by its invariants. In order to carry through the numerical computations, it is necessary to calculate a pair of periods, knowing g_2 and g_3, and also to be able to find a root of the equation $p(u) = A$, where A is a given constant. For the details of the methods to be followed, and for information regarding the use of tables, we can only refer the reader to special treatises.*

80. Application to cubics in a plane. When $g_2^3 - 27\, g_3^2$ is not zero, the equation

$$(75) \qquad y^2 = 4\,x^3 - g_2 x - g_3$$

represents a cubic without double points. This equation is satisfied by putting $x = p(u)$, $y = p'(u)$, where the invariants of the function $p(u)$ are precisely g_2 and g_3. To each point of the cubic corresponds a single value of u in a suitable parallelogram of periods. For the equation $p(u) = x$ has two roots u_1 and u_2 in a parallelogram of periods, the sum $u_1 + u_2$ is a period, and the two values $p'(u_1)$ and $p'(u_2)$ are the negatives of each other. They are therefore equal respectively to the two values of y which correspond to the same value of x.

In general, the coördinates of a point of a plane cubic without double points can be expressed by elliptic functions of a parameter. We know, in fact, that the equation of a cubic can be reduced to the form (75) by means of a projective transformation, but this transformation cannot be effected unless we know a point of inflection of the cubic, and the determination of the points of inflections depend upon the solution of a ninth-degree equation of a special form. We shall now show that the parametric representation of a cubic by means of elliptic functions of a parameter can be obtained without having to solve any equation, provided that we know the coördinates of a point of the cubic.

Suppose first that the equation of the cubic is of the form

$$(76) \qquad y^2 = b_0 x^3 + 3\,b_1 x^2 + 3\,b_2 x + b_3,$$

---

* The formulæ (39) which give the development of $\sigma(u)$ in a power series, and those which result from it by differentiation, enable us, at least theoretically, to calculate $\sigma(u)$, $\sigma'(u)$, $\sigma''(u)$, and consequently $\zeta(u)$ and $p(u)$, for all systems of values of u, g_2, g_3.

in which case the point at infinity is a point of inflection. This equation can be reduced to the preceding form by putting $y = 4\,y'/b_0$, $x = -\,b_1/b_0 + 4\,x'/b_0$, which gives

$$y'^2 = 4\,x'^3 - g_2 x' - g_3,$$

where the invariants g_2, g_3 are given by the formulæ

$$g_2 = \frac{12\,(b_1^2 - b_0 b_2)}{16}, \qquad g_3 = \frac{3\,b_0 b_1 b_2 - 2\,b_1^3 - b_0^2 b_3}{16}.$$

Hence we obtain for the coördinates of a point of the cubic (76) the following formulæ :

$$x = -\frac{b_1}{b_0} + \frac{4}{b_0}\,\mathrm{p}(u), \qquad y = \frac{4}{b_0}\,\mathrm{p}'(u).$$

Let us now consider a cubic C_3, and let (α, β) be the coördinates of a point of that cubic. The tangent to the cubic at this point (α, β) meets the cubic at a second point (α', β') whose coördinates can be obtained rationally. If the point (α', β') is taken as origin of coördinates, the equation of the cubic is of the form

$$\phi_3(x, y) + \phi_2(x, y) + \phi_1(x, y) = 0,$$

where $\phi_i(x, y)$ denotes a homogeneous polynomial of the ith degree $(i = 1, 2, 3)$. Let us cut the cubic by the secant $y = tx$; then x is determined by an equation of the second degree,

$$x^2 \phi_3(1, t) + x \phi_2(1, t) + \phi_1(1, t) = 0,$$

whence we obtain

$$x = \frac{-\,\phi_2(1, t) \pm \sqrt{R(t)}}{2\,\phi_3(1, t)}, \qquad y = tx,$$

where $R(t)$ denotes the polynomial $\phi_2^2(1, t) - 4\,\phi_3(1, t)\,\phi_1(1, t)$, which is in general of the fourth degree. The roots of this polynomial are precisely the slopes of the tangents to the cubic which pass through the origin.[*] We know a priori one root of this polynomial, the slope t_0 of the straight line which joins the origin to the point (α, β). Putting $t = t_0 + 1/t'$, we find

$$\sqrt{R(t)} = \frac{\sqrt{R_1(t')}}{t'^2},$$

where the polynomial $R_1(t')$ is now only of the third degree. The coördinates (x, y) of a point of the cubic C_3 are therefore expressible rationally in terms of a parameter t' and of the square root of a

---

[*] Two roots cannot be equal (see Vol. I, § 103, 2d ed. ; § 108, 1st ed.). — TRANS.

polynomial $R_1(t')$ of the third degree. We have just seen how to express t' and $\sqrt{R_1(t')}$ as elliptic functions of a parameter u; hence we can express x and y also as elliptic functions of u.

It follows from the nature of the methods used above that to a point (x, y) of the cubic correspond a single value of t and a definite value of $\sqrt{R(t)}$, and hence completely determined values of t' and $\sqrt{R_1(t')}$. Now to each system of values of t' and $\sqrt{R_1(t')}$ corresponds only one value of u in a suitable parallelogram of periods, as we have already pointed out. The expressions $x = f(u)$, $y = f_1(u)$, obtained for the coördinates of a point of C_3, are therefore such that all the determinations of u which give the same point of the cubic can be obtained from any one of them by adding to it various periods.

This parametric representation of plane cubics by means of elliptic functions is very important.* As an example we shall show how it enables us to determine the points of inflection. Let the expressions for the coördinates be $x = f(u)$, $y = f_1(u)$; the arguments of the points of intersections of the cubic with the straight line $Ax + By + C = 0$ are the roots of the equation

$$Af(u) + Bf_1(u) + C = 0.$$

Since to a point (x, y) corresponds only one value of u in a parallelogram of periods, it follows that the elliptic function $Af(u) + Bf_1(u) + C$ must be, in general, of the third order. The poles of that function are evidently independent of A, B, C; hence if u_1, u_2, u_3 are the three arguments corresponding respectively to the three points of intersections of the cubic and the straight line, we must have, by § 68,

$$u_1 + u_2 + u_3 = K + 2\,m_1\omega + 2\,m_2\omega',$$

where K is the sum of the poles in a parallelogram. Replacing u by $K/3 + u$ in $f(u)$ and $f_1(u)$, the relation can be written in the simpler form

$$u_1 + u_2 + u_3 = \text{period}.$$

Conversely, this condition is sufficient to insure that the three points M_1 $(u = u_1)$, M_2 $(u = u_2)$, M_3 $(u = u_3)$ on the cubic shall lie on a straight line. For let M_3' be the third point of intersection of the straight line $M_1 M_2$ with the cubic, and u_3' the corresponding argument. Since the sum $u_1 + u_2 + u_3'$ is equal to a period, u_3 and u_3' differ only by a period, and consequently M_3' coincides with M_3.

If u is the value of the parameter at a point of inflection, the tangent at that point meets the curve in three coincident points, and $3\,u$ must be equal to a period.. We must have, then, $u = (2\,m_1\omega + 2\,m_2\omega')/3$. All the points of inflection can be obtained by giving to the integers m_1 and m_2 the values 0, 1, 2. Hence there are *nine* points of inflections. The straight line which passes through

---

* CLEBSCH, *Ueber diejenigen Curven, deren Coordinaten sich als elliptische Functionen eines Parameters darstellen lassen* (*Crelle's Journal*, Vol. LXIV).

the two points of inflection $(2\,m_1\omega + 2\,m_2\omega')/3$ and $(2\,m_1'\omega + 2\,m_2'\omega')/3$ meets the cubic in a third point whose argument,

$$-\frac{2\,(m_1 + m_1')\,\omega + 2\,(m_2 + m_2')\,\omega'}{3},$$

is again one third of a period, that is, in a new point of inflection. The number of straight lines which meet the cubic in three points of inflection is therefore equal to $(9 \cdot 8)/(3 \cdot 2)$, that is, to *twelve*.

Note. The points of intersection of the standard cubic (75) with the straight line $y = mx + n$ are given by the equation $p'(u) - mp(u) - n = 0$, the left-hand side of which has a pole of the third order at the point $u = 0$. The sum of the arguments of the points of intersection is then equal to a period. If u_1 and u_2 are the arguments of two of these points, we can take $-u_1 - u_2$ for the argument of the third point of intersection, and the abscissas of these three points are respectively $p(u_1)$, $p(u_2)$, $p(u_1 + u_2)$. We can deduce from this a new proof of the addition formula for $p(u)$. In fact, the abscissas of the points of intersection are roots of the equation

$$4\,x^3 - g_2 x - g_3 = (mx + n)^2\,;$$

hence

$$x_1 + x_2 + x_3 = p(u_1) + p(u_2) + p(u_1 + u_2) = \frac{m^2}{4}.$$

On the other hand, from the straight line passing through the two points $M_1(u_1)$, $M_2(u_2)$, we have the two relations $p'(u_1) = mp(u_1) + n$, $p'(u_2) = mp(u_2) + n$, whence

$$m = \frac{p'(u_2) - p'(u_1)}{p(u_2) - p(u_1)},$$

and this leads to the relation already found in § 74,

$$p(u_1) + p(u_2) + p(u_1 + u_2) = \frac{1}{4}\left[\frac{p'(u_2) - p'(u_1)}{p(u_2) - p(u_1)}\right]^2.$$

81. General formulæ for parameter representation. Let $R(x)$ be a polynomial of the fourth degree prime to its derivative. Consider the curve C_4 represented by the equation

$$(77) \qquad y^2 = R(x) = a_0 x^4 + 4\,a_1 x^3 + 6\,a_2 x^2 + 4\,a_3 x + a_4.$$

We shall show how the coördinates x and y of a point of this curve can be expressed as elliptic functions of a parameter. If we know a root a of the equation $R(x) = 0$, we have already seen in the treatment of cubics how to proceed. Putting $x = a + 1/x'$, the relation (77) becomes

$$y^2 = R\left(a + \frac{1}{x'}\right) = \frac{R_1(x')}{x'^4},$$

where $R_1(x')$ is a polynomial of the third degree. Hence the curve C_4, by means of the relations $x = a + 1/x'$, $y = y'/x'^2$, corresponds point for point to the curve C_3' of the third degree whose equation is $y'^2 = R_1(x')$. Now x' and y' can be expressed by means of a parameter u, in the form $x' = \alpha p(u) + \beta$, $y' = \alpha p'(u)$, by a suitable choice of α, β and of the invariants of $p(u)$. We deduce from these relations the following expressions for x and y:

$$(78) \qquad x = a + \frac{1}{\alpha p(u) + \beta}, \qquad y = \frac{\alpha p'(u)}{[\alpha p(u) + \beta]^2};$$

whence we find $du = - dx/y$, so that the parameter u is identical, except for sign, with the integral of the first kind, $\int dx / \sqrt{R(x)}$, and the formulæ (78) constitute a generalization of the results for the simple case of parametric representation in § 80.

Let us consider now the general case in which we do not know any root of the equation $R(x) = 0$. We are going to show that x *and* y *can be expressed rationally in terms of an elliptic function* $p(u)$ *with known invariants, and of its derivative* $p'(u)$, *without introducing any other irrationality than a square root.* Let us replace for the moment x and y by t and v respectively, so that the relation (77) becomes

$$(77') \qquad v^2 = R(t) = a_0 t^4 + 4 a_1 t^3 + 6 a_2 t^2 + 4 a_3 t + a_4.$$

The polynomial $R(t)$ can be expressed in the form

$$R(t) = [\phi_2(t)]^2 - \phi_1(t)\,\phi_3(t)$$

in an infinite number of ways, where ϕ_1, ϕ_2, ϕ_3 are polynomials of the degrees indicated by their subscripts. For let (α, β) be the coördinates of any point on the curve C_4. Let us take a polynomial $\phi_2(t)$ such that $\phi_2(\alpha) = \beta$, which can be done in an infinite number of ways; then the equation

$$R(t) - [\phi_2(t)]^2 = 0$$

will have the root $t = \alpha$, and we can put $\phi_1(t) = t - \alpha$. The polynomial $R(t)$ having been put in the preceding form, let us consider the auxiliary cubic C_3 represented by the equation

$$(79) \qquad x^3 \phi_3\!\left(\frac{y}{x}\right) + 2 x^2 \phi_2\!\left(\frac{y}{x}\right) + x\phi_1\!\left(\frac{y}{x}\right) = 0.$$

If we cut this cubic by the secant $y = tx$, the abscissas of the two variable points of intersection are roots of the equation

$$x^2 \phi_3(t) + 2 x\phi_2(t) + \phi_1(t) = 0$$

and can be expressed in the form

$$x = \frac{-\phi_2(t) + v}{\phi_3(t)},$$

where v is determined by the equation (77'). Conversely, we see that t and v can be expressed rationally in terms of the coördinates x, y of a point of C_3 by the equations

$$(80) \qquad t = \frac{y}{x}, \qquad v = x\phi_3\left(\frac{y}{x}\right) + \phi_2\left(\frac{y}{x}\right).$$

Now x and y can be expressed as elliptic functions of a parameter u, since we know a point on the cubic C_3 that is the origin. Then t and v can also be expressed as elliptic functions of u. The method is evidently susceptible of a great many variations, and we have introduced only the irrational $\beta = \sqrt{R(\alpha)}$, where α is arbitrary.

We are going to carry through the actual calculation, supposing, as is always admissible, that we have first made the coefficient a_1 of t^3 disappear in $R(t)$. We can then write

$$a_0 R(t) = (a_0 t^2)^2 + 6\,a_0 a_2 t^2 + 4\,a_0 a_3 t + a_0 a_4$$

and put

$$\phi_1(t) = -1, \quad \phi_2(t) = a_0 t^2, \quad \phi_3(t) = 6\,a_0 a_2 t^2 + 4\,a_0 a_3 t + a_0 a_4.$$

The auxiliary cubic C_3 has the form

$$(81) \qquad 6\,a_0 a_2 xy^2 + 4\,a_0 a_3 x^2 y + a_0 a_4 x^3 + 2\,a_0 y^2 - x = 0.$$

Following the general method, let us cut this cubic with the secant $y = tx$; the equation obtained can be written in the form

$$\left(\frac{1}{x}\right)^2 - 2\,a_0 t^2 \frac{1}{x} - (6\,a_0 a_2 t^2 + 4\,a_0 a_3 t + a_0 a_4) = 0;$$

whence we obtain

$$\frac{1}{x} = a_0 t^2 + \sqrt{a_0 R(t)}.$$

Conversely, we can express t and $\sqrt{a_0 R(t)}$ in terms of x and y:

$$(82) \qquad t = \frac{y}{x}, \qquad \sqrt{a_0 R(t)} = \frac{1}{x} - a_0\left(\frac{y}{x}\right)^2.$$

On the other hand, solving the equation (81) for y, we have

$$y = \frac{-2\,a_0 a_3 x^2 + \sqrt{4\,a_0^2 a_3^2 x^4 - x(a_0 a_4 x^2 - 1)(6\,a_0 a_2 x + 2\,a_0)}}{6\,a_0 a_2 x + 2\,a_0}.$$

The polynomial under the radical has the root $x = 0$. Applying the method explained above, we can then express x and y as elliptic functions of a parameter. Doing so, we obtain the results

$$(83) \qquad x = \frac{1}{2\,a_0 \mathrm{p}(u) - a_2}, \qquad y = \frac{a_0 \mathrm{p}'(u) - a_3}{2[a_0 \mathrm{p}(u) + a_2][2\,a_0 \mathrm{p}(u) - a_2]},$$

where the invariants g_2, g_3 of the elliptic function $p(u)$ have the following values:

(84) $$g_2 = \frac{a_0 a_4 + 3\, a_2^2}{a_0^2}, \qquad g_3 = \frac{a_0 a_2 a_4 - a_2^3 - a_0 a_3^2}{a_0^3}.$$

Substituting the preceding values for x and y in the expressions (82), we find

(85) $$\left\{ \begin{aligned} t &= \frac{1}{2} \frac{\left[p'(u) - \dfrac{a_3}{a_0} \right]}{p(u) + \dfrac{a_2}{a_0}}, \\ \sqrt{R(t)} &= \sqrt{a_0} \left\{ 2\, p(u) - \frac{a_2}{a_0} - \frac{1}{4} \left[\frac{p'(u) - \dfrac{a_3}{a_0}}{p(u) + \dfrac{a_2}{a_0}} \right]^2 \right\}. \end{aligned} \right.$$

We can write these results in a somewhat simpler form by noting that the relations

(86) $$p(v) = -\frac{a_2}{a_0}, \qquad p'(v) = \frac{a_3}{a_0}$$

are compatible according to the values (84) of the invariants g_2 and g_3. On the other hand, we can substitute for

$$\frac{1}{4} \left[\frac{p'(u) - p'(v)}{p(u) - p(v)} \right]^2$$

its equivalent $p(u + v) + p(u) + p(v)$. Combining these results and replacing t and $\sqrt{R(t)}$ by x and y respectively, we may formulate the result in the following proposition:

The coördinates (x, y) of any point on the curve C_4, represented by the equation (77) (where $a_1 = 0$), can be expressed in terms of a variable parameter u by the formulæ

(87) $$x = \frac{1}{2} \frac{p'(u) - p'(v)}{p(u) - p(v)}, \qquad y = \sqrt{a_0}\,[p(u) - p(u + v)],$$

where the invariants g_2 and g_3 have the values given by the relations (84), and where $p(v)$, $p'(v)$ are determined by the compatible equations (86).

From the formula (45), established above (§ 74), we derive, by differentiating the two sides of that equality,

$$\frac{1}{2} \frac{d}{du} \left[\frac{p'(u) - p'(v)}{p(u) - p(v)} \right] = p(u) - p(u + v);$$

that is, $dx/du = y/\sqrt{a_0}$, or $du = [\sqrt{a_0}/y]dx$. The parameter u, therefore, represents the elliptic integral of the first kind, $\sqrt{a_0}\int dx/\sqrt{R(x)}$, and the formulæ (87) furnish the solution of the generalized problem of parameter representation.

82. Curves of deficiency one. An algebraic plane curve C_n of degree n cannot have more than $(n-1)(n-2)/2$ double points without degenerating into several distinct curves. If the curve C_n is not degenerate and has d double points, the difference

$$p = \frac{(n-1)(n-2)}{2} - d$$

is called the deficiency of that curve. Curves of deficiency zero are called unicursal curves; the coördinates of a point of such a curve can be expressed as rational functions of a parameter. The next simplest curves are those of deficiency *one*; a curve of deficiency one has $(n-1)(n-2)/2 - 1 = n(n-3)/2$ double points.

The coördinates of a point of a curve of deficiency one can be expressed as elliptic functions of a parameter.

In order to prove this theorem, let us consider the *adjoint* curves of the $(n-2)$th order, that is, the curves C_{n-2} which pass through the $n(n-3)/2$ double points of C_n. Since $(n-2)(n+1)/2$ points are necessary to determine a curve of the $(n-2)$th degree, the adjoint curves C_{n-2} depend still upon

$$\frac{(n-2)(n+1) - n(n-3)}{2} = (n-1)$$

arbitrary parameters. If we also require that these curves pass through $n-3$ other simple points taken at pleasure on C_n, we obtain a system of adjoint curves which have, in common with C_n, the $n(n-3)/2$ double points of C_n and $n-3$ of its simple points. Let $F(x, y) = 0$ be the equation of C_n, and let

$$f_1(x, y) + \lambda f_2(x, y) + \mu f_3(x, y) = 0$$

be the equation of the system of curves C_{n-2}, where λ and μ are arbitrary parameters. Any curve of this system meets C_n in only three variable points, for each double point counts as two simple points, and we have

$$n(n-3) + n - 3 = n(n-2) - 3.$$

Let us now put

$$(88) \qquad x' = \frac{f_2(x, y)}{f_1(x, y)}, \qquad y' = \frac{f_3(x, y)}{f_1(x, y)};$$

when the point (x, y) describes the curve C_n, the point (x', y') describes an algebraic curve C' whose equation would be obtained by the elimination of x and y between the equations (88) and $F(x, y) = 0$. The two curves C' and C_n correspond to each other point for point by means of a *birational transformation*. This means that, conversely, the coördinates (x, y) of a point of C_n can be expressed rationally in terms of the coördinates (x', y') of the corresponding point of C'. To prove this we need only show that to a point (x', y') of C' there corresponds only one point of C_n, or that the equations (88), together with $F(x, y) = 0$, have only a single system of solutions for x and y, which vary with x' and y'.

Suppose that to a point of C' there correspond actually two points (a, b), (a', b') of C_n which are not among the points taken as the basis of the system of curves C_{n-2}. Then we should have

$$\frac{f_1(a', b')}{f_1(a, b)} = \frac{f_2(a', b')}{f_2(a, b)} = \frac{f_3(a', b')}{f_3(a, b)},$$

and all the curves of the system which pass through the point (a, b) would also pass through the point (a', b'). The curves of the system which pass through these two points would still depend *linearly* upon a variable parameter and would meet the curve C_n in a single variable point. The coördinates of this last point of intersection with C_n would then be rational functions of a variable parameter, and the curve C_n would be unicursal. But this is impossible, since it has only $n(n - 3)/2$ double points. Hence to a point (x', y') of C' corresponds only one point of C_n, and the coördinates of this point are, by the theory of elimination, rational functions of x' and y':

(89) $x = \phi_1(x', y'), \qquad y = \phi_2(x', y').$

In order to obtain the degree of the curve C', let us try to find the number of points common to this curve and any straight line $ax' + by' + c = 0$. This amounts to finding the number of points common to the curve C_n and the curve

$$af_2(x, y) + bf_3(x, y) + cf_1(x, y) = 0,$$

since to a point of C' corresponds a single point of C_n, and conversely. Now there are only three points of intersection which vary with a, b, c. The curve C' is therefore of the third degree. To sum up, the coördinates of a point of the curve C_n can be expressed rationally in terms of the coördinates of a point of a plane cubic; and since the coördinates of a point of a cubic are elliptic functions of a parameter, the same thing must be true of the coördinates of a point of C_n.

It results also from the demonstration, and from what has been seen above for cubics, that the representation can be made in such a way that to a point (x, y) of C_n corresponds only one value of u in a parallelogram of periods.

Let $x = \psi(u)$, $y = \psi_1(u)$ be the expressions for x and y derived above; then every Abelian integral $w = \int R(x, y)\,dx$ associated with the curve C_n (I, § 103, 2d ed.; § 108, 1st ed.) is reduced by this change of variables to the integral of an elliptic function; hence this integral w can be expressed in terms of the transcendentals p, ζ, σ of the theory of elliptic functions. The introduction of these transcendentals in analysis has doubled the scope of the integral calculus.

Example. Bicircular quartics. A curve of the fourth degree with two double points is of deficiency one. If the double points are the circular points at infinity, the curve C_4 is called a *bicircular quartic.* If we take for the origin a point of the curve, we can take for the adjoint curves C_{n-2} circles passing through the origin
$$x^2 + y^2 + \lambda x + \mu y = 0.$$

In order to have a cubic corresponding point for point to the quartic C_4, we need only follow the general method and put $x' = x/(x^2 + y^2)$, $y' = y/(x^2 + y^2)$. We have, conversely, $x = x'/(x'^2 + y'^2)$, $y = y'/(x'^2 + y'^2)$. These formulæ define an inversion with respect to a circle of *unit* radius described with the origin as center. To obtain the equation of the cubic C_3', it will suffice to replace x and y in the equation of C_4 by the preceding values. Suppose, for example, that the equation of the quartic C_4 is $(x^2 + y^2)^2 - ay = 0$; the cubic C_3' will have for its equation $ay'(y'^2 + x'^2) - 1 = 0$.

Note. When a plane curve C_n has singular points of a higher order, it is of deficiency one, provided that all its singular points are equivalent to $n(n-3)/2$ ordinary double points. For example, a curve of the fourth degree having a single double point at which two branches of the curve are tangent to each other without having any other singularity is of deficiency one; to verify this it suffices to cut the quartic by a system of conics tangent to the two branches of the quartic at the double point and passing through another point of the quartic. The curve $y^2 = R(x)$, where $R(x)$ is a polynomial of the fourth degree prime to its derivative, has a singularity of this kind at the point at infinity. It is reduced to a cubic by the following birational transformation :
$$x = x', \qquad y = y' + \sqrt{a_0}\,x'^2,$$
from which it is easy to obtain the formulæ (87).

EXERCISES

1. Prove that an integral doubly periodic function is a constant by means of the development
$$f(z) = \sum_{-\infty}^{+\infty} A_n e^{\frac{2 n i \pi z}{\omega}}.$$

(The condition $f(z + \omega') = f(z)$ requires that we have $A_n = 0$ if $n \neq 0$.)

2. If a is not a multiple of π, we have the formula

$$\frac{\sin (z + a)}{\sin a} = \left(1 + \frac{z}{a}\right) \prod_{-\infty}^{+\infty}{}' \left(1 + \frac{z}{a - n\pi}\right) e^{\frac{z}{n\pi}}.$$

(Change z to $z + a$ in the expansion for $\operatorname{ctn} z$, then integrate between the limits 0 and z.)

3. Deduce from the preceding result the new infinite products

$$\frac{\cos (z + a)}{\cos a} = \left(1 + \frac{2z}{2a + \pi}\right) \prod_{-\infty}^{+\infty} \left[1 + \frac{2z}{2a - (2n - 1)\pi}\right] e^{\frac{z}{n\pi}},$$

$$\frac{\sin \alpha - \sin z}{\sin \alpha} = \left(1 - \frac{z}{\alpha}\right)\left(1 + \frac{z}{\alpha + \pi}\right) \prod_{-\infty}^{+\infty}{}' \left(1 - \frac{z}{\alpha + 2n\pi}\right)\left(1 - \frac{z}{(2n - 1)\pi - \alpha}\right) e^{\frac{z}{n\pi}},$$

$$\frac{\cos z - \cos \alpha}{1 - \cos \alpha} = \left(1 - \frac{z^2}{\alpha^2}\right) \prod_{-\infty}^{+\infty}{}' \left(1 - \frac{z}{2n\pi + \alpha}\right)\left(1 - \frac{z}{2n\pi - \alpha}\right) e^{\frac{z}{n\pi}}.$$

Transform these new products into products of primary functions or into products that no longer contain exponential factors, such as

$$\cos z = \left(1 - \frac{4z^2}{\pi^2}\right)\left(1 - \frac{4z^2}{9\pi^2}\right) \cdots \left[1 - \frac{4z^2}{(2n + 1)^2 \pi^2}\right] \cdots.$$

4. Derive the relations

$$\tan z = 2z \left[\frac{1}{\frac{\pi^2}{4} - z^2} + \frac{1}{\frac{9\pi^2}{4} - z^2} + \cdots + \frac{1}{\frac{(2n + 1)^2 \pi^2}{4} - z^2} + \cdots\right],$$

$$\frac{1}{\sin z} = \frac{1}{z} - 2z \left[\frac{1}{z^2 - \pi^2} - \frac{1}{z^2 - 4\pi^2} + \cdots + (-1)^{n-1}\frac{1}{z^2 - n^2\pi^2} + \cdots\right].$$

Establish analogous relations for

$$\frac{1}{\sin z - \sin a}, \qquad \frac{1}{\cos z - \cos a}.$$

5. Establish the relation

$$\frac{\sin \pi z}{\pi z} = 1 - \frac{z^2}{1} + \frac{z^2 (z^2 - 1)}{[2!]^2} - \frac{z^2 (z^2 - 1)(z^2 - 4)}{[3!]^2} + \cdots$$

$$+ (-1)^{n-1} \frac{z^2 (z^2 - 1) \cdots (z^2 - n^2)}{[(n + 1)!]^2} + \cdots.$$

6. Decompose the functions

$$\frac{1}{\mathrm{p}'(u)}, \qquad \frac{1}{\mathrm{p}'^2(u)}$$

into simple elements.

7. If $g_2 = 0$, we have

$$\mathrm{p}(\alpha u; 0, g_3) = \alpha \mathrm{p}(u; 0, g_3), \qquad \mathrm{p}'(\alpha u; 0, g_3) = \mathrm{p}'(u; 0, g_3),$$

where α is one of the cube roots of unity. From this deduce the decomposition of $1/[\mathrm{p}'(u) - \mathrm{p}'(v)]$ into simple elements when $g_2 = 0$.

8. Given the integrals

$$\int \frac{ax+b}{(x-1)\sqrt{x^3-1}}\,dx, \qquad \int \frac{ax^2+b}{\sqrt{1+x^4}}\,dx,$$

$$\int \frac{dx}{x^3\sqrt{x^3-x}}, \qquad \int \frac{ax^2+b}{\sqrt{(1-x^2)(1-k^2x^2)}}\,dx,$$

it is required to express the variable x and each one of these integrals in terms of the transcendentals p, ζ, σ.

9. Establish Hermite's decomposition formula (§ 73) by equating to zero the sum of the residues of the function $F(z)[\zeta(x-z)-\zeta(x_0-z)]$ in a parallelogram of periods, where $F(x)$ is an elliptic function and where x, x_0 are considered as constants.

10. Deduce from the formula (60) the relation $\eta = -\theta'''(0)/12\,\omega\theta'(0)$.

(It should be noticed that the series for $\sigma(u)$ does not contain any terms in u^3.)

11*. Express the coördinates x and y of one of the following curves as elliptic functions of a parameter:

$$y^3 = A\,[(x-a)\ (x-b)\ (x-c)]^2, \qquad y^3 = A\,[(x-a)\ (x-b)]^2,$$

$$y^4 = A\ (x-a)^2(x-b)^3(x-c)^3, \qquad y^4 = A\ (x-a)^2(x-b)^3,$$

$$y^4 = A\,(x-a)^3(x-b)^3,$$

$$y^6 = A\ (x-a)^3(x-b)^4(x-c)^5, \qquad y^6 = A\ (x-a)^3(x-b)^4,$$

$$y^6 = A\ (x-a)^3(x-b)^5, \qquad y^6 = A\ (x-a)^4(x-b)^5,$$

$$y^3 + (lx^2+mx+n)\,y^2 + A\,[(x-a)(x-b)(x-c)]^2 = 0,$$

$$y^4 + Axy^3 + x^3\left(Bx + \frac{3^3}{4^4}\frac{A^4}{4\,B}\right)^2 = 0, \qquad y^4 + Axy^3 + x^2\left(Bx^2 + \frac{3^3}{4^4}\frac{A^4}{4\,B}\right)^2 = 0,$$

$$y^4 + Axy^3 + \left(Bx^4 + \frac{3^3}{4^4}\frac{A^4}{4\,B}\right)^2 = 0,$$

$$y^5 + Axy^4 + x^4\left(Bx - \frac{4^4}{5^5}\frac{A^5}{4\,B}\right)^2 = 0, \qquad y^5 + Axy^4 + \left(Bx^5 - \frac{4^4}{5^5}\frac{A^4}{4\,B}\right)^2 = 0.$$

The variable parameter is equal, except for a constant, to the integral $\int (1/y)\,dx$.

[BRIOT ET BOUQUET, *Théorie des fonctions doublement périodiques*, 2d ed., pp. 388–412.]

CHAPTER IV

ANALYTIC EXTENSION

I. DEFINITION OF AN ANALYTIC FUNCTION BY MEANS OF ONE OF ITS ELEMENTS

83. Introduction to analytic extension. Let $f(z)$ be an analytic function in a connected portion A of the plane, bounded by one or more curves, closed or not, where the word *curve* is to be understood in the usual elementary sense as heretofore.

If we know the value of the function $f(z)$ and the values of all its successive derivatives at a definite point a of the region A, we can deduce from them the value of the function at any other point b of the same region. To prove this, join the points a and b by a path L lying entirely in the region A; for example, by a broken line or by any form of curve whatever. Let δ be the lower limit of the distance from any point of the path L to any point of the boundary of the region A, so that a circle with the radius δ and with its center at any point of L will lie entirely in that region. By hypothesis we know the value of the function $f(a)$ and the values of its successive derivatives $f'(a)$, $f''(a)$, $\cdots$, for $z = a$. We can therefore write the power series which represents the function $f(z)$ in the neighborhood of the point a :

$$(1) \quad f(z) = f(a) + \frac{z-a}{1} f'(a) + \cdots + \frac{(z-a)^n}{n!} f^{(n)}(a) + \cdots.$$

The radius of convergence of this series is at least equal to δ, but it may be greater than δ. If the point b is situated in the circle of convergence C_0 of the preceding series, it will suffice to replace z by b in order to have $f(b)$. Suppose that the point b lies outside the circle C_0, and let α_1 be the point where the path L leaves C_0^* (Fig. 30). Let us take on this path a point z_1 within C_0 and near α_1, so that the

---

* Since the value of $f(z)$ at the point b does not depend on the path so long as it does not leave the region A, we may suppose that the path cuts the circle C_0 in only one point, as in the figure, and the successive circles C_1, C_2, $\cdots$ in at most two points. This amounts to taking for α_1 the last point of intersection of L and C_0, and similarly for the others.

distance between the two points z_1 and α_1 shall be less than $\delta/2$. The series (1) and those obtained from it by successive differentiations enable us to calculate the values of the function $f(z)$ and of all its derivatives, $f(z_1), f'(z_1), \cdots, f^{(n)}(z_1), \cdots$, for $z = z_1$. The coefficients of the series which represents the function $f(z)$ in the neighborhood of the point z_1 are therefore determined if we know the coefficients of the first series (1), and we have in the neighborhood of the point z_1

$$(2) \quad f(z) = f(z_1) + \frac{z - z_1}{1} f'(z_1) + \cdots + \frac{(z - z_1)^n}{n!} f^{(n)}(z_1) + \cdots.$$

The radius of the circle of convergence C_1 of this series is at least equal to δ; this circle contains, then, the point α_1 within it, and there is also a part of it out-side of the circle C_0. If the point b is in this new circle C_1, it will suffice to put $z = b$ in the series (2) in order to have the value of $f(b)$. Sup-pose that the point b is again outside of C_1, and let α_2 be the point where the path $z_1 b$ leaves the circle. Let us take on the path L a point z_2 within C_1 and such that the

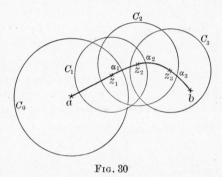

FIG. 30

distance between the two points z_2 and α_2 shall be less than $\delta/2$. The series (2) and those which we obtain from it by successive dif-ferentiations will enable us to calculate the values of $f(z)$ and its derivatives $f(z_2), f'(z_2), f''(z_2), \cdots$ at the point z_2. We shall then form a new series,

$$(3) \quad f(z) = f(z_2) + \frac{z - z_2}{1} f'(z_2) + \cdots + \frac{(z - z_2)^n}{n!} f^{(n)}(z_2) + \cdots,$$

which represents the function $f(z)$ in a new circle C_2 with a radius greater than or equal to δ. If the point b is in this circle C_2, we shall replace z by b in the preceding equality (3); if not, we shall continue to apply the same process. At the end of a finite number of such operations we shall finally have a circle containing the point b within it (in the case of the figure, b is in the interior of C_3); for we can always choose the points $z_1, z_2, z_3, \cdots$ in such a way that the dis-tance between any two consecutive points shall be greater than $\delta/2$. On the other hand, let S be the length of the path L. The length of the broken line $a z_1 z_2 \cdots z_{p-1} z_p$ is always less than S; hence we have $p \delta / 2 + |z_p - b| < S$. Let p be an integer such that $(p/2 + 1) \delta > S$. The preceding inequality shows that after p operations, at most, we shall come upon a point z_p of the path L whose distance from the point b will be less than δ; the point b will be in the interior of the circle of convergence C_p of the power series which represents the function $f(z)$ in the neighborhood of the point z_p, and it will suffice to replace z by b in this series in order to have $f(b)$. In the same way all the derivatives $f'(b), f''(b), \cdots$ can be calculated.

The above reasoning proves that it is possible, at least theoretically, to calculate the value of a function analytic in a region A, and of all its derivatives at any point of that region, provided we know the sequence of values,

$$(4) \qquad f(a), \quad f'(a), \quad f''(a), \quad \cdots, \quad f^{(n)}(a), \quad \cdots,$$

of the function and of its successive derivatives at a *given point* a of that region. It follows that any function analytic in a region A is completely determined in the whole of that region if it is known in a region, however small, surrounding any point a taken in A, or even if it is known at all points of an arc of a curve, however short, ending at the point a. For if the function $f(z)$ is determined at every point on the whole length of an arc of a curve, the same must be true of its derivative $f'(z)$, since the value $f'(z_1)$ at any point of that arc is equal to the limit of the quotient $[f(z_2) - f(z_1)]/(z_2 - z_1)$ when the point z_2 approaches z_1 along the arc considered; the derivative $f'(z)$ being known, we deduce from it in the same way $f''(z)$, and from that we deduce $f'''(z), \cdots$. All the successive derivatives of the function $f(z)$ will then be determined for $z = a$. We shall say for brevity that the knowledge of the numerical values of all the terms of the sequence (4) determines an *element* of the function $f(z)$. The result reached can now be stated in the following manner: *A function analytic in a region A is completely determined if we know any one of its elements.* We can say further that two functions analytic in the same region cannot have a common element without being identical.

We have supposed for definiteness that the function considered, $f(z)$, was analytic in the whole region; but the reasoning can be extended to any function analytic in the region except at certain singular points, provided the path L, followed by the variable in going from a to b, does not pass through any singular point of the function. It suffices for this to break up the path into several arcs, as we have already done (§ 31), so that each one can be inclosed in a closed boundary inside of which the branch of the function $f(z)$ considered shall be analytic. The knowledge of the initial element and of the path described by the variable suffices, at least theoretically, to find the final element, that is, the numerical values of all the terms of the analogous sequence

$$(5) \qquad f(b), \quad f'(b), \quad \cdots, \quad f^{(n)}(b), \quad \cdots.$$

84. New definition of analytic functions. Up to the present we have studied analytic functions which were defined by expressions which give their values for all values of the variable in the field in which they were studied. We now know, from what precedes, that it is possible to define an analytic function for any value of the variable as soon as we know a single element of the function; but in order to present the theory satisfactorily from this new point of view, we must add to the definition of analytic functions according to Cauchy a new convention, which seems to be worth stating in considerable detail.

Let $f_1(z), f_2(z)$ be two functions analytic respectively in the two regions A_1, A_2 having one and only one part A' in common (Fig. 31). If in the common part A' we have $f_2(z) = f_1(z)$, which will be the case if these two functions have a single common element in this region, we shall regard $f_1(z)$ and $f_2(z)$ as forming a single function $F(z)$, analytic in the region $A_1 + A_2$, by means of the following equalities: $F(z) = f_1(z)$ in A_1, and $F(z) = f_2(z)$ in A_2.

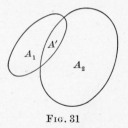

FIG. 31

We shall also say that $f_2(z)$ is the *analytic extension* into the region $A_2 - A'$ of the analytic function $f_1(z)$, which is supposed to be defined only in the region A_1. It is clear that the analytic extension of $f_1(z)$ into the region of A_2 exterior to A_1 is possible in only one way.*

---

*In order to show that the preceding convention is distinct from the definition of functions analytic in general, it suffices to notice that it leads at once to the following consequence: *If a function $f(z)$ is analytic in a region A, every other analytic function $f_1(z)$, under these conventions, which coincides with $f(z)$ in a part of the region A is identical with $f(z)$ in A.* Now let us consider a function $F(z)$ defined for all values of the complex variable z in the following manner:

$$F(z) = \sin z, \text{ if } z \neq \frac{\pi}{2}; \quad F\!\left(\frac{\pi}{2}\right) = 0.$$

However odd this sort of convention may appear, it has nothing in it contradictory to the previous definition of functions in general analytic. The function thus defined would be analytic for all values of z except for $z = \pi/2$, which would

Let us now consider an infinite sequence of numbers, real or imaginary,

(6) $a_0, a_1, a_2, \cdots, a_n, \cdots,$

subject to the single condition that the series

(7) $a_0 + a_1 z + a_2 z^2 + \cdots + a_n z^n + \cdots$

converges for some value of z different from zero. (We take $z = 0$ for the initial value of the variable, which does not in any way restrict the generality.) The series (7) has, then, by hypothesis, a circle of convergence C_0 whose radius R is not zero. If R is infinite, the series is convergent for every value of z and represents an integral function of the variable. If the radius R has a finite value different from zero, the sum of the series (7) is an analytic function $f(z)$ in the interior of the circle C_0. But since we know only the sequence of coefficients (6), we cannot say anything a priori regarding the nature of the function outside of the circle C_0. We do not know whether or not it is possible to add to the circle C_0 an adjoining region forming with the circle a connected region A such that there exists a function analytic in A and coinciding with $f(z)$ in the interior of C_0. The method of the preceding paragraph enables us to determine whether this is the case or not. Let us take in the circle C_0 a point a different from the origin. By means of the series (7), and the series obtained from it by term-by-term differentiation we can calculate the element of the function $f(z)$ which corresponds to the point a, and consequently we can form the power series

(8) $f(a) + \dfrac{z - a}{1} f'(a) + \cdots + \dfrac{(z - a)^n}{n!} f^{(n)}(a) + \cdots,$

which represents the function $f(z)$ in the neighborhood of the point a. This series is certainly convergent in a circle about a as center with a radius $R - |a|$ (§ 8), but it may be convergent in a larger circle whose radius cannot exceed $R + |a|$. For if it were convergent in

---

be a singular point of a particular nature. But the properties of this function $F(z)$ would be in contradiction to the convention which we have just adopted, since the two functions $F(z)$ and $\sin z$ would be identical for all the values of z except for $z = \pi/2$, which would be a singular point for only one of the two functions.

Weierstrass, in Germany, and Méray, in France, developed the theory of analytic functions by starting only with the properties of power series; their investigations are also entirely independent. Méray's theory is presented in his large treatise, *Leçons nouvelles sur l'Analyse infinitésimale*. It is shown in the text how we can define an analytic function step by step, knowing one of its elements but always supposing known the theorems of Cauchy on analytic functions.

a circle of radius $R + |a| + \delta$, the series (7) would be convergent in a circle of radius $R + \delta$ about the origin as center, contrary to the hypothesis. Let us suppose first that the radius of the circle of convergence of the series (8) is always equal to $R - |a|$, wherever the point a may be taken in the circle C_0. Then there exists no means of extending the function $f(z)$ analytically outside of the circle, at least if we make use of power series only. We can say that there does not exist any function $F(z)$ analytic in a region A of the plane greater than and containing the circle C_0 and coinciding with $f(z)$ in the circle C_0, for the method of analytic extension would enable us to determine the value of that function at a point exterior to the circle C_0, as we have just seen. The circle C_0 is then said to be a *natural boundary* for the function $f(z)$. Further on we shall see some examples of this.

Suppose, in the second place, that with a suitably chosen point a in the circle C_0 the circle of convergence C_1 of the series (8) has a radius greater than $R - |a|$. This circle C_1 has a part exterior to C_0 (Fig. 32), and the sum of the series (8) is an analytic function $f_1(z)$ in the circle C_1. In the interior of the circle γ with the center a, which is tangent to the circle C_0 internally, we have $f_1(z) = f(z)$ (§ 8); hence this equality must subsist in the whole of the region common to the two circles C_0, C_1. The

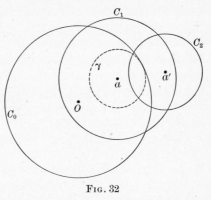

Fig. 32

series (8) gives us the analytic extension of the function $f(z)$ into the portion of the circle C_1 exterior to the circle C_0. Let a' be a new point taken in this region; by proceeding in the same way we shall form a new power series in powers of $z - a'$, which will be convergent in a circle C_2. If the circle C_2 is not entirely within C_1, the new series will give the extension of $f(z)$ in a more extended region, and so on in the same way. We see, then, how it is possible to extend, step by step, the region of existence of the function $f(z)$, which at first was defined only in the interior of the circle C_0.

It is clear that the preceding process can be carried out in an infinite number of ways. In order to keep in mind how the extension was obtained, we must define precisely the path followed by the variable. Let us suppose that we can obtain the analytic extension of the function defined by the series (7) along a path L, as we have just explained. Each point x of the path L is the center of a circle of convergence of radius r in the interior of which the function is represented by a convergent series arranged in powers of $z - x$. *The radius r of this circle varies continuously with x.* For let x and x' be two neighboring points of the path L, and r and r' the corresponding radii. If x' is near enough to x to satisfy the inequality $|x' - x| < r$, the radius r' will lie between $r - |x' - x|$ and $r + |x' - x|$, as we have seen above. Hence the difference $r' - r$ approaches zero with $|x' - x|$. Now let C_0' be a circle with the radius $R/2$ described with the origin as center; if a is any point on the circle C_0', the radius of convergence of the series (8) is at least equal to $R/2$, but it may be greater. Since this radius varies in a continuous manner with the position of the point a, it passes through a *minimum* value $R/2 + r$ at a point of the circle C_0'. *We cannot have $r > 0$,* for if r were actually positive, there would exist a function $F(z)$ analytic in the circle of radius $R + r$ about the origin as center and coinciding with $f(z)$ in the interior of C_0. For a value of z whose absolute value lies between R and $R + r$, $F(z)$ would be equal to the sum of any one of the series (8), where a is a point on C_0' such that $|z - a| < R/2 + r$. According to Cauchy's theorem, $F(z)$ would be equal to the sum of a power series convergent in the circle of radius $R + r$, and this series would be identical with the series (7), which is impossible.

There is, therefore, on the circumference of C_0' at least one point a such that the circle of convergence of the series (8) has $R/2$ for its radius, and this circle is tangent internally to the circle C_0 at a point α where the radius Oa meets that circle. The point α is a *singular* point of $f(z)$ on the circle C_0. In a circle c with the point α for center, however small the radius may be taken, there cannot exist an analytic function which is identical with $f(z)$ in the part common to the two circles C_0 and c. It is also clear that the circle of convergence of the series (8) having any point of the radius $O\alpha$ for center is tangent internally to the circle C_0 at the point α.[*]

---

[*] If all the coefficients a_n of the series (7) are *real and positive*, the point $z = R$ is *necessarily a singular point* on C_0. In fact, if it were not, the power series

$$f\left(\frac{R}{2}\right) + \left(z - \frac{R}{2}\right) f'\left(\frac{R}{2}\right) + \cdots + \frac{\left(z - \dfrac{R}{2}\right)^n}{n!} f^{(n)}\left(\frac{R}{2}\right) + \cdots,$$

which represents $f(z)$ in the neighborhood of the point $z = R/2$, would have a radius of convergence greater than $R/2$. The same would be true a fortiori of the series

Let us consider now a path L starting at the origin and ending at any point Z outside of the circle C_0, and let us imagine a moving point to describe this path, moving always in the same sense from O to Z. Let α_1 be the point where the moving point leaves the circle; if this point α_1 were a singular point, it would be impossible to continue on the path L beyond this point. We shall suppose that it is not a singular point; we can then form a power series arranged in powers of $z - \alpha_1$ and convergent in a circle C_1 with the center α_1, whose sum coincides with $f(z)$ in the part common to the two circles C_0 and C_1. To calculate $f(\alpha_1)$, $f'(\alpha_1)$, $\cdots$ we could employ, for example, an intermediate point on the radius $O\alpha_1$. The sum of the second series would furnish us with the analytic extension of $f(z)$ along the path L from α_1, so long as the moving point does not leave the circle C_1. In particular, if all the path starting from α_1 lies in the interior of C_1, that series will give the value of the function at the point Z. If the path leaves the circle C_1 at the point α_2, we shall form, similarly, a new power series convergent in a circle C_2 with the center α_2, and so on. We shall suppose first that after a finite number of operations we arrive at a circle C_p with the center α_p, containing all the portion of the path L which follows α_p, and in particular the point Z. It will suffice to replace z by Z in the last series used and in those which we have obtained from it by term-by-term differentiation in order to find the values of $f(Z)$, $f'(Z)$, $f''(Z)$, $\cdots$, with which we arrive at the point Z, that is, the final element of the function.

It is clear that we arrive at any point of the path L with completely determined values for the function and all its derivatives. Let us note also that we could replace the circles C_0, C_1, C_2, $\cdots$, C_p by a sequence of circles similarly defined, having any points z_1, z_2, $\cdots$, z_q of the path L as centers, provided that the circle with the center z_i contains the portion of the path L included between z_i and z_{i+1}. We can also modify the path L, keeping the same extremities, without changing the final values of $f(z)$, $f'(z)$, $f''(z)$, $\cdots$; for the

$$f\left(\frac{Re^{i\omega}}{2}\right) + \left(z - \frac{Re^{i\omega}}{2}\right)f'\left(\frac{Re^{i\omega}}{2}\right) + \cdots,$$

whatever the angle ω may be, for we have evidently

$$\left| f^{(n)}\left(\frac{Re^{i\omega}}{2}\right) \right| \leqq f^{(n)}\left(\frac{R}{2}\right),$$

since all the coefficients a_n are positive. The minimum of the radius of convergence of the series (8), when a describes the circle C_0', would then be greater than $R/2$.

circles $C_0, C_1, \cdots, C_p$ cover a portion of the plane forming a kind of strip in which the path L lies, and we can replace the path L by any other path L' going from $z = 0$ to the point Z and situated in that

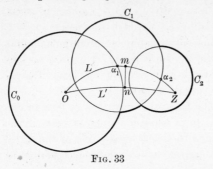

strip. Let us suppose, for definiteness, that we have to make use of three consecutive circles C_0, C_1, C_2 (Fig. 33). Let L' be a new path lying in the strip formed by these three circles, and let us join the two points m and n. If we go from O to m first by the path $O\alpha_1 m$, then by the path Onm, it is clear that we arrive

Fig. 33

at m with the same element, since we have an analytic function in the region formed by C_0 and C_1. Similarly, if we go from m to Z by the path $m\alpha_2 Z$ or by the path mnZ, we arrive in each case at the point Z with the same element. The path L is therefore equivalent to the path $OnmZ$, that is, to the path L'. The method of proof is the same, whatever may be the number of the successive circles. In particular, we can always replace a path of any form whatever by a broken line.*

85. Singular points. If we proceed as we have just explained, it may happen that we cannot find a circle containing all that part of the path L which remains to be described, however far we continue the process. This will be the case when the point α_p is a singular point on the circle C_{p-1}, for the process will be checked just at that point. If the process can be continued forever, without arriving at a circle inclosing all that part of the path L which remains to be described, the points $\alpha_{p-1}, \alpha_p, \alpha_{p+1}, \cdots$ approach a limit point λ of the path L, which may be either the point Z itself or a point lying between O and Z. The point λ is again a *singular point*, and it is impossible to push the analytic extension of the function $f(z)$ along the path L beyond the point λ. But if λ is different from Z, it does not follow that the point Z is itself a singular point, and that we cannot go from O to Z by some other path. Let us consider, for example, either of the two functions $\sqrt{1 + z}$ and $\mathrm{Log}\,(1 + z)$; we could not go from

---

* The reasoning requires a little more attention when the path L has double points, since then the strip formed by the successive circles C_0, C_1, C_2, $\cdots$ may return and cover part of itself. But there is no essential difficulty.

the origin to the point $z = -2$ along the axis of reals, since we could not pass through the singular point $z = -1$. But if we cause the variable z to describe a path not going through this point, it is clear that we shall arrive at the point $z = -2$ after a finite number of steps, for all the successive circles will pass through the point $z = -1$. It should be noticed that the preceding definition of singular points depends upon the path followed by the variable; a point λ may be a singular point for a certain path, and may not for some other, if the function has several distinct branches.

When two paths L_1, L_1', going from the origin to Z, lead to different elements at Z, there exists at least one singular point in the interior of the region which would be swept out by one of the paths, L_1, for example, if we were to deform it in a continuous manner so as to bring it into coincidence with L_1', retaining always the same extremities during the change. Let us suppose, as is always permissible, that the two paths L_1, L_1' are broken lines composed of the same number of segments $0\,a_1 b_1 c_1 \cdots l_1 Z$ and $0\,a_1' b_1' c_1' \cdots l_1' Z$ (Fig. 34). Let $a_2, b_2, c_2, \cdots, l_2$ be the middle points of the segments $a_1 a_1'$, $b_1 b_1', c_1 c_1', \cdots, l_1 l_1'$; the path L_2 formed by the broken line $0\,a_2 b_2 c_2 \cdots l_2 Z$ cannot be equivalent at the same time to the two paths L_1, L_1' if it does not contain a singular point. If the path L_2 does contain a singular point, the theorem is established. If the two paths L_1 and L_2 are not equivalent, we can deduce from them a new path L_3 lying between L_1 and L_2

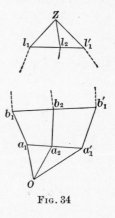

FIG. 34

by the same process. Continuing in this way, we shall either reach a path L_p containing a singular point or we shall have an infinite sequence of paths $L_1, L_2, L_3, \cdots$. These paths will approach a limiting path Λ, for the points $a_1, a_2, a_3, \cdots$ approach a limit point lying between a_1 and $a_1', \cdots$, and similarly for the others. This limiting path Λ must necessarily contain a singular point, since we can draw two paths as near as we please to Λ, one on each side of it, and leading to different elements for the function at Z. This could not be true if Λ did not contain any singular points, since the paths sufficiently close to Λ must lead to the same elements at Z as does Λ.

The preceding definition of singular points is purely negative and does not tell us anything about the nature of the function in the neighborhood. No hypothesis on these singular points or on their distribution in the plane can be discarded a priori without danger of leading to some contradiction. A study of the analytic extension is required to determine all the possible cases.*

86. General problem. From what precedes, it follows that an analytic function is *virtually* determined when we know one of its elements, that is, when we know a sequence of coefficients $a_0, a_1, a_2, \cdots, a_n, \cdots$ such that the series

$$a_0 + a_1(x - \alpha) + \cdots + a_n(x - \alpha)^n + \cdots$$

has a radius of convergence different from zero. These coefficients being known, we are led to consider the following general problem: *To find the value of the function at any point β of the plane when the variable is made to describe a definitely chosen path from the point α to the point β.* We can also consider the problem of determining a priori the singular points of the analytic function; it is also clear that the two problems are closely related to each other. The method of analytic extension itself furnishes a solution of these two problems, at least theoretically, but it is practicable only in very particular cases. For example, as nothing indicates a priori the number of intermediate series which must be employed to go from the point α to the point β, and since we can calculate the sum of each of these series with only a certain degree of approximation, it appears impossible to obtain any idea of the final approximation which we shall reach. So the investigation of simpler solutions was necessary, at least in particular cases. Only in recent years, however, has this problem been the object of thorough investigations, which have already led to some important results.†

---

* Let $f(x)$ be a function analytic along the whole length of the segment ab of the real axis. In the neighborhood of any point α of this segment the function can be represented by a power series whose radius of convergence $R(\alpha)$ is not zero. This radius R, being a continuous function of α, has a *positive* minimum r. Let ρ be a positive number less than r, and E the region of the plane swept out by a circle with the radius ρ when its center describes the segment ab. The function $f(x)$ is analytic in the region E and on its boundary; let M be an upper bound for its absolute value; from the general formulæ (14) (§ 33) it follows that at any point x of ab we have the inequality

$$|f^{(n)}(x)| < \frac{Mn!}{\rho^n}.$$

(Cf. I, § 197, 2d ed.; § 191, 1st ed.)

† For everything regarding this matter we refer the reader to Hadamard's excellent work, *La série de Taylor et son prolongement analytique* (Naud, 1901). It contains a very complete bibliography.

The fact that these researches are so recent must not be attributed entirely to the difficulty of the question, however great it may be. The functions which have actually been studied successively by mathematicians have not been chosen by them arbitrarily; rather, the study of these functions was forced upon them by the very nature of the problems which they encountered. Now, aside from a small number of transcendentals, all these functions, after the explicit elementary functions, are defined either as the roots of equations which do not admit a formal solution or as integrals of algebraic differential equations. It is clear, then, that the study of implicit functions and of functions defined by differential equations must logically have preceded the study of the general problem of which these two problems are essentially only very particular cases.

It is easy to show how the study of algebraic differential equations leads to the theory of analytic extension. Let us consider, for concreteness, two power series $y(x)$, $z(x)$, arranged according to positive powers of x and convergent in a circle C of radius R described about the point $x = 0$ as center. On the other hand, let $F(x, y, y', y''$, $\cdots, y^{(p)}, z, z', \cdots, z^{(q)})$ be a polynomial in $x, y, y', \cdots, y^{(p)}, z, z', \cdots, z^{(q)}$. Let us suppose that we replace y and z in this polynomial by the preceding series, $y', y'', \cdots, y^{(p)}$ by the successive derivatives of the series $y(x)$, and $z', z'', \cdots, z^{(q)}$ by the derivatives of the series $z(x)$; the result is again a power series convergent in the circle C. If all the coefficients of that series are zero, the analytic functions $y(x)$ and $z(x)$ satisfy, *in the circle C*, the relation

$$(9) \qquad F(x, y, y', \cdots, y^{(p)}, z, z', \cdots, z^{(q)}) = 0.$$

We are now going to prove that *the functions obtained by the analytic extension of the series $y(x)$ and $z(x)$ satisfy the same relation in the whole of their domain of existence.* More precisely, if we cause the variable x to describe a path L starting at the origin and proceeding from the circle C to reach any point α of the plane, and if it is possible to continue the analytic extension of the two series $y(x)$ and $z(x)$ along the whole length of this path without meeting any singular point, the power series $Y(x - \alpha)$ and $Z(x - \alpha)$ with which we arrive at the point α represent, in the neighborhood of that point, two analytic functions which satisfy the relation (9). For let x_1 be a point of the path L within the circle C and near the point where the path L leaves the circle C. With the point x_1 as center we can describe a circle C_1, partly exterior to the circle C, and there exist two power series $y(x - x_1)$, $z(x - x_1)$ that are convergent in the circle C_1 and whose values are identical with the values of the two series $y(x)$ and $z(x)$ in the part common to the two circles C, C_1. Substituting for y and z in F the two corresponding series, the result obtained is a power series $P(x - x_1)$ convergent in the circle C_1. Now in the part common to the two circles C, C_1 we have $P(x - x_1) = 0$; the series $P(x - x_1)$ has therefore all its coefficients zero, and the two new series $y(x - x_1)$ and $z(x - x_1)$ satisfy the relation (9) in the circle C_1. Continuing in this way, we see that the relation never ceases to be satisfied by the analytic extension of the two series $y(x)$ and $z(x)$, whatever the path followed by the variable may be; the proposition is thus demonstrated.

The study of a function defined by a differential equation is, then, essentially only a particular case of the general problem of analytic extension. But, on the other hand, it is easy to see how the knowledge of a particular relation between the analytic function and some of its derivatives may in certain cases facilitate the solution of the problem. We shall have to return to this point in the study of differential equations.

II. NATURAL BOUNDARIES. CUTS

The study of modular elliptic functions furnished Hermite the first example of an analytic function defined only in a portion of the plane. We shall point out a very simple method of obtaining analytic functions having any curve whatever of the plane for a natural boundary (see § 84), under certain hypotheses of a very general character concerning the curve.

87. Singular lines. Natural boundaries. We shall first demonstrate a preliminary proposition.*

Let a_1, a_2, $\cdots$, a_n, $\cdots$ and c_1, c_2, $\cdots$, c_n, $\cdots$ be two sequences of any kind of terms, the second of which is such that Σc_ν is absolutely convergent and has all its terms different from zero. Let C be a circle with the center z_0, containing none of the points a_i in its interior and passing through a *single one* of these points; then the series

$$(10) \qquad F(z) = \sum_{\nu=1}^{+\infty} \frac{c_\nu}{a_\nu - z}$$

---

*POINCARÉ, *Acta Societatis Fennicæ*, Vol. XIII, 1881; GOURSAT, *Bulletin des sciences mathématiques*, 2d series, Vol. XI, p. 109, and Vol. XVII, p. 247.

represents an analytic function in the circle C which can be developed in a series of powers of $z - z_0$. *The circle of convergence of this series is precisely the circle C.*

We can clearly suppose that $z_0 = 0$, for if we change z to $z_0 - z'$, a_ν is replaced by $a_\nu - z_0$, and c_ν does not change. We shall also suppose that we have $|a_1| = R$, where R denotes the radius of the circle C, and $|a_i| > R$ for $i > 1$. In the circle C the general term $c_\nu/(a_\nu - z)$ can be developed in a power series, and that series has $(|c_\nu|/R)/(1 - z/R)$ for a dominant function, as is easily verified. By a general theorem demonstrated above (§ 9), the series $\Sigma|c_\nu|$ being convergent, the function $F(z)$ can be developed in a power series in the circle C, and that series can be obtained by adding term by term the power series which represent the different terms. We have, then, in the circle C

$$(10')\qquad F(z) = A_0 + A_1 z + A_2 z^2 + \cdots + A_n z^n + \cdots, \qquad A_n = \sum_{\nu=1}^{+\infty} \frac{c_\nu}{a_\nu^{n+1}}.$$

Let us choose an integer p such that $\displaystyle\sum_{\nu=p+1}^{+\infty}|c_\nu|$ shall be smaller than $|c_1|/2$, which is always possible, since c_1 is not zero and since the series $\Sigma|c_\nu|$ is convergent. Having chosen the integer p in this way, we can write $F(z) = F_1(z) + F_2(z)$, where we have set

$$F_1(z) = \sum_{\nu=2}^{p} \frac{c_\nu}{a_\nu - z}, \qquad F_2(z) = \frac{c_1}{a_1 - z} + \sum_{\nu=p+1}^{+\infty} \frac{c_\nu}{a_\nu - z}.$$

$F_1(z)$ is a rational function which has only poles exterior to the circle C; it is therefore developable in a power series in a circle C' with a radius $R' > R$. As for $F_2(z)$, we have

$$(11)\qquad F_2(z) = B_0 + B_1 z + \cdots + B_n z^n + \cdots,$$

where

$$B_n = \frac{c_1}{a_1^{n+1}} + \frac{c_{p+1}}{(a_{p+1})^{n+1}} + \frac{c_{p+2}}{(a_{p+2})^{n+1}} + \cdots.$$

We can write this coefficient again in the form

$$B_n = \frac{1}{a_1^{n+1}}\left[c_1 + \sum_{\nu=p+1}^{+\infty} c_\nu \left(\frac{a_1}{a_\nu}\right)^{n+1} \right];$$

but we have, by hypothesis, $|a_1/a_\mu| < 1$, and the absolute value of the sum of the series

$$\sum_{\nu=p+1}^{+\infty} c_\nu \left(\frac{a_1}{a_\nu}\right)^{n+1}$$

is less than $|c_1|/2$, by the method of choosing the integer p. The absolute value of the coefficient B_n is therefore between $|c_1|/2\,R^{n+1}$ and $3|c_1|/2\,R^{n+1}$ in magnitude, and the absolute value of the general term of the series (11) lies between $(|c_1|/2\,R)|z/R|^n$ and $(3|c_1|/2\,R)|z/R|^n$; that series is therefore divergent if $|z| > R$. By adding to the series $F_2(z)$, convergent in the circle with the radius R, a series $F_1(z)$, convergent in a circle of radius $R' > R$, it is clear that the sum $F(z)$ has the circle C with the radius R for its circle of convergence; this proves the proposition which was stated.

Let now L be a curve, closed or not, having at each point a definite radius of curvature. The series Σc_ν being absolutely convergent, let us suppose that the points of the sequence $a_1, a_2, \cdots, a_i, \cdots$ are all on the curve L and are distributed on it in such a way that on a finite arc of this curve there are always an infinite number of points of that sequence. The series

$$(12) \qquad F(z) = \sum_{\nu=1}^{+\infty} \frac{c_\nu}{a_\nu - z}$$

is convergent for every point z_0 not belonging to the curve L, and represents an analytic function in the neighborhood of that point. To prove this it would suffice to repeat the first part of the preceding proof, taking for the circle C any circle with the center z_0 and not containing any of the points a_i. If the curve L is not closed, and does not have any double points, the series (12) represents an analytic function in the whole extent of the plane except for the points of the curve L. We cannot conclude from this that the curve L is a singular line; we have yet to assure ourselves that the analytic extension of $F(z)$ is not possible across any portion of L, however small it may be. To prove this it suffices to show that the circle of convergence of the power series which represents $F(z)$ in the neighborhood of any point z_0 not on L can never inclose an arc of that curve, however small it may be. Suppose that the circle C, with the center z_0, actually incloses an arc $\alpha\beta$ of the curve L. Let us take a point a_i on this arc $\alpha\beta$, and on the normal to this arc at a_i let us take a point z' so close to the point a_i that the circle C_i, described about the point z' as center with the radius $|z' - a_i|$, shall lie entirely in the interior of C and not have any point in common with the arc $\alpha\beta$ other than the point a_i itself. By the theorem which has just been demonstrated, the circle C_i is the circle of convergence for the power series which represents $F(z)$ in the neighborhood of the point z'. But this is in contradiction to the general properties of power series, for that circle of convergence cannot be smaller than the circle with the center z' which is tangent internally to the circle C.

If the curve L is closed, the series (12) represents two distinct analytic functions. One of these exists only in the interior of the curve L, and for it that curve is a natural boundary; the other function, on the contrary, exists only in the region exterior to the curve L and has the same curve as a natural boundary. Thus the curve L is a *natural* boundary for each of these functions.

Given several curves, $L_1, L_2, \cdots, L_p$, closed or not, it will be possible to form in this way series of the form (12) having these curves for natural boundaries; the sum of these series will have all these curves for natural boundaries.

88. Examples. Let AB be a segment of a straight line, and α, β the complex quantities representing the extremities A, B. All the points $\gamma = (m\alpha + n\beta)/(m+n)$, where m and n are two positive integers varying from 1 to $+\infty$, are on the segment AB, and on a finite portion of this segment there are always an infinite number of points of that kind, since the point γ divides the segment AB in the ratio m/n. On the other hand, let $C_{m,n}$ be the general term of an absolutely convergent double series. The double series

$$F(z) = \sum \frac{C_{m,n}}{\dfrac{m\alpha + n\beta}{m+n} - z}$$

represents an analytic function having the segment AB for a natural boundary. We can, in fact, transform this series into a simple series with a single index in an infinite number of ways. It is clear that by adding several series of this kind it will be possible to form an analytic function having the perimeter of any given polygon as a natural boundary.

Another example, in which the curve L is a circle, may be defined as follows: Let α be a positive irrational number, and let ν be a positive integer. Let us put

$$a = e^{2i\pi\alpha}, \qquad a_\nu = a^\nu = e^{2i\pi\nu\alpha}.$$

Then all the points a^ν are distinct and are situated on the circle C of unit radius having its center at the origin. Moreover, we know that we can find two integers m and n such that the difference $2\pi(n\alpha - m)$ will be less in absolute value than a number ϵ, however small ϵ be taken.

There exist, then, powers of a whose angle is as near zero as we wish, and consequently on a finite arc of the circumference there will always be an infinite number of points a^ν. Let us next put $c_\nu = a^\nu/2^\nu$; the series

$$F(z) = \sum_{\nu=1}^{+\infty} \frac{1}{2^\nu} \frac{1}{1 - \dfrac{z}{a^\nu}}$$

represents, by the general theorem, an analytic function in the circle C which has the whole circumference of this circle for a natural boundary.

Developing each term in powers of z, we obtain for the development of $F(z)$ the power series

$$(13) \qquad F(z) = 1 + \frac{z}{2\,a-1} + \frac{z^2}{2\,a^2-1} + \cdots + \frac{z^n}{2\,a^n-1} + \cdots.$$

It is easy to prove directly that the function represented by this power series cannot be extended analytically beyond the circle C; for if we add to it the series for $1/(1-z)$, there results

$$F(z) + \frac{1}{1-z} = 2 + z\Big(\frac{1}{2\,a-1}+1\Big) + \cdots + z^n\Big(\frac{1}{2\,a^n-1}+1\Big) + \cdots = 2\,F(az),$$

or

$$F(az) = \frac{1}{2}F(z) + \frac{1}{2}\frac{1}{1-z}.$$

Changing in this relation z to az, then to $a^2z, \cdots$, we find the general relation

$$(14) \qquad F(a^n z) = \frac{1}{2^n}F(z) + \frac{1}{2^n(1-z)} + \frac{1}{2^{n-1}(1-az)} + \cdots + \frac{1}{2(1-a^{n-1}z)},$$

which shows that the difference $2^n F(a^n z) - F(z)$ is a rational function $\phi(z)$ having the n poles of the first order $1, 1/a, \cdots, 1/a^{n-1}$.

The result (14) has been established on the supposition that we have $|z| < 1$ and $|a| = 1$. If the angle of a is commensurable with π, the equality (14) shows that $F(z)$ is a rational function; to show this it would suffice to take for n an integer such that $a^n = 1$. If the angle of a is incommensurable with π, it is impossible for the function $F(z)$ to be analytic on a finite arc AB of the circumference, however small it may be. For let a^{-p} and a^{n-p} be two points on the arc $AB(n > p)$. The numbers n and p having been chosen in this way, let us suppose that z is made to approach a^{-p}; $a^n z$ will approach a^{n-p}, and the two functions $F(z)$ and $F(a^n z)$ would approach finite limits if $F(z)$ were analytic on the arc AB. Now the relation (14) shows that this is impossible, since the function $\phi(z)$ has the pole a^{-p}.

An analogous method is applicable, as Hadamard has shown, to the series considered by Weierstrass,

$$(15) \qquad F(z) = \sum b^n z^{a^n},$$

where a is a positive integer > 1 and b is a constant whose absolute value is less than one. This series is convergent if $|z|$ is not greater than unity, and divergent if $|z|$ is greater than unity. The circle C with a *unit* radius is therefore the circle of convergence. The circumference is a natural boundary for the function $F(z)$. For suppose that there are no singular points of the function on a finite arc $\alpha\beta$ of the circumference. If we replace the variable z in $F(z)$ by $ze^{2k\pi i/c^h}$, where k and h are two positive integers and c a divisor of a, all the terms of the series (15) after the term of the rank h are unchanged, and the difference $F(z) - F(ze^{2k\pi i/c^h})$ is a polynomial. Neither would the function $F(z)$ have any singular points on the arc $\alpha_k\beta_k$, which is derived from the arc $\alpha\beta$ by a rotation through an angle $2\,k\pi/c^h$ around the origin. Let us take h large enough to make $2\,\pi/c^h$ smaller than the arc $\alpha\beta$; taking successively $k = 1, 2, \cdots, c^h$, it is clear that the arcs $\alpha_1\beta_1, \alpha_2\beta_2, \cdots$ cover the circumference completely. The function $F(z)$ would therefore not have any singular points on the circumference, which is absurd (§ 84).

This example presents an interesting peculiarity; the series (15) is absolutely and uniformly convergent along the circumference of C. It represents, then, a continuous function of the angle θ along this circle.*

89. Singularities of analytical expressions. Every analytical expression (such as a series whose different terms are functions of a variable z, or a definite integral in which that variable appears as a parameter) represents, under certain conditions, an analytic function in the neighborhood of each of the values of z for which it has a meaning. If the set of these values of z covers completely a connected region A of the plane, the expression considered represents an analytic function of z in that region A; but if the set of these values of z forms two or more distinct and *separated* regions, it may happen that the analytical expression considered represents entirely distinct functions in these different regions. We have already met an example of this in § 38. There we saw how we could form a series of rational terms, convergent in two curvilinear triangles PQR, $P'Q'R'$ (Fig. 16), whose value is equal to a given analytic function $f(z)$ in the triangle PQR and to zero in the triangle $P'Q'R'$. By adding two such series we shall obtain a series of rational terms whose value is equal to $f(z)$ in the triangle PQR and to another analytic function $\phi(z)$ in the triangle $P'Q'R'$. These two functions $f(z)$ and $\phi(z)$ being

---

* Fredholm has shown, similarly, that the function represented by the series

$$\sum_{0}^{\infty} a^n z^{n^2},$$

where a is a positive quantity less than one, cannot be extended beyond the circle of convergence (*Comptes rendus*, March 24, 1890). This example leads to a result which is worthy of mention. On the circle of unit radius the series is convergent and the value

$$F(\theta) = \Sigma\, a^n [\cos{(n^2\theta)} + i \sin{(n^2\theta)}]$$

is a continuous function of the angle θ which has an infinite number of derivatives. This function $F(\theta)$ cannot, however, be developed in a Taylor's series in any interval, however small it may be. Suppose that in the interval $(\theta_0 - \alpha,\ \theta_0 + \alpha)$ we actually have

$$F(\theta) = A_0 + A_1(\theta - \theta_0) + \cdots + A_n(\theta - \theta_0)^n + \cdots.$$

The series on the right represents an analytic function of the complex variable θ in the circle c with the radius α described with the point θ_0 for center. To this circle c corresponds, by means of the relation $z = e^{\theta i}$, a closed region A of the plane of the variable z containing the arc γ of the unit circle extending from the point with the angle $\theta_0 - \alpha$ to the point with the angle $\theta_0 + \alpha$. There would exist, then, in this region A an analytic function of z coinciding with the value of the series $\Sigma a^n z^{n^2}$ along γ and also in the part of A within the unit circle; this is impossible, since we cannot extend the sum of the series beyond the circle.

arbitrary, it is clear that the value of the series in the triangle $P'Q'R'$ will in general bear no relation to the analytic extension of the value of that series in the triangle PQR.

The following is another very simple example, analogous to an example pointed out by Schröder and by Tannery. The expression $(1 - z^n)/(1 + z^n)$, where n is a positive integer which increases indefinitely, approaches the limit $+1$ if $|z| < 1$, and the limit -1 if $|z| > 1$. If $|z| = 1$, this expression has no limit except for $z = 1$. Now the sum of the first n terms of the series

$$S(z) = \frac{1-z}{1+z} + \left(\frac{1-z^2}{1+z^2} - \frac{1-z}{1+z}\right) + \cdots + \left(\frac{1-z^n}{1+z^n} - \frac{1-z^{n-1}}{1+z^{n-1}}\right) + \cdots$$

is equal to the preceding expression. This series is therefore convergent if $|z|$ is different from unity. Hence it represents $+1$ in the interior of the circle C with the radius *unity* about the origin as center, and -1 at all points outside of this circle. Now let $f(z)$, $\phi(z)$ be any two analytic functions whatever; for example, two integral functions. Then the expression

$$\psi(z) = \frac{1}{2}[f(z) + \phi(z)] + \frac{1}{2} S(z)[f(z) - \phi(z)]$$

is equal to $f(z)$ in the interior of C, and to $\phi(z)$ in the region exterior to C. The circumference itself is a *cut* for that expression, but of a quite different nature from the natural boundaries which we have just mentioned. The function which is equal to $\psi(z)$ in the interior of C can be extended analytically beyond C; and, similarly, the function which is equal to $\psi(z)$ outside of C can be extended analytically into the interior.

Analogous singularities present themselves in the case of functions represented by definite integrals. The simplest example is furnished by Cauchy's integral; if $f(z)$ is a function analytic within a closed curve Γ and also on that curve itself, the integral

$$\left(\frac{1}{2\pi i}\right) \int_\Gamma \frac{f(z)\, dz}{z - x}$$

represents $f(x)$ if the point x is in the interior of Γ. The same integral is zero if the point x is outside of the curve Γ, for the function $f(z)/(z - x)$ is then analytic inside of the curve. Here again the curve Γ is not a natural boundary for the definite integral. Similarly, the definite integral $\int_0^{2\pi} \operatorname{ctn}[(z - x)/2]\, dz$ has the real axis as a cut; it is equal to $+2\pi i$ or $-2\pi i$, according as x is above or below that cut (§ 45).

90. Hermite's formula. An interesting result due to Hermite can be brought into relation with the preceding discussion.* Let $F(t, z)$, $G(t, z)$ be two analytic functions of each of the variables t and z ; for example, two polynomials or two power series convergent for all the values of these two variables. Then the definite integral

$$(16) \qquad \Phi(z) = \int_{\alpha}^{\beta} \frac{F(t, z)}{G(t, z)} \, dt,$$

taken over the segment of a straight line which joins the two points α and β, represents, as we shall see later (§ 95), an analytic function of z except for the values of z which are roots of the equation $G(t, z) = 0$, where t is the complex quantity corresponding to a point on the segment $\alpha\beta$. This equation therefore determines a finite or an infinite number of curves for which the integral $\Phi(z)$ ceases to have a meaning. Let AB be one of these curves not having any double points. In order to consider a very precise case, we shall suppose that when t describes the segment $\alpha\beta$, one of the roots of the equation $G(t, z) = 0$ describes the arc AB, and that all the other roots of the same equation, if there are any, remain outside of a suitably chosen closed curve surrounding the arc AB, so that the segment $\alpha\beta$ and the arc AB correspond to each other point to point. The integral (16) has no meaning when z falls upon the arc AB; we wish to calculate the difference between the values of the function $\Phi(z)$ at two points N, N', lying on opposite sides of the arc AB, whose distances from a fixed point M of the arc AB are infinitesimal. Let ζ, $\zeta + \epsilon$, $\zeta + \epsilon'$ be the three values of z corresponding to the three points M, N, N' respectively. To these three points correspond in the plane of the variable t, by means of the equation $G(t, z) = 0$, the point m on $\alpha\beta$, and the two points n, n' on opposite sides of $\alpha\beta$ at infinitesimal distances from m. Let θ, $\theta + \eta$, $\theta + \eta'$ be the cor-

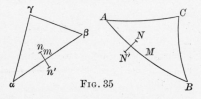

FIG. 35

responding values of t. In the neighborhood of the segment $\alpha\beta$ let us take a point γ so near $\alpha\beta$ that the equation $G(t, \zeta + \epsilon) = 0$ has no other root than $t = \theta + \eta$ in the interior of the triangle $\alpha\beta\gamma$ (Fig. 35). The function $F(t, \zeta + \epsilon)/G(t, \zeta + \epsilon)$ of the variable t has but a single pole $\theta + \eta$ in the interior of the triangle $\alpha\beta\gamma$, and, according to the hypotheses made above, this pole is a simple pole. Applying Cauchy's theorem, we have, then, the relation

$$(17) \qquad \left\{ \begin{aligned} &\int_{\alpha}^{\beta} \frac{F(t, \zeta + \epsilon)}{G(t, \zeta + \epsilon)} \, dt + \int_{\beta}^{\gamma} \frac{F(t, \zeta + \epsilon)}{G(t, \zeta + \epsilon)} \, dt \\ &\qquad + \int_{\gamma}^{\alpha} \frac{F(t, \zeta + \epsilon)}{G(t, \zeta + \epsilon)} \, dt = 2 \, i\pi \, \frac{F(\theta + \eta, \zeta + \epsilon)}{G'_t(\theta + \eta, \zeta + \epsilon)}. \end{aligned} \right.$$

The two integrals $\int_{\beta}^{\gamma}$, $\int_{\gamma}^{\alpha}$ are of the same form as $\Phi(z)$; they represent respectively two functions, $\Phi_1(z)$, $\Phi_2(z)$, which are analytic so long as the variable is not situated upon certain curves. Let AC and BC be the curves which correspond to the two segments $\alpha\gamma$ and $\beta\gamma$ of the t plane, and which are at infinitesimal distances from the cut AB associated with $\Phi(z)$. Let us now give

* HERMITE, *Sur quelques points de la théorie des fonctions* (*Crelle's Journal*, Vol. XCI).

the value $\zeta + \epsilon'$ to z; the corresponding value of t is $\theta + \eta'$, represented by the point n', and the function $F(t, \zeta + \epsilon')/G(t, \zeta + \epsilon')$ of t is analytic in the interior of the triangle $\alpha\beta\gamma$. We have, then, the relation

(18) $$\int_\alpha^\beta \frac{F(t, \zeta + \epsilon')}{G(t, \zeta + \epsilon')}\, dt + \int_\beta^\gamma \frac{F(t, \zeta + \epsilon')}{G(t, \zeta + \epsilon')}\, dt + \int_\gamma^\alpha \frac{F(t, \zeta + \epsilon')}{G(t, \zeta + \epsilon')}\, dt = 0;$$

subtracting the two formulæ (17) and (18) term by term, we can write the result as follows:

$$\Phi(\zeta + \epsilon) - \Phi(\zeta + \epsilon') + [\Phi_1(\zeta + \epsilon) - \Phi_1(\zeta + \epsilon')]$$
$$+ [\Phi_2(\zeta + \epsilon) - \Phi_2(\zeta + \epsilon')] = 2\, i\pi\, \frac{F(\theta + \eta, \zeta + \epsilon)}{G'_t(\theta + \eta, \zeta + \epsilon)}.$$

But since neither of the functions $\Phi_1(z)$, $\Phi_2(z)$ has the line AB as a cut, they are analytic in the neighborhood of the point $z = \zeta$, and by making ϵ and ϵ' approach zero we obtain at the limit the difference of the values of $\Phi(z)$ in two points infinitely near each other on opposite sides of AB. We shall write the result in the abridged form

(19) $$\Phi(N) - \Phi(N') = 2\,\pi i\, \frac{F(\theta, \zeta)}{\dfrac{\partial G(\theta, \zeta)}{\partial \theta}};$$

this is Hermite's formula. It is seen that it is very simply related to Cauchy's theorem.* The demonstration indicates clearly how we must take the points N and N'; the point $N(\zeta + \epsilon)$ must be such that an observer describing the segment $\alpha\beta$ has the corresponding point $\theta + \eta$ on his left.

It is to be noticed that the arc AB is not a natural boundary for the function $\Phi(z)$. In the neighborhood of the point N' we can replace $\Phi(z)$ by $- [\Phi_1(z) + \Phi_2(z)]$ according to the relation (18). Now the sum $\Phi_1(z) + \Phi_2(z)$ is an analytic function in the curvilinear triangle ACB and on the arc AB itself, as well as in the neighborhood of N'. Therefore we can make the variable z cross the arc AB at any one of its points except the extremities A and B without meeting any obstacle to the analytic extension. The same thing would be true if we were to make the variable z cross the arc AB in the opposite sense.

Example. Let us consider the integral

(20) $$\Phi(z) = \int_\alpha^\beta \frac{f(t)\, dt}{t - z},$$

where the integral is to be taken over a segment AB of the real axis, and where $f(t)$ denotes an analytic function along that segment AB. Let us represent z on the same plane as t. The function $\Phi(z)$ is an analytic function of z in the neighborhood of every point not located on the segment AB itself, which is a cut for the integral. The difference $\Phi(N) - \Phi(N')$ is here equal to $\pm\, 2\,\pi i f(\zeta)$, where ζ is a point of the segment AB. When the variable z crosses the line AB, the analytic extension of $\Phi(z)$ is represented by $\Phi(z) \pm \pi i f(z)$.

This example gives rise to an important observation. The function $\Phi(z)$ is still an analytic function of z, even when $f(t)$ is not an analytic function of t, provided that $f(t)$ is continuous between α and β (§ 33). But in this case the preceding reasoning no longer applies, and the segment AB is in general a natural boundary for the function $\Phi(z)$.

---

* GOURSAT, *Sur un théorème de M. Hermite* (*Acta mathematica*, Vol. I).

EXERCISES

1. Find the lines of discontinuity for the definite integrals

$$F(z) = \int_0^1 \frac{zdt}{1+z^2t^2}, \qquad \Phi(z) = \int_a^b \frac{dt}{t+iz},$$

taken along the straight line which joins the points $(0, 1)$ and (a, b) respectively; determine the value of these integrals for a point z not located on these boundaries.

2. Consider four circles with radii $1/\sqrt{2}$, having for centers the points $+1$, $+i$, -1, $-i$. The region *exterior* to these four circles is composed of a finite region A_1 containing the origin, and of an infinite region A_2. Construct, by the method of § 38, a series of rational functions which converge in these regions, and whose value in A_1 is equal to 1 and in A_2 to 0. Verify the result by finding the sum of the series obtained.

3. Treat the same questions, considering the two regions *interior* to the circle of radius 2 with the center for origin, and *exterior* to the two circles of radius 1 with centers at the points $+1$ and -1 respectively.

[APPELL, *Acta mathematica*, Vol. I.]

4. The definite integral

$$\Phi(z) = \int_0^{+\infty} \frac{t^a \sin z}{1 + 2t\cos z + t^2}\, dt,$$

taken along the real axis, has for cuts the straight lines $x = (2k+1)\pi$, where k is an integer. Let $\zeta = (2k+1)\pi + i\xi$ be a point on one of these cuts. The difference in the values of the integral in two points infinitely close to that point on each side of the cut is equal to $\pi(e^{a\xi} + e^{-a\xi})$.

[HERMITE, *Crelle's Journal*, Vol. XCI.]

5. The two definite integrals

$$J = \int_{-\infty}^{+\infty} \frac{e^{i(t-z)}}{t-z}\, dt, \qquad J_0 = \int_{-\infty}^{+\infty} \frac{e^{-i(t-z)}}{t-z}\, dt,$$

taken along the real axis, have the axis of reals for a cut in the plane of the variable z. Above the axis we have $J = 2\pi i$, $J_0 = 0$, and below we have $J = 0$, $J_0 = -2\pi i$. From these results deduce the values of the definite integrals

$$\int_{-\infty}^{+\infty} \frac{e^{it}}{t-z}\, dt, \qquad \int_{-\infty}^{+\infty} \frac{\cos(t-z)}{t-z}\, dt,$$

$$\int_{-\infty}^{+\infty} \frac{e^{-it}}{t-z}\, dt, \qquad \int_{-\infty}^{+\infty} \frac{\sin(t-z)}{t-z}\, dt.$$

[HERMITE, *Crelle's Journal*, Vol. XCI.]

6. Establish by means of cuts the formula (Chap. II, Ex. 15)

$$\int_{-\infty}^{+\infty} \frac{e^{at}}{1+e^t}\, dt = \frac{\pi}{\sin a\pi}.$$

[HERMITE, *Crelle's Journal*, Vol. XCI.]

(Consider the integral

$$\Phi(z) = \int_{-\infty}^{+\infty} \frac{e^{a(t+z)}}{1+e^{(t+z)}}\, dt,$$

which has all the straight lines $y = (2k + 1)\pi$ for cuts, and which remains constant in the strip included between two consecutive cuts. Then establish the relations

$$\Phi(z + 2\pi i) = \Phi(z) + 2\pi i e^{\pi a i}, \qquad \Phi(z + 2\pi i) = e^{2\pi a i}\Phi(z),$$

where z and $z + 2\pi i$ are two points separated by the cut $y = \pi$.)

7*. Let $f(z)$ be an analytic function in the neighborhood of the origin, so that $f(z) = \Sigma a_n z^n$. Denote by $F(z) = \Sigma a_n z^n / n!$ the *associated* integral function. It is easily proved that we have

$$(1) \qquad F(az) = \frac{1}{2\pi i} \int_{(C)} \frac{f(u)}{\mu} e^{\frac{az}{u}} du,$$

where the integral is taken along a closed curve C, including the origin within it, inside of which $f(z)$ is analytic. From this it follows that

$$(2) \qquad \int_0^l e^{-a} F(az)\, da = \frac{1}{2\pi i} \int_C \frac{f(u)}{u}\, du \int_0^l e^{a\left(\frac{z}{u} - 1\right)} da,$$

where l denotes a real and positive number.

If the real part of z/u remains less than $1 - \epsilon$ (where $\epsilon > 0$) when u describes the curve C, the integral

$$\int_0^l e^{a\left(\frac{u}{z} - 1\right)} da$$

approaches $u/(u - z)$ uniformly as l becomes infinite, and the formula (2) becomes at the limit

$$(3) \qquad \int_0^{+\infty} e^{-a} F(az)\, da = \frac{1}{2\pi i} \int_{(C)} \frac{f(u)\, du}{u - z} = f(z).$$

This result is applicable to all the points within the negative pedal curve of C.

[BOREL, *Leçons sur les séries divergentes*.]

8*. Let $f(z) = \Sigma a_n z^n$, $\phi(z) = \Sigma b_n z^n$ be two power series whose radii of convergence are r and ρ respectively. The series

$$\psi(z) = \Sigma a_n b_n z^n$$

has a radius of convergence at least equal to $r\rho$, and the function $\psi(z)$ has no other singular points than those which are obtained by multiplying the quantities corresponding to the different singular points of $f(z)$ by those corresponding to the singular points of $\phi(z)$.

[HADAMARD, *Acta mathematica*, Vol. XXIII, p. 55.]

CHAPTER V

ANALYTIC FUNCTIONS OF SEVERAL VARIABLES

I. GENERAL PROPERTIES

In this chapter we shall discuss analytic functions of several independent complex variables. For simplicity, we shall suppose that there are *two* variables only, but it is easy to extend the results to functions of any number of variables whatever.

91. Definitions. Let $z = u + vi$, $z' = w + ti$ be two independent complex variables; every other complex quantity Z whose value depends upon the values of z and z' can be said to be a *function* of the two variables z and z'. Let us represent the values of these two variables z and z' by the two points with the coördinates (u, v) and (w, t) in two systems of rectangular axes situated in two planes P, P', and let A, A' be any two portions of these two planes. We shall say that a function $Z = f(z, z')$ is *analytic* in the two regions A, A' if to every system of two points z, z', taken respectively in the regions A, A', corresponds a definite value of $f(z, z')$, varying continuously with z and z', and if each of the quotients

$$\frac{f(z + h, z') - f(z, z')}{h}, \qquad \frac{f(z, z' + k) - f(z, z')}{k}$$

approaches a definite limit when, z and z' remaining fixed, the absolute values of h and k approach zero. These limits are the partial derivatives of the function $f(z, z')$, and they are represented by the same notation as in the case of real variables.

Let us separate in $f(z, z')$ the real part and the coefficient of i, $f(z, z') = X + Yi$; X and Y are real functions of the four independent real variables u, v, w, t, satisfying the four relations

$$\frac{\partial X}{\partial u} = \frac{\partial Y}{\partial v}, \qquad \frac{\partial X}{\partial v} = -\frac{\partial Y}{\partial u}, \qquad \frac{\partial X}{\partial w} = \frac{\partial Y}{\partial t}, \qquad \frac{\partial X}{\partial t} = -\frac{\partial Y}{\partial w},$$

the significance of which is evident.* We can eliminate Y in six

---

* If z and z' are analytic functions of another variable x, these relations enable us to demonstrate easily that the derivative of $f(z, z')$ with respect to x is obtained by the usual rule which gives the derivative of a function of other functions. The formulæ of the differential calculus, in particular those for the change of variables, apply, therefore, to analytic functions of complex variables.

different ways by passing to derivatives of the second order, but the six relations thus obtained reduce to only four:

$$(1) \quad \begin{cases} \dfrac{\partial^2 X}{\partial u\, \partial t} - \dfrac{\partial^2 X}{\partial v\, \partial w} = 0, & \dfrac{\partial^2 X}{\partial u\, \partial w} + \dfrac{\partial^2 X}{\partial v\, \partial t} = 0, \\[2ex] \dfrac{\partial^2 X}{\partial u^2} + \dfrac{\partial^2 X}{\partial v^2} = 0, & \dfrac{\partial^2 X}{\partial w^2} + \dfrac{\partial^2 X}{\partial t^2} = 0. \end{cases}$$

Up to the present time little use has been made of these relations for the study of analytic functions of two variables. One reason for this is that they are too numerous to be convenient.

92. Associated circles of convergence. The properties of power series in two real variables (I, §§ 190–192, 2d ed.; §§ 185–186, 1st ed.) are easily extended to the case where the coefficients and the variables have complex values. Let

$$(2) \quad F(z, z') = \Sigma a_{mn} z^m z'^n$$

be a double series with coefficients of any kind, and let

$$A_{mn} = |a_{mn}|.$$

We have seen (I, § 190, 2d ed.) that there exist, in general, an infinite number of systems of two *positive* numbers R, R' such that the series of absolute values

$$(3) \quad \Sigma A_{mn} Z^m Z'^n$$

is convergent if we have at the same time $Z < R$ and $Z' < R'$, and divergent if we have $Z > R$ and $Z' > R'$. Let C be the circle described in the plane of the variable z about the origin as center with the radius R; similarly, let C' be the circle described in the plane of the variable z' about the point $z' = 0$ as center with the radius R' (Fig. 36). The double series (2) is absolutely convergent when the variables z and z' are respectively in the interior of the two circles C and C', and divergent when these variables are respectively exterior to these two circles (I, § 191, 2d ed.; § 185, 1st ed.). The circles C, C' are said to form a system of *associated* circles of convergence. This set of two circles plays the same part as the circle of convergence for a power series in one variable, but in place of a single circle there is an infinite number of systems of associated circles for a power series in two variables. For example, the series

$$\sum \frac{(m+n)!}{m!\, n!} z^m z'^n$$

is absolutely convergent if $|z| + |z'| < 1$, and in that case only. Every pair of circles C, C' whose radii R, R' satisfy the relation $R + R' = 1$ is a system of associated circles. It may happen that we can limit ourselves to the consideration of a single system of associated circles; thus, the series $\Sigma z^m z'^n$ is convergent only if we have at the same time $|z| < 1$ and $|z'| < 1$.

Let C_1 be a circle of radius $R_1 < R$ concentric with C; similarly, let C_1' be a circle of radius $R_1' < R'$ concentric with C'; when the variables z and z' remain within the circles C_1 and C_1' respectively,

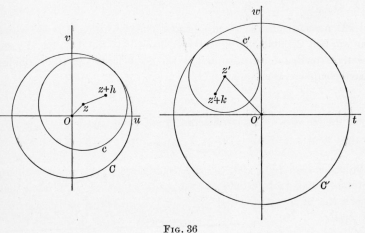

Fig. 36

the series (2) is uniformly convergent (see I, § 191, 2d ed.; § 185, 1st ed.) and the sum of the series is therefore a continuous function $F(z, z')$ of the two variables z, z' in the interior of the two circles C and C'.

Differentiating the series (2) term by term with respect to the variable z, for example, the new series obtained, $\Sigma m a_{mn} z^{m-1} z'^n$, is again absolutely convergent when z and z' remain in the two circles C and C' respectively, and its sum is the derivative $\partial F/\partial z$ of $F(z, z')$ with respect to z. The proof is similar in all respects to the one which has been given for real variables (I, § 191, 2d ed.; § 185, 1st ed.). Similarly, $F(z, z')$ has a partial derivative $\partial F/\partial z'$ with respect to z', which is represented by the double series obtained by differentiating the series (2) term by term with respect to z'. The function $F(z, z')$ is therefore an analytic function of the two variables z, z' in the preceding region. The same thing is evidently true of the two derivatives $\partial F/\partial z$, $\partial F/\partial z'$, and therefore $F(z, z')$ can be differentiated term by term any number of times; all its partial derivatives are also analytic functions.

Let us take any point z of absolute value r in the interior of C, and from this point as center let us describe a circle c with radius $R - r$ tangent internally to the circle C. In the same way let z' be any point of absolute value $r' < R'$, and c' the circle with the point z' as center and $R' - r'$ as radius. Finally, let $z + h$ and $z' + k$ be any two points taken in the circles c and c' respectively, so that we have

$$|z| + |h| < R, \qquad |z'| + |k| < R'.$$

If we replace z and z' in the series (2) by $z + h$ and $z' + k$, we can develop each term in a series proceeding according to powers of h and k, and the multiple series thus obtained is absolutely convergent. Arranging the series according to powers of h and k, we obtain the Taylor expansion

$$(4) \qquad F(z + h,\ z' + k) = \sum \frac{\dfrac{\partial^{m+n} F}{\partial z^m \partial z'^n}}{m!\ n!} h^m k^n.$$

93. Double integrals. When we undertake to extend to functions of several complex variables the general theorems which Cauchy deduced from the consideration of definite integrals taken between imaginary limits, we encounter difficulties which have been completely elucidated by Poincaré.* We shall study here only a very

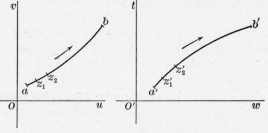

Fig. 37

simple particular case, which will, however, suffice for our subsequent developments. Let $f(z, z')$ be an analytic function when the variables z, z' remain within the two regions A, A' respectively. Let us consider a curve ab lying in A (Fig. 37) and a curve $a'b'$ in A', and let us divide each of these curves into smaller arcs by any number of points of division. Let $z_0, z_1, z_2, \cdots, z_{k-1}, z_k, \cdots, Z$

---

* POINCARÉ, *Sur les résidus des intégrales doubles (Acta mathematica*, Vol. **IX**).

be the points of division of ab, where z_0 and Z coincide with a and b, and let z_0', z_1', z_2', $\cdots$, z_{h-1}', z_h', $\cdots$, z_{m-1}', Z' be the points of division of $a'b'$, where z_0' and Z' coincide with a' and b'. The sum

$$(5) \qquad S = \sum_{k=1}^{n} \sum_{h=1}^{m} f(z_{k-1}, z_{h-1}')(z_k - z_{k-1})(z_h' - z_{h-1}'),$$

taken with respect to the two indices, approaches a limit, when the two numbers m and n become infinite, in such a way that the absolute values $|z_k - z_{k-1}|$ and $|z_h' - z_{h-1}'|$ approach zero. Let $f(z, z') = X + Yi$, where X and Y are real functions of the four variables u, v, w, t; and let us put $z_k = u_k + v_k i$, $z_h' = w_h + t_h i$. The general term of the sum S can be written in the form

$$[X(u_{k-1}, v_{k-1};\ w_{h-1}, t_{h-1}) + iY(u_{k-1}, v_{k-1};\ w_{h-1}, t_{h-1})]$$
$$\times [u_k - u_{k-1} + i(v_k - v_{k-1})][w_h - w_{h-1} + i(t_h - t_{h-1})],$$

and if we carry out the indicated multiplication, we have eight partial products. Let us show, for example, that the sum of the partial products,

$$(6) \qquad \sum_{k=1}^{n} \sum_{h=1}^{m} X(u_{k-1}, v_{k-1};\ w_{h-1}, t_{h-1})(u_k - u_{k-1})(w_h - w_{h-1}),$$

approaches a limit. We shall suppose, as is the case in the figure, that the curve ab is met in only one point by a parallel to the axis Ov, and, similarly, that a parallel to the axis Ot meets the curve $a'b'$ in at most one point. Let $v = \phi(u)$, $t = \psi(w)$ be the equations of these two curves, u_0 and U the limits between which u varies, and w_0 and W the limits between which w varies. If we replace the variables v and t in X by $\phi(u)$ and $\psi(w)$ respectively, it becomes a continuous function $P(u, w)$ of the variables u and w, and the sum (6) can again be written in the form

$$(6') \qquad \sum_{k=1}^{n} \sum_{h=1}^{m} P(u_{k-1}, w_{h-1})(u_k - u_{k-1})(w_h - w_{h-1}).$$

As m and n become infinite, this sum has for its limit the double integral $\iint P(u, w)\,du\,dw$ extended over the rectangle bounded by the straight lines $u = u_0$, $u = U$, $w = w_0$, $w = W$.

This double integral can also be expressed in the form

$$\int_{u_0}^{U} du \int_{w_0}^{W} P(u, w)\,dw,$$

or again, by introducing line integrals, in the form

$$(7) \qquad \int_{(ab)} du \int_{(a'b')} X(u,\, v;\, w,\, t)\, dw.$$

In this last expression we suppose that u and v are the coördinates of any point of the arc ab, and w, t the coördinates of any point of the arc $a'b'$. The point (u, v) being supposed fixed, the point (w, t) is made to describe the arc $a'b'$, and the line integral $\int X\, dw$ is taken along $a'b'$. The result is a function of u, v, say $R(u, v)$; we then calculate the line integral $\int R(u, v)\, du$ along the arc ab.

The last expression (7) obtained for the limit of the sum (6) is applicable whatever may be the paths ab and $a'b'$. It suffices to break up the arcs ab and $a'b'$ (as we have done repeatedly before) into arcs small enough to satisfy the previous requirements, to associate in all possible ways a portion of ab with a portion of $a'b'$, and then to add the results. Proceeding in this way with all the sums of partial products similar to the sum (6), we see that S has for its limit the sum of eight double integrals analogous to the integral (7). Representing that limit by $\iint F(z, z')\, dz\, dz'$, we have the equality

$$(8)\ \left\{ \begin{aligned} \iint F(z,\, z')\, dz\, dz' =\ & \int_{(ab)} du \int_{(a'b')} X\, dw - \int_{(ab)} dv \int_{(a'b')} X\, dt \\ & - \int_{(ab)} du \int_{(a'b')} Y\, dt - \int_{(ab)} dv \int_{(a'b')} Y\, dw \\ & + i \int_{(ab)} du \int_{(a'b')} Y\, dw - i \int_{(ab)} dv \int_{(a'b')} Y\, dt \\ & + i \int_{(ab)} du \int_{(a'b')} X\, dt + i \int_{(ab)} dv \int_{(a'b')} X\, dw, \end{aligned} \right.$$

which can be written in an abridged form,

$$\iint F(z,\, z')\, dz\, dz' = \int_{(ab)} (du + i\, dv) \int_{(a'b')} (X + iY)(dw + i\, dt),$$

or, again,

$$(9) \qquad \iint F(z,\, z')\, dz\, dz' = \int_{(ab)} dz \int_{(a'b')} F(z,\, z')\, dz'.$$

The formula (9) is precisely similar to the formula for calculating an ordinary double integral taken over the area of a rectangle by means of two successive quadratures (I, § 120, 2d ed.; § 123, 1st ed.). We calculate first the integral $\int F(z, z')\, dz'$ along the arc $a'b'$, supposing

z constant; the result is a function $\Phi(z)$ of z, which we integrate next along the arc ab. As the two paths ab and $a'b'$ enter in exactly the same way, it is clear that we can interchange the order of integrations.

Let M be a positive number greater than the absolute value of $F(z, z')$ when z and z' describe the arcs ab and $a'b'$. If L and L' denote the lengths of the respective arcs, the absolute value of the double integral is less than MLL' (§ 25). When one of the paths, $a'b'$ for example, forms a closed curve, the integral $\int_{(a'b')} F(z, z')\,dz'$ will be zero if the function $F(z, z')$ is analytic for all the values of z' in the interior of that curve and for the values of z on ab. The same thing will then be true of the double integral.

94. Extension of Cauchy's theorems. Let C, C' be two closed curves without double points, lying respectively in the planes of the variables z and z', and let $F(z, z')$ be a function that is analytic when z and z' remain in the regions limited by these two curves or on the curves themselves. Let us consider the double integral

$$I = \int_{(C)} dz \int_{(C')} \frac{F(z, z')\,dz'}{(z - x)(z' - x')},$$

where x is a point inside of the boundary C and where x' is a point inside of the boundary C'; and let us suppose that these two boundaries are described in the positive sense. The integral

$$\int_{(C')} \frac{F(z, z')\,dz'}{(z - x)(z' - x')},$$

where z denotes a fixed point of the boundary C, is equal to $2\pi i\, F(z, x')/(z - x)$. We have, then,

$$I = 2\pi i \int_{(C)} \frac{F(z, x')}{z - x}\,dz,$$

or, applying Cauchy's theorem once more,

$$I = -4\pi^2 F(x, x').$$

This leads us to the formula

$$(10) \qquad F(x, x') = -\frac{1}{4\pi^2} \int_{(C)} dz \int_{(C')} \frac{F(z, z')\,dz'}{(z - x)(z' - x')},$$

which is completely analogous to Cauchy's fundamental formula, and from which we can derive similar conclusions. From it we deduce the existence of the partial derivatives of all orders of the function $F(z, z')$ in the regions considered, the derivative $\partial^{m+n} F/\partial x^m \partial x'^n$ having a value given by the expression

$$(11) \quad \frac{\partial^{m+n} F}{\partial x^m \partial x'^n} = -\frac{m!\, n!}{4\,\pi^2} \int_{(C)} dz \int_{(C')} \frac{F(z, z')\, dz'}{(z-x)^{m+1}(z'-x')^{n+1}}.$$

In order to obtain Taylor's formula, let us suppose that the boundaries C and C' are the circumferences of circles. Let a be the center of C, and R its radius; b the center of C', and R' its radius. The points x and x' being taken respectively in the interior of these circles, we have $|x-a| = r < R$ and $|x'-b| = r' < R'$. Hence the rational fraction

$$\frac{1}{(z-x)(z'-x')} = \frac{1}{[z-a-(x-a)][z'-b-(x'-b)]}$$

can be developed in powers of $x - a$ and $x' - b$,

$$\frac{1}{(z-x)(z'-x')} = \sum_{m=0}^{+\infty} \sum_{n=0}^{+\infty} \frac{(x-a)^m (x'-b)^n}{(z-a)^{m+1}(z'-b)^{n+1}},$$

where the series on the right is uniformly convergent when z and z' describe the circles C and C' respectively, since the absolute value of the general term is $(r/R)^m (r'/R')^n/RR'$. We can therefore replace $1/(z-x)(z'-x')$ by the preceding series in the relation (10) and integrate term by term, which gives

$$F(x, x') =$$
$$-\frac{1}{4\,\pi^2} \sum_{m=0}^{+\infty} \sum_{n=0}^{+\infty} (x-a)^m (x'-b)^n \int_{(C)} dz \int_{(C')} \frac{F(z, z')\, dz'}{(z-a)^{m+1}(z'-b)^{n+1}}.$$

Making use of the results obtained by replacing x and x' by a and b in the relations (10) and (11), we obtain Taylor's expansion in the form

$$(12) \quad F(x, x') = F(a, b) + \sum_{m=0}^{+\infty} \sum_{n=0}^{+\infty} \frac{\partial^{m+n} F}{\partial a^m \partial b^n} \frac{(x-a)^m (x'-b)^n}{m!\, n!},$$

where the combination $m = n = 0$ is excluded from the summation.

Note. The coefficient a_{mn} of $(x-a)^m (x'-b)^n$ in the preceding series is equal to the double integral

$$-\frac{1}{4\,\pi^2} \int_{(C)} dz \int_{(C')} \frac{F(z, z')\, dz'}{(z-a)^{m+1}(z'-b)^{n+1}}.$$

If M is an upper bound for $|F(z, z')|$ along the circles C and C', we have, by a previous general remark,

$$|a_{mn}| < \frac{1}{4\,\pi^2}\,\frac{M}{R^{m+1}R'^{n+1}}\,2\,\pi R . 2\,\pi R' = \frac{M}{R^m R'^n}.$$

The function

$$\frac{M}{\left(1 - \dfrac{x - a}{R}\right)\left(1 - \dfrac{x' - b}{R'}\right)}$$

is therefore a dominant function for $F(x, x')$ (I, § 192, 2d ed.; § 186, 1st ed.).

95. Functions represented by definite integrals. In order to study certain functions, we often seek to express them as definite integrals in which the independent variable appears as a parameter under the integral sign. We have already given sufficient conditions under which the usual rules of differentiation may be applied when the variables are real (I, §§ 98, 100, 2d ed.; § 97, 1st ed.). We shall now reconsider the question for complex variables.

Let $F(z, z')$ be an analytic function of the two variables z and z' when these variables remain within the two regions A and A' respectively. Let us take a definite path L of finite length in the region A, and let us consider the definite integral

$$(13) \qquad \Phi(x) = \int_{(L)} F(z, x)\,dz,$$

where x is any point of the region A'. To prove that this function $\Phi(x)$ is an analytic function of x, let us describe about the point x as center a circle C with radius R, lying entirely in the region A'. Since the function $F(z, z')$ is analytic, Cauchy's fundamental formula gives

$$F(z, x) = \frac{1}{2\,\pi i}\int_{(C)}\frac{F(z, z')\,dz'}{z' - x};$$

whence the integral (13) can be written in the form

$$\Phi(x) = \frac{1}{2\,\pi i}\int_{(L)} dz \int_{(C)}\frac{F(z, z')\,dz'}{z' - x}.$$

Let $x + \Delta x$ be a point near x in the circle C; we have, similarly,

$$\Phi(x + \Delta x) = \frac{1}{2\,\pi i}\int_{(L)} dz \int_{(C)}\frac{F(z, z')\,dz'}{z' - x - \Delta x},$$

and consequently, by repeating the calculation already made (§ 33),

$$\frac{\Phi(x + \Delta x) - \Phi(x)}{\Delta x} = \frac{1}{2\pi i} \int_{(L)} dz \int_{(C)} \frac{F(z, z')\,dz'}{(z' - x)^2}$$

$$+ \frac{\Delta x}{2\pi i} \int_{(L)} dz \int_{(C)} \frac{F(z, z')\,dz'}{(z' - x)^2(z' - x - \Delta x)}.$$

Let M be a positive number greater than the absolute value of $F(z, z')$ when the variables z and z' describe the curves L and C respectively; let S be the length of the curve L; and let ρ denote the absolute value of Δx. The absolute value of the second integral is less than

$$\frac{\rho}{2\pi} \frac{M}{R^2(R - \rho)} 2\pi R . S = \frac{\rho M S}{R(R - \rho)};$$

hence it approaches zero when the point $x + \Delta x$ approaches x indefinitely. It follows that the function $\Phi(x)$ has a unique derivative which is given by the expression

$$\Phi'(x) = \frac{1}{2\pi i} \int_{(L)} dz \int_{(C)} \frac{F(z, z')\,dz'}{(z' - x)^2}.$$

But we have also (§ 33)

$$\frac{\partial F}{\partial x} = \frac{1}{2\pi i} \int_{(C)} \frac{F(z, z')\,dz'}{(z' - x)^2},$$

and the preceding relation can be again written

$$(14) \qquad \Phi'(x) = \int_{(L)} \frac{\partial F}{\partial x}\,dz.$$

Thus we obtain again the usual formula for differentiation under the integral sign.

The reasoning is no longer valid if the path of integration L extends to infinity. Let us suppose, for definiteness, that L is a ray proceeding from a point a_0 and making an angle θ with the real axis. We shall say that the integral

$$\Phi(x) = \int_{a_0}^{\infty} F(z, x)\,dz$$

is uniformly convergent if to every positive number ϵ there can be made to correspond a positive number N such that we have

$$\left| \int_{a_0 + \rho e^{i\theta}}^{\infty} F(z, x)\,dz \right| < \epsilon,$$

provided that ρ is greater than N, wherever x may be in A'. By dividing the path of integration into an infinite number of rectilinear segments we prove that every uniformly convergent integral is equal to the value of a uniformly convergent series whose terms are the integrals along certain segments of the infinite ray L. All these integrals are analytic functions of x; therefore the same is true of the integral $\int_{a_0}^{\infty} F(z,\, x)\, dz$ (§ 39).

It is seen, in the same way, that the ordinary formula for differentiation can be applied, provided the integral obtained, $\int_{a_0}^{\infty} (\partial F/\partial x)\, dz$, is itself uniformly convergent.

If the function $F(z,\, z')$ becomes infinite for a limit a_0 of the path of integration, we shall also say that the integral is uniformly convergent in a certain region if to every positive number ϵ a point $a_0 + \eta$ on the line L can be made to correspond in such a way that

$$\left| \int_{a_0 + \eta}^{b} F(z,\, x)\, dz \right| < \epsilon,$$

where b is any point of the path L lying between a_0 and $a_0 + \eta$, the inequality holding for all values of x in the region considered. The conclusions are the same as in the case where one of the limits of the integral is moved off to infinity, and they are established in the same way.

96. Application to the Γ function. The definite integral taken along the real axis

(15) $$\Gamma(z) = \int_0^{+\infty} t^{z-1} e^{-t}\, dt,$$

which we have studied only for real and positive values of z (I, § 94, 2d ed.; § 92, 1st ed.), has a finite value, provided the real part of z, which we will denote by $\mathcal{R}(z)$, is positive. In fact, let $z = x + yi$; this gives $|t^{z-1} e^{-t}| = t^{x-1} e^{-t}$. Since the integral

$$\int_0^{+\infty} t^{x-1} e^{-t}\, dt$$

has a finite value if x is positive, it is clear that the same is true of the integral (15) (I, §§ 91, 92, 2d ed.; §§ 90, 91, 1st ed.). This integral is uniformly convergent in the whole region defined by the conditions $N > \mathcal{R}(z) > \eta$, where N and η are two arbitrary positive numbers. In fact, we can write

$$\Gamma(z) = \int_0^1 t^{z-1} e^{-t}\, dt + \int_1^{+\infty} t^{z-1} e^{-t}\, dt,$$

and it suffices to prove that each of these integrals on the right is uniformly convergent. Let us prove this for the second integral, for example. Let l be a positive number greater than one. If $\mathcal{R}(z) < N$, we have

$$\left| \int_l^{+\infty} t^{z-1} e^{-t}\, dt \right| < \int_l^{+\infty} t^{N-1} e^{-t}\, dt,$$

and a positive number Λ can be found large enough to make the last integral less than any positive number ϵ whenever $l \geqq \Lambda$. The function $\Gamma(z)$, defined by the integral (15), is therefore an analytic function in the whole region of the plane lying to the right of the y-axis. This function $\Gamma(z)$ satisfies again the relation

$$(16) \qquad \Gamma(z+1) = z\Gamma(z),$$

obtained by integration by parts, and consequently the more general relation

$$(17) \qquad \Gamma(z+n) = z(z+1) \cdots (z+n-1)\Gamma(z),$$

which is an immediate consequence of the other.

This property enables us to extend the definition of the Γ function to values of z whose real part is negative. For consider the function

$$(18) \qquad \psi(z) = \frac{\Gamma(z+n)}{z(z+1) \cdots (z+n-1)},$$

where n is a positive integer. The numerator $\Gamma(z+n)$ is an analytic function of z defined for values of z for which $\mathcal{R}(z) > -n$; hence the function $\psi(z)$ is a function analytic except for poles, defined for all the values of the variable whose real part is greater than $-n$. Now this function $\psi(z)$ coincides with the analytic function $\Gamma(z)$ to the right of the y-axis, by the relation (17); hence it is identical with the analytic extension of the analytic function $\Gamma(z)$ in the strip included between the two straight lines $\mathcal{R}(z) = 0$, $\mathcal{R}(z) = -n$. Since the number n is arbitrary, we may conclude that there exists a function which is analytic except for the poles of the first order at the points $z = 0$, $z = -1$, $z = -2, \cdots, z = -n, \cdots$, and which is equal to the integral (15) at all points to the right of the y-axis. This function, which is analytic except for poles in the finite plane, is again represented by $\Gamma(z)$; but the formula (15) enables us to compute its numerical value only if we have $\mathcal{R}(z) > 0$. If $\mathcal{R}(z) < 0$, we must also make use of the relation (17) in order to obtain the numerical value of that function.

We shall now give an expression for the Γ function which is valid for all values of z. Let $S(z)$ be the integral function

$$S(z) = z \prod_{n=1}^{+\infty} \left(1 + \frac{z}{n}\right) e^{-\frac{z}{n}},$$

which has the poles of $\Gamma(z)$ for zeros. The product $S(z)\,\Gamma(z)$ must then be an integral function. It can be shown that this integral function is equal to e^{-Cz}, where C is Euler's constant* (I, § 18, Ex., 2d ed.; § 49, Note, 1st ed.), and we derive from it the result

$$(19) \qquad \frac{1}{z\,\Gamma(z)} = \frac{1}{\Gamma(z+1)} = e^{Cz} \prod_{n=1}^{+\infty} \left(1 + \frac{z}{n}\right) e^{-\frac{z}{n}},$$

which shows that $1/\Gamma(z+1)$ is a transcendental integral function.

---

* HERMITE, *Cours d'Analyse*, 4th ed., p. 142.

97. Analytic extension of a function of two variables. Let $u = F(z, z')$ be an analytic function of the two variables z and z' when these two variables remain respectively in two connected regions A and A' of the two planes in which we represent them. It is shown, as in the case of a single variable (§ 83), that the value of this function for any pair of points z, z' taken in the regions A, A' is determined if we know the values of F and of all its partial derivatives for a pair of points $z = a$, $z' = b$ taken in the same regions. It now appears easy to extend the notion of analytic extension to functions of two complex variables. Let us consider a double series Σa_{mn} such that there exist two positive numbers r, r' having the following property : the series

$$(20) \qquad\qquad F(z, z') = \Sigma a_{mn} z^m z'^n$$

is convergent if we have at the same time $|z| < r$, $|z'| < r'$, and divergent if we have at the same time $|z| > r$, $|z'| > r'$. The preceding series defines, then, a function $F(z, z')$ which is analytic when the variables z, z' remain respectively in the circles C, C' of radii r and r'; but it does not tell us anything about the nature of this function when we have $|z| > r$ or $|z'| > r'$. Let us suppose for definiteness that we cause the variable z to move over a path L from the origin to a point Z exterior to the circle C, and the variable z' to travel over another path L' from the point $z' = 0$ to a point Z' exterior to the circle C'. Let α and β be two points taken respectively on the two paths L and L', α being in the interior of C and β in the interior of C'. The series (20) and those which are obtained from it by successive differentiations enable us to form a new power series,

$$(21) \qquad\qquad \Sigma b_{mn} (z - \alpha)^m (z' - \beta)^n,$$

which is absolutely convergent if we have $|z - \alpha| < r_1$ and $|z' - \beta| < r'_1$, where r_1 and r'_1 are two suitably chosen positive numbers. Let us call C_1 the circle of radius r_1 described about the point α as center in the plane of z, and C'_1 the circle of radius r'_1 described in the plane of z' about the point β as center. If z is in the part common to the two circles C and C_1, and the point z' in the part common to the two circles C' and C'_1, the value of the series (21) is the same as the value of the series (20). If it is possible to choose the two numbers r_1 and r'_1 in such a way that the circle C_1 will be partly exterior to the circle C, or the circle C'_1 partly exterior to the circle C', we shall have extended the definition of the function $F(z, z')$ to a region extending beyond the first. Continuing in this manner, it is easy to see how the function $F(z, z')$ may be extended step by step. But there appears here an important new consideration : *It is necessary to take into account the way in which the variables move with respect to each other on their respective paths.* The following is a very simple example of this, due to Sauvage.* Let $u = \sqrt{z - z' + 1}$; for the initial values let us take $z = z' = 0$, $u = 1$, and let the paths described by the variables z, z' be defined as follows : 1) The path described by the variable z' is composed of the rectilinear segment from the origin to the point $z' = 1$. 2) The path described by z is composed of three semicircumferences : the first, OMA (Fig. 38), has its center on the real axis to

---

* *Premiers principes de la théorie générale des fonctions de plusieurs variables* (*Annales de la Faculté des Sciences de Marseille*, Vol. XIV). This memoir is an excellent introduction to the study of analytic functions of several variables.

the left of the origin and a radius less than 1/2 ; the second, ANB, also has its center on the real axis and is so placed that the point -1 is on its diameter AB ; finally, the third, BPC, has for its center the middle point of the segment joining the point B to the point C $(z = 1)$. The first and the third of these semicircumferences are above the real axis, and the second is below, so that the boundary $OMANBPCO$ incloses the point $z = -1$. Let us now select the following movements :

1) z' remains zero, and z describes the entire path $OABC$;

2) z remains equal to 1, and z' describes its whole path.

If we consider the auxiliary variable $t = z - z'$, it is easily seen that the path described by the variable t, when that variable is represented by a point on the

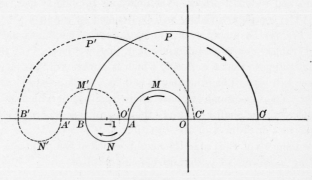

Fɪɢ. 38

z plane, is precisely the closed boundary $OABCO$ which surrounds the critical point $t = -1$ of the radical $\sqrt{t + 1}$. The final value of u is therefore $u = -1$.

On the other hand, let us select the following procedure :

1) z remains zero and z' varies from 0 to $1 - \epsilon$ (ϵ being a very small positive number);

2) z' remains equal to $1 - \epsilon$, and z describes the path $OABC$;

3) z remains equal to 1, and z' varies from $1 - \epsilon$ to 1.

When z' varies from 0 to $1 - \epsilon$, the auxiliary variable t describes a path OO' ending in a point O' very near the point -1 on the real axis. When z describes next the path $OABC$, t moves over a path $O'A'B'C'$ congruent to the preceding and ending in the point C' $(OC' = \epsilon)$ on the real axis. Finally, when z' varies from $1 - \epsilon$ to 1, t passes from C' to the origin. Thus the auxiliary variable t describes the closed boundary $OO'A'B'C'O$ which leaves the point -1 on its exterior, provided ϵ is taken small enough. The final value of u will therefore be equal to $+ 1$.

Very much less is known about the nature of the singularities of analytic functions of several variables than about those of functions of a single variable. One of the greatest difficulties of the problem lies in the fact that the pairs of singular values are not isolated.*

---

*For everything regarding this matter see a memoir by Poincaré in the *Acta mathematica* (Vol. XXVI), and P. Cousin's thesis (Ibid. Vol. XIX).

II. IMPLICIT FUNCTIONS. ALGEBRAIC FUNCTIONS

98. Weierstrass's theorem. We have already established (I, § 193, 2d ed.; § 187, 1st ed.) the existence of implicit functions defined by equations in which the left-hand side can be developed in a power series proceeding in positive and increasing powers of the two variables. The arguments which were made supposing the variables and coefficients real apply without modification when the variables and the coefficients have any values, real or imaginary, provided we retain the other hypotheses. We shall establish now a more general theorem, and we shall preserve the notations previously used in that study. The complex variables will be denoted by x and y.

Let $F(x, y)$ be an analytic function in the neighborhood of a pair of values $x = \alpha$, $y = \beta$, and such that we have $F(\alpha, \beta) = 0$. We shall suppose that $\alpha = \beta = 0$, which is always permissible. The equation $F(0, y) = 0$ has the root $y = 0$ to a certain degree of multiplicity. The case which we have studied is that in which $y = 0$ is a simple root; we shall now study the general case where $y = 0$ is a multiple root of order n of the equation $F(0, y) = 0$. If we arrange the development of $F(x, y)$ in the neighborhood of the point $x = y = 0$ according to powers of y, that development will be

$$(22) \quad F(x, y) = A_0 + A_1 y + \cdots + A_n y^n + A_{n+1} y^{n+1} + \cdots,$$

where the coefficients A_i are power series in x, of which the first n are zero for $x = 0$, while A_n does not vanish for $x = 0$. Let C and C' be two circles of radii R and R' described in the planes of x and y respectively about the origin as center. We shall suppose that the function $F(x, y)$ is analytic in the region defined by these two circles and also on the circles themselves; since A_n is not zero for $x = 0$, we may suppose that the radius R of the circle C is sufficiently small so that A_n does not vanish in the interior of the circle C nor on the circle. Let M be an upper bound for $|F(x, y)|$ in the preceding region and B a lower bound for $|A_n|$. By Cauchy's fundamental theorem we have

$$F(x, y) = \frac{1}{2 \pi i} \int_{(C')} \frac{F(x, y') \, dy'}{y' - y},$$

where x and y are any two points taken in the circles C and C'; from this we conclude that the absolute value of the coefficient A_m of y^m in the formula (22) is less than M/R'^m, whatever may be the value of x in the circle C.

We can now write

(23) $$F(x, y) = A_n y^n (1 + P + Q),$$

where

$$P = \frac{A_{n+1}}{A_n} y + \frac{A_{n+2}}{A_n} y^2 + \cdots,$$

$$Q = \frac{A_0}{A_n} \frac{1}{y^n} + \cdots + \frac{A_{n-1}}{A_n} \frac{1}{y}.$$

Let ρ be the absolute value of y; we have

$$|P| < \frac{M}{BR'^m}\left(\frac{\rho}{R'} + \frac{\rho^2}{R'^2} + \cdots\right) = \frac{M}{BR'^m} \frac{\dfrac{\rho}{R'}}{1 - \dfrac{\rho}{R'}},$$

and this absolute value will be less than $1/2$ if we have

(24) $$\rho < R' \frac{BR'^m}{BR'^m + 2M}.$$

On the other hand, let $\mu(r)$ be the maximum value of the absolute values of the functions $A_0, A_1, \cdots, A_{n-1}$ for all the values of x for which the absolute value does not exceed a number $r < R$. Since these n functions are zero for $x = 0$, $\mu(r)$ approaches zero with r, and we can always take r so small that

(25) $$\frac{\mu(r)}{B}\left(\frac{1}{\rho} + \frac{1}{\rho^2} + \cdots + \frac{1}{\rho^n}\right) < \frac{1}{2}, \qquad (r < R),$$

where ρ is a definite positive number. The numbers r and ρ having been determined so as to satisfy the preceding conditions, let us replace the circle C by the circle C_r described in the x-plane with the radius r about the point $x = 0$ as center, and similarly in the y-plane the circle C' by the concentric circle C'_ρ with the radius ρ. If we give to x a value such that $|x| \leqq r$, and then cause the variable y to describe the circle C'_ρ, along the entire circumference of this circle we have, from the manner in which the numbers r and ρ have been chosen, $|P| < 1/2$, $|Q| < 1/2$, and therefore $|P + Q| < 1$. If the variable y describes the circle C'_ρ in the positive sense, the angle of $1 + P + Q$ returns to its initial value, whereas the angle of the factor $A_n y^n$ increases by $2n\pi$. *The equation $F(x, y) = 0$, in which $|x| \leqq r$, therefore has n roots whose absolute values are less than ρ, and only n.*

All the other roots of the equation $F(x, y) = 0$, if there are any, have their absolute values greater than ρ. Since we can replace the number ρ by a number as small as we wish, less than ρ, if we replace at the same time r by a smaller number satisfying always the condition (25), we see that the equation $F(x, y) = 0$ has n roots and only n which approach zero with x.

If the variable x remains in the interior of the circle C_r or on its circumference, the n roots $y_1, y_2, \cdots, y_n$, whose absolute values are less than ρ, remain within the circle C'_ρ. These roots are not in general analytic functions of x in the circle C_r, but every symmetric integral rational function of these n roots is an analytic function of x in this circle. It evidently suffices to prove this for the sum $y_1^k + y_2^k + \cdots + y_n^k$, where k is a positive integer. Let us consider for this purpose the double integral

$$ I = \int_{(C'_\rho)} dy' \int_{(C_r)} y'^k \frac{\dfrac{\partial F(x', y')}{\partial y'}}{F(x', y')} \frac{dx'}{x' - x}, $$

where we suppose $|x| < r$. If $|y'| = \rho$, the function $F(x', y')$ cannot vanish for any value of the variable x' within or on C_r, and the only pole of the function under the integral sign in the interior of the circle C_r is the point $x' = x$. We have, then,

$$ \int_{(C_r)} y'^k \frac{\dfrac{\partial F(x', y')}{\partial y'}}{F(x', y')} \frac{dx'}{x' - x} = 2\pi i y'^k \frac{\dfrac{\partial F(x, y')}{\partial y'}}{F(x, y')}, $$

and consequently

$$ I = 2\pi i \int_{(C'_\rho)} y'^k \frac{\dfrac{\partial F(x, y')}{\partial y'}}{F(x, y')} dy'. $$

By a general theorem (§ 48) this integral is equal to

$$ -4\pi^2 (y_1^k + y_2^k + \cdots + y_n^k), $$

where $y_1, y_2, \cdots, y_n$ are the n roots of the equation $F(x, y) = 0$ with absolute values less than ρ. On the other hand, the integral I is an analytic function of x in the circle C_r, for we can develop $1/(x' - x)$ in a uniformly convergent series of powers of x, and then calculate the integral term by term. The different sums Σy_i^k being analytic functions in the circle C_r, the same thing must be true of the sum of the roots, of the sum of the products taking two at a time, and so on, and therefore the n roots $y_1, y_2, \cdots, y_n$ are also roots of an equation of the nth degree

$$ (26) \quad f(x, y) = y^n + a_1 y^{n-1} + a_2 y^{n-2} + \cdots + a_{n-1} y + a_n = 0, $$

whose coefficients $a_1, a_2, \cdots, a_n$ are analytic functions of x in the circle C_r vanishing for $x = 0$.

The two functions $F(x, y)$ and $f(x, y)$ vanish for the same pairs of values of the variables x, y in the interior of the circles C_r and C'_ρ. We shall now show that the quotient $F(x, y)/f(x, y)$ is an analytic function in this region. Let us take definite values for these variables such that $|x| < r$, $|y| < \rho$, and let us consider the double integral

$$J = \int_{(C'_\rho)} dy' \int_{(C_r)} \frac{F(x', y')}{f(x', y')} \frac{dx'}{(x' - x)(y' - y)}.$$

For a value of y' of absolute value ρ the function $f(x', y')$ of the variable x' cannot vanish for any value of x' within or on the circle C_r. The function under the integral sign has therefore the single pole $x' = x$ within C_r, and the corresponding residue is

$$\frac{F(x, y')}{f(x, y')(y' - y)}.$$

Hence we have also

$$J = 2\pi i \int_{(C'_\rho)} \frac{F(x, y')}{f(x, y')} \frac{dy'}{y' - y};$$

but the two analytic functions $F(x, y')$, $f(x, y')$ of the variable y' have the same zeros with the same degrees of multiplicity in the interior of C'_ρ. Their quotient is therefore an analytic function of y' in C'_ρ, and the only pole of the function to be integrated in this circle is $y' = y$; hence we have

$$J = -4\pi^2 \frac{F(x, y)}{f(x, y)}.$$

On the other hand, we can replace $1/(x' - x)(y' - y)$ in the integral by a uniformly convergent series arranged in positive powers of x and y. Integrating term by term, we see that the integral is equal to the value of a power series proceeding according to powers of x and y and convergent in the circles C_r, C'_ρ. Hence we may write

$$F(x, y) = f(x, y) H(x, y)$$

or

(27) $$F(x, y) = (y^n + a_1 y^{n-1} + \cdots + a_n) H(x, y),$$

where the function $H(x, y)$ is analytic in the circles C_r, C'_ρ.

The coefficient A_n of y^n in $F(x, y)$ contains a constant term different from zero; since $a_1, a_2, \cdots, a_n$ are zero for $x = 0$, the development of $H(x, y)$ necessarily contains a constant term different from zero, and the decomposition given by the expression (27) throws into relief the fact that the roots of $F(x, y) = 0$ which approach zero with x are obtained by putting the first factor equal to zero. The preceding important theorem is due to Weierstrass.* It generalizes, at least as far as that is possible for a function of several variables, the decomposition into factors of functions of a single variable.

99. Critical points. In order to study the n roots of the equation $F(x, y) = 0$ which become infinitely small with x, we are thus led to study the roots of an equation of the form

$$(28) \quad f(x, y) = y^n + a_1 y^{n-1} + a_2 y^{n-2} + \cdots + a_{n-1} y + a_n = 0$$

for values of x near zero, where $a_1, a_2, \cdots, a_n$ are analytic functions that vanish for $x = 0$. When n is greater than unity (the only case which concerns us), the point $x = 0$ is in general a *critical point*. Let us eliminate y between the two equations $f = 0$ and $\partial f / \partial y = 0$; the resultant $\Delta(x)$ is a polynomial in the coefficients $a_1, a_2, \cdots, a_n$, and therefore an analytic function in the neighborhood of the origin. This resultant † is zero for $x = 0$, and, since the zeros of an analytic function form a system of isolated points, we may suppose that we have taken the radius r of the circle C_r so small that in the interior of C_r the equation $\Delta(x) = 0$ has no other root than $x = 0$. For every point x_0 taken in that circle other than the origin, the equation $f(x_0, y) = 0$ will have n distinct roots. According to the case already studied (I, § 194, 2d ed.; § 188, 1st ed.), the n roots of the equation (28) will be analytic functions of x in the neighborhood of the point x_0. Hence there cannot be any other critical point than the origin in the interior of the circle C_r.

Let $y_1, y_2, \cdots, y_n$ be the n roots of the equation $f(x_0, y) = 0$. Let us cause the variable x to describe a loop around the point $x = 0$, starting from the point x_0; along the whole loop the n roots of the equation $f(x, y) = 0$ are distinct and vary in a continuous manner. If we start from the point x_0 with the root y_1, for example, and follow the continuous variation of that root along the whole loop, we return to the point of departure with a final value equal to one of the roots of the equation $f(x_0, y) = 0$. If that final value is y_1, the root

---

* *Abhandlungen aus der Functionenlehre von K. Weierstrass* (Berlin, 1860). The proposition can also be demonstrated by making use only of the properties of power series and the existence theorem for implicit functions (*Bulletin de la Société mathématique*, Vol. XXXVI, 1908, pp. 209–215).

† We disregard the case where the resultant is identically zero. In this case $f(x, y)$ would be divisible by a factor $[f_1(x, y)]^k$, where $k > 1$, $f_1(x, y)$ being of the same form as $f(x, y)$.

considered is single-valued in the neighborhood of the origin. If
that final value is different from y_1, let us suppose that it is equal
to y_2. A new loop described in the same sense will lead from the
root y_2 to one of the roots $y_1, y_2, \cdots, y_n$. The final value cannot be
y_2, since the reverse path must lead from y_2 to y_1. That final value
must, then, be one of the roots $y_1, y_3, \cdots, y_n$. If it is y_1, we see that
the two roots y_1 and y_2 are permuted when the variable describes
a loop around the origin. If that final value is not y_1, it is one
of the remaining $(n-2)$ roots; let y_3 be that root. A new loop
described in the same sense will lead from the root y_3 to one of the
roots $y_1, y_2, y_3, y_4, \cdots, y_n$. It cannot be y_3, for the same reason as
before; neither is it y_2, since the reverse path leads from y_2 to y_1.
Hence that final value is either y_1 or one of the remaining $(n-3)$
roots $y_4, y_5, \cdots, y_n$. If it is y_1, the three roots y_1, y_2, y_3 permute
themselves cyclically when the variable x describes a loop around
the origin. If the final value is different from y_1, we shall continue
to cause the variable to turn around the origin, and at the end of
a finite number of operations we shall necessarily come back to a
root already obtained, which will be the root y_1. Suppose, for example, that this happens after p operations; the p roots obtained,
$y_1, y_2, \cdots, y_p$, permute themselves cyclically when the variable x
describes a loop around the origin. We say that they form a *cyclic
system of p roots*. If $p = n$, the n roots form a single cyclic system.
If p is less than n, we shall repeat the reasoning, starting with one
of the remaining $n - p$ roots and so on. It is clear that if we continue in this way we shall end by exhausting all the roots, and we
can state the following proposition: *The n roots of the equation
$F(x, y) = 0$, which are zero for $x = 0$, form one or several cyclic
systems in the neighborhood of the origin.*

To render the statement perfectly general, it is sufficient to agree
that a cyclic system can be composed of a single root; that root is
then a single-valued function in the neighborhood of the origin.

The roots of the same cyclic system can be represented by a unique
development. Let $y_1, y_2, \cdots, y_p$ be the p roots of a cyclic system; let
us put $x = x'^p$. Each of these roots becomes an analytic function
of x' for all values of x' other than $x' = 0$; on the other hand, when
x' describes a loop around $x' = 0$, the point x describes p successive loops in the same sense around the origin. Each of the roots
$y_1, y_2, \cdots, y_p$ returns then to its initial value; they are single-valued
functions in the neighborhood of the origin. Since these roots approach zero when x' approaches zero, the origin $x' = 0$ cannot be

other than an ordinary point, and one of these roots is represented
by a development of the form

$$(29) \qquad y = a_1 x' + a_2 x'^2 + \cdots + a_m x'^m + \cdots,$$

or, replacing x' by $x^{1/p}$,

$$(30) \qquad y = a_1 x^{\frac{1}{p}} + a_2 \left(x^{\frac{1}{p}}\right)^2 + \cdots + a_m \left(x^{\frac{1}{p}}\right)^m + \cdots.$$

We may now say that *the development* (30) *represents all the roots
of the same cyclic system, provided that we give to* $x^{1/p}$ *all of its
p determinations.* For, let us suppose that, taking for the radical $\sqrt[p]{x}$
one of its determinations, we have the development of the root y_1.
If the variable x describes a loop around the origin in the positive
sense, y_1 changes into y_2, and $x^{1/p}$ is multiplied by $e^{2\pi i/p}$. It will be
seen, similarly, that we shall obtain y_q by replacing $x^{1/p}$ by $x^{1/p} e^{2q\pi i/p}$
in the equality (30). This unique development for the system shows
up clearly the cyclic permutation of the p roots. It would now remain
to show how we could separate the n roots of the equation $F(x, y) = 0$
into cyclic systems and calculate the coefficients a_i of the developments (30). We have already considered the case where the point
$x = y = 0$ is a double point (I, § 199, 2d ed.). We shall now treat
another particular case.

If for $x = y = 0$ the derivative $\partial F/\partial x$ is not zero, the development of $F(x, y)$ contains a term of the first degree in x, and we have

$$(31) \qquad F(x, y) = Ax + By^n + \cdots, \qquad (AB \neq 0)$$

where the terms not written are divisible by one of the factors x^2, xy,
y^{n+1}. Let us consider y for a moment as the independent variable;
the equation $F(x, y) = 0$ has a single root approaching zero with y,
and that root is analytic in the neighborhood of the origin. The
development which we have already seen how to calculate (I, §§ 35,
193, 2d ed.; §§ 20, 187, 1st ed.) runs as follows:

$$(32) \qquad x = y^n(a_0 + a_1 y + \cdots). \qquad (a_0 \neq 0)$$

Extracting the nth root of the two sides, we find

$$(33) \qquad x^{\frac{1}{n}} = y \sqrt[n]{a_0 + a_1 y + \cdots}.$$

For $y = 0$ the auxiliary equation $u^n = a_0 + a_1 y + \cdots$ has n distinct roots, each of which is developable in a power series according
to powers of y. Since these n roots are deducible from one of them
by multiplying it by the successive powers of $e^{2\pi i/n}$, we can take for
$\sqrt[n]{a_0 + a_1 y + \cdots}$ in the equality (33) any one of these roots, subject
to the condition of assigning successively to $x^{1/n}$ its n determinations.

We can therefore write the equation (33) in the form

$$x^{\frac{1}{n}} = b_1 y + b_2 y^2 + \cdots, \qquad\qquad (b_1 \neq 0)$$

and from this we derive, conversely, a development of y in powers of $x^{1/n}$:

$$(34) \qquad\qquad y = c_1 x^{\frac{1}{n}} + c_2 \left(x^{\frac{1}{n}}\right)^2 + \cdots.$$

This development, if we give successively to $x^{1/n}$ its n values, represents the n roots which approach zero with x. These n roots form, then, a single cyclic system.

For a study of the general case we refer the reader to treatises devoted to the theory of algebraic functions.*

100. Algebraic functions. Up to the present time the implicit functions most carefully studied are the *algebraic functions*, defined by an equation $F(x, y) = 0$, in which the left-hand side is an *irreducible* polynomial in x and y. A polynomial is said to be irreducible when it is not possible to find two other polynomials of lower degree, $F_1(x, y)$ and $F_2(x, y)$, such that we have identically

$$F(x, y) = F_1(x, y) \times F_2(x, y).$$

If the polynomial $F(x, y)$ were equal to a product of that kind, it is clear that the equation $F(x, y) = 0$ could be replaced by two distinct equations $F_1(x, y) = 0$, $F_2(x, y) = 0$.

Let, then,

$$(35) \quad F(x, y) = \phi_0(x) y^n + \phi_1(x) y^{n-1} + \cdots + \phi_{n-1}(x) y + \phi_n(x) = 0$$

be the proposed equation of degree n in y, where $\phi_0, \phi_1, \cdots, \phi_n$ are polynomials in x. Eliminating y between the two relations $F = 0$, $\partial F/\partial y = 0$, we obtain a polynomial $\Delta(x)$ for the resultant, which cannot be identically zero, since $F(x, y)$ is supposed to be irreducible. Let us mark in the plane the points $\alpha_1, \alpha_2, \cdots, \alpha_k$, which represent the roots of the equation $\Delta(x) = 0$, and the points $\beta_1, \beta_2, \cdots, \beta_h$, which represent the roots of $\phi_0(x) = 0$. Some of the points α_i may also be among the roots of $\phi_0(x) = 0$. For a point a different from the points α_i, β_j the equation $F(a, y) = 0$ has n distinct and finite roots, $b_1, b_2, \cdots, b_n$. In the neighborhood of the point a the equation (35) has therefore n analytic roots which approach $b_1, b_2, \cdots, b_n$ respectively when x approaches a. Let α_i be a root of the equation

---

* See also the noted memoir of Puiseux on algebraic functions (*Journal de Mathématiques*, Vol. XV, 1850).

$\Delta(x) = 0$. The equation $F(a_i, y) = 0$ has a certain number of equal roots; let us suppose, for example, that it has p roots equal to b. The p roots which approach b when x approaches a_i group themselves into a certain number of cyclic systems, and the roots of the same cyclic system are represented by a development in series arranged according to fractional powers of $x - a_i$. If the value a_i does not cause $\phi_0(x)$ to vanish, all the roots of the equation (35) in the neighborhood of the point a_i group themselves into a certain number of cyclic systems, some of which may contain only one root. For a point β_j which makes $\phi_0(x)$ zero, some of the roots of the equation (35) become infinite; in order to study these roots, we put $y = 1/y'$, and we are led to study the roots of the equation

$$F_1(x, y') = y'^m F(x, 1/y') = 0,$$

which become zero for $x = \beta_j$. These roots group themselves again into a certain number of cyclic systems, the roots of the same system being represented by a development in series of the form

$$(36) \quad . \ y' = a_m(x - \beta_j)^{\frac{m}{p}} + a_{m+1}(x - \beta_j)^{\frac{m+1}{p}} + \cdots, \quad (a_m \neq 0).$$

The corresponding roots of the equation in y will be given by the development

$$(37) \quad y = (x - \beta_j)^{-\frac{m}{p}} \left[a_m + a_{m+1}(x - \beta_j)^{\frac{1}{p}} + \cdots \right]^{-1},$$

which can be arranged in increasing powers of $(x - \beta_j)^{1/p}$, but there will be at first a *finite* number of terms with negative exponents.

To study the values of y for the infinite values of x, we put $x = 1/x'$, and we are led to study the roots of an equation of the same form in the neighborhood of the origin. To sum up, in the neighborhood of any point $x = a$ the n roots of the equation (35) are represented by a certain number of series arranged according to increasing powers of $x - a$ or of $(x - a)^{1/p}$, containing perhaps a finite number of terms with negative exponents, and this statement applies also to infinite values of x by replacing $x - \infty$ by $1/x$.

It is to be observed that the fractional powers or the negative exponents present themselves only for the exceptional points. The only singular points of the roots of the equation are therefore the critical points around which some of these roots permute themselves cyclically, and the poles where some of these roots become infinite; moreover, a point may be at the same time a pole and a critical point. These two kinds of singular points are often called *algebraic singular points*.

We have so far studied the roots of the proposed equation only in the neighborhood of a fixed point. Suppose now that we join two points $x = a$, $x = b$, for which the equation (35) has n distinct and finite roots, by a path AB not passing through any singular point of the equation. Let y_1 be a root of the equation $F(a, y) = 0$; the root $y = f(x)$, which reduces to y_1 for $x = a$, is represented in the neighborhood of the point a by a power-series development $P(x - a)$. We can propose to ourselves the problem of finding its analytic extension by causing the variable to describe the path AB. This is a particular case of the general problem, and we know in advance that we shall arrive at the point B with a final value which will be a root of the equation $F(b, y) = 0$ (§ 86). We shall surely arrive at the point b at the end of a *finite* number of operations; in fact, the radii of the circles of convergence of the series representing the different roots of the equation $F(x, y) = 0$, having their centers at different points of the path AB, have a lower limit* $\delta > 0$, since this path does not contain any critical points; and it is clear that we could always take the radii of the different circles which we use for the analytic extension at least equal to δ.

Among all the paths joining the points A and B we can always find one leading from the root y_1 to any given one of the roots of the equation $F(b, y) = 0$ as the final value. The proof of this can be made to depend on the following proposition: *If an analytic function z of the variable x has only p distinct values for each value of x, and if it has in the whole plane (including the point at infinity) only algebraic singular points, the p determinations of z are roots of an equation of degree p whose coefficients are rational functions of x.* Let $z_1, z_2, \cdots, z_p$ be the p determinations of z; when the variable x describes a closed curve, these p values $z_1, z_2, \cdots, z_p$ can only change into each other. The symmetric function $u_k = z_1^k + z_2^k + \cdots + z_p^k$, where k is a positive integer, is therefore single-valued. Moreover, that function can have only polar singularities, for in the neighborhood of any point in the finite plane $x = a$ the developments of $z_1, z_2, \cdots, z_p$ have only a finite number of terms with negative exponents. The same thing is therefore true of the development of u_k. Also, the function u_k being single-valued, its development cannot contain fractional powers. The point a is therefore a pole or an ordinary point for u_k, and similarly for the point at infinity. The function u_k

---

* To prove this rigorously it suffices to make use of a form of reasoning analogous to that of § 84.

is therefore a rational function of x, whatever may be the integer k; consequently the same thing is true of the simple symmetric functions, such as Σz_i, $\Sigma z_i z_k$, $\cdots$, which proves the theorem stated.

Having shown this, let us now suppose that in going from the point a to any other point x of the plane by all possible paths we can obtain as final values only p of the roots of the equation

$$F(x, y) = 0, \qquad\qquad (p < n).$$

These p roots can evidently only be permuted among themselves when the variable x describes a closed boundary, and they possess all the properties of the p branches $z_1, z_2, \cdots, z_p$ of the analytic function z which we have just studied. We conclude from this that $y_1, y_2, \cdots, y_p$ would be roots of an equation of degree p, $F_1(x, y) = 0$, with rational coefficients. The equation $F(x, y) = 0$ would have, then, all the roots of the equation $F_1(x, y) = 0$, whatever x may be, and the polynomial $F(x, y)$ would not be irreducible, contrary to hypothesis. If we place no restriction upon the path followed by the variable x, the n roots of the equation (35) must then be regarded as the distinct branches of a single analytic function, as we have already remarked in the case of some simple examples (§ 6).

Let us suppose that from each of the critical points we make an infinite cut in the plane in such a way that these cuts do not cross each other. If the path followed by x is required not to cross any of these cuts, the n roots are single-valued functions in the whole plane, for two paths having the same extremities will be transformable one into the other by a continuous deformation without passing over any critical point (§ 85). In order to follow the variation of a root along any path, we need only know the law of the permutation of these roots when the variable describes a loop around each of the critical points.

Note. The study of algebraic functions is made relatively easy by the fact that we can determine a priori by algebraic computation the singular points of these functions. This is no longer true in general of implicit functions that are not algebraic, which may have transcendental singular points. As an example, the implicit function $y(x)$, defined by the equation $e^y - x - 1 = 0$, has no algebraic critical point, but it has the transcendental singular point $x = -1$.

101. Abelian integrals. Every integral $I = \int R(x, y)\, dx$, where $R(x, y)$ is a rational function of x and y, and where y is an algebraic function defined by the equation $F(x, y) = 0$, is called an *Abelian integral attached to that curve.* To complete the determination of that integral, it is necessary to assign a lower limit x_0 and the corresponding value y_0 chosen among the roots of the equation $F(x_0, y) = 0$. We shall now state some of the most important general properties of such integrals. When we go from the point x_0 to any point x by all the possible paths, all the values of the integral I are included in one of the formulæ

$$(38) \qquad I = I_k + m_1\omega_1 + m_2\omega_2 + \cdots + m_r\omega_r, \qquad (k = 1, 2, \cdots, n)$$

where $I_1, I_2, \cdots, I_n$ are the values of the integral which correspond to certain definite paths, $m_1, m_2, \cdots, m_r$ are arbitrary integers, and $\omega_1, \omega_2, \cdots, \omega_r$ are periods. These periods are of two kinds; one kind results from loops described about the poles of the function $R(x, y)$; these are the *polar periods*. The others come from closed paths surrounding several critical points, called *cycles*; these are called *cyclic* periods. The number of the distinct cyclic periods depends only on the algebraic relation considered, $F(x, y) = 0$; it is equal to $2p$, where p denotes the deficiency of the curve (§ 82). On the other hand, there may be any number of polar periods. From the point of view of the singularities three classes of Abelian integrals are distinguished. Those which remain finite in the neighborhood of every value of x are called the *first kind*; if their absolute value becomes infinite, it can only happen through the addition of an infinite number of periods. The integrals of the *second kind* are those which have a single pole, and the integrals of the *third kind* have two logarithmic singular points. Every Abelian integral is a sum of integrals of the three kinds, and the number of distinct integrals of the first kind is equal to the deficiency.

The study of these integrals is made very easy by the aid of plane surfaces composed of several sheets, called *Riemann surfaces*. We shall not have occasion to consider them here. We shall only give, on account of its thoroughly elementary character, the demonstration of a fundamental theorem, discovered by Abel.

102. Abel's theorem. In order to state the results more easily, let us consider the plane curve C represented by the equation $F(x, y) = 0$, and let $\Phi(x, y)$ be the equation of another plane algebraic curve C'. These two curves have N points in common, $(x_1, y_1), (x_2, y_2), \cdots, (x_N, y_N)$, the number N being equal to the product of the degrees of the two curves. Let $R(x, y)$ be a rational function, and let us consider the following sum:

$$(39) \qquad I = \sum_{i=1}^{N} \int_{(x_0, y_0)}^{(x_i, y_i)} R(x, y)\, dx,$$

where

$$\int_{(x_0, y_0)}^{(x_i, y_i)} R(x, y)\, dx$$

denotes the Abelian integral taken from the fixed point x_0 to a point x_i along a path which leads y from the initial value y_0 to the final value y_i, the initial value y_0 of y being the same for all these integrals. It is clear that the sum I is determined except for a period, since this is the case with each of the integrals. Suppose, now, that some of the coefficients, $a_1, a_2, \cdots, a_k$, of the polynomial $\Phi(x, y)$ are variable. When these coefficients vary continuously, the points x_i themselves vary continuously, and if none of these points pass through a point of discontinuity of the integral $\int R(x, y)\, dx$, the sum I itself varies continuously, provided that we follow the continuous variation of each of the integrals contained in it along the entire path described by the corresponding upper limit. The sum I is therefore a function of the parameters $a_1, a_2, \cdots, a_k$, whose analytic form we shall now investigate.

Let us denote in general by δV the total differential of any function V with respect to the variables $a_1, a_2, \cdots, a_k$:

$$\delta V = \frac{\partial V}{\partial a_1}\, \delta a_1 + \cdots + \frac{\partial V}{\partial a_k}\, \delta a_k.$$

By the expression (39) we have

$$\delta I = \sum_{i=1}^{N} R(x_i, y_i)\, \delta x_i.$$

From the two relations $F(x_i, y_i) = 0$, $\Phi(x_i, y_i) = 0$ we derive

$$\frac{\partial F}{\partial x_i}\, \delta x_i + \frac{\partial F}{\partial y_i}\, \delta y_i = 0, \qquad \frac{\partial \Phi}{\partial x_i}\, \delta x_i + \frac{\partial \Phi}{\partial y_i}\, \delta y_i + \delta \Phi_i = 0,$$

and consequently $\delta x_i = \Psi(x_i, y_i)\, \delta \Phi_i$, where $\Psi(x_i, y_i)$ is a rational function of $x_i, y_i, a_1, a_2, \cdots, a_k$, and where Φ_i is put for $\Phi(x_i, y_i)$. We have, then,

$$\delta I = \sum_{i=1}^{i=N} R(x_i, y_i)\, \Psi(x_i, y_i)\, \delta \Phi_i.$$

The coefficient of δa_1 on the right is a rational symmetric function of the coördinates of the N points (x_i, y_i) common to the two curves C, C'. The theory of elimination proves that this function is a rational function of the coefficients of the two polynomials $F(x, y)$ and $\Phi(x, y)$, and consequently a rational function of $a_1, a_2, \cdots, a_k$. Evidently the same thing is true of the coefficients of $\delta a_2, \cdots, \delta a_k$, and I will be obtained by the integration of a total differential

$$I = \int \pi_1 \delta a_1 + \pi_2 \delta a_2 + \cdots + \pi_k \delta a_k,$$

where $\pi_1, \pi_2, \cdots, \pi_k$ are rational functions of $a_1, a_2, \cdots, a_k$. Now the integration cannot introduce any other transcendentals than logarithms. *The sum I is therefore equal to a rational function of the coefficients $a_1, a_2, \cdots, a_k$, plus a sum of logarithms of rational functions of the same coefficients, each of these logarithms being multiplied by a constant factor.* This is the statement of Abel's theorem in its most general form. In geometric language we can also say that *the sum of the values of any Abelian integral, taken from a common origin to the N points of intersection of the given curve with a variable curve of degree m, $\Phi(x, y) = 0$, is equal to a rational function of the coefficients of $\Phi(x, y)$, plus a sum of a finite number of logarithms of rational functions of the same coefficients, each logarithm being multiplied by a constant factor.*

The second statement appears at first sight the more striking, but in applications we must always keep in mind the analytic statement in the evaluation of the continuous variation of the sum I which corresponds to a continuous variation of the parameters $a_1, a_2, \cdots, a_k$. The theorem has a precise meaning only if we take into account the paths described by the N points $x_1, x_2, \cdots, x_N$ on the plane of the variable x.

The statement becomes of a remarkable simplicity when the integral is of the first kind. In fact, if $\pi_1, \pi_2, \cdots, \pi_k$ were not identically zero, it would be possible to find a system of values $a_1 = a_1', \cdots, a_k = a_k'$ for which I would become infinite. Let $(x_1', y_1'), \cdots, (x_N', y_N')$ be the points of intersection of the curve C with the curve C' which correspond to the values $a_1', \cdots, a_k'$ of the parameters. The integral

$$\int_{(x_0, y_0)}^{(x, y)} R(x, y)\, dx$$

would become infinite when the upper limit approaches one of the points (x_i', y_i'), which is impossible if the integral is of the first kind. Therefore we have $\delta I = 0$, and, when $a_1, a_2, \cdots, a_k$ vary continuously, I remains constant; Abel's theorem can then be stated as follows:

Given a fixed curve C and a variable curve C' of degree m, the sum of the increments of an Abelian integral of the first kind attached to the curve C along the continuous curves described by the points of intersection of C with C' is equal to zero.

Note. We suppose that the degree of the curve C' remains constant and equal to m. If for certain particular values of the coefficients $a_1, a_2, \cdots, a_k$ that degree were lowered, some of the points of intersections of C with C' should be regarded as thrown off to infinity, and it would be necessary to take account of this in the application of the theorem. We mention also the almost evident fact that if some of the points of intersection of C with C' are fixed, it is unnecessary to include the corresponding integrals in the sum I.

103. Application to hyperelliptic integrals. The applications of Abel's theorem to Analysis and to Geometry are extremely numerous and important. We shall calculate δI explicitly in the case of hyperelliptic integrals.

Let us consider the algebraic relations

$$(40) \qquad y^2 = R(x) = A_0 x^{2p+2} + A_1 x^{2p+1} + \cdots + A_{2p+2},$$

where the polynomial $R(x)$ is prime to its derivative. We shall suppose that A_0 may be zero, but that A_0 and A_1 may not be zero at the same time, so that $R(x)$ is of degree $2p+1$ or of degree $2p+2$. Let $Q(x)$ be any polynomial of degree q. We shall take for the initial value x_0 a value of x which does not make $R(x)$ vanish, and for y_0 a root of the equation $y^2 = R(x_0)$. We shall put

$$v(x, y) = \int_{(x_0, y_0)}^{(x, y)} \frac{Q(x)\, dx}{\sqrt{R(x)}},$$

where the integral is taken along a path going from x_0 to x, and where y denotes the final value of the radical $\sqrt{R(x)}$ when we start from x_0 with the value y_0. In order to study the system of points of intersection of the curve C represented by the equation (40) with another algebraic curve C', we may evidently replace in the equation of the latter curve an even power of y, such as y^{2r}, by $[R(x)]^r$, and an odd power y^{2r+1} by $y[R(x)]^r$. These substitutions having been made, the equation obtained will now contain y only to the first degree, and we may suppose the equation of the curve C' of the form

$$(41) \qquad y\phi(x) - f(x) = 0,$$

where $f(x)$ and $\phi(x)$ are two polynomials prime to each other, of degrees λ and μ respectively, some of the coefficients of which we shall suppose to be variable. The abscissas of the points of intersection of the two curves C and C' are roots of the equation

$$(42) \qquad \psi(x) = R(x)\,\phi^2(x) - f^2(x) = 0,$$

of degree N. For special systems of values of the variable coefficients in the two polynomials $f(x)$ and $\phi(x)$ the degree of the equation may turn out to be less than N; some of the points of intersection are then thrown off to infinity, but the corresponding integrals must be included in the sum which we are about to study. To each root x_i of the equation (42) corresponds a completely determined value of y given by $y_i = f(x_i)/\phi(x_i)$. Let us now consider the sum

$$I = \sum_{i=1}^{N} v(x_i, y_i) = \sum_{i=1}^{N} \int_{(x_0, y_0)}^{(x_i, y_i)} \frac{Q(x)\, dx}{\sqrt{R(x)}}.$$

We have

$$\delta I = \sum_{i=1}^{N} \frac{Q(x_i)\, \delta x_i}{\sqrt{R(x_i)}} = \sum_{i=1}^{N} \frac{Q(x_i)\, \phi(x_i)}{f(x_i)} \delta x_i,$$

for the final value of the radical at the point x_i must be equal to y_i, that is, to $f(x_i)/\phi(x_i)$. On the other hand, from the equation $\psi(x_i) = 0$ we derive

$$\psi'(x_i)\, \delta x_i + 2R(x_i)\, \phi(x_i)\, \delta \phi_i - 2f(x_i)\, \delta f_i = 0,$$

and therefore

$$\delta I = \sum_{i} \frac{Q(x_i)\, \phi(x_i)}{f(x_i)} \times \frac{2f(x_i)\, \delta f_i - 2R(x_i)\, \phi(x_i)\, \delta \phi_i}{\psi'(x_i)},$$

or, making use of the equation (42),

$$(43) \qquad \delta I = \sum_{i=1}^{N} \frac{2Q(x_i)\,(\phi_i \delta f_i - f_i \delta \phi_i)}{\psi'(x_i)}.$$

Let us calculate, for example, the coefficient of δa_k in δI, where a_k is the coefficient, supposed variable, of x^k in the polynomial $f(x)$. The term δa_k does not appear in $\delta \phi_i$, and it is multiplied by x_i^k in δf_i. The desired coefficient of δa_k is therefore equal to

$$\sum_{i=1}^{N} \frac{2Q(x_i)\, \phi(x_i)\, x_i^k}{\psi'(x_i)} = 2 \sum_{i=1}^{N} \frac{\pi(x_i)}{\psi'(x_i)},$$

where $\pi(x) = Q(x)\, \phi(x)\, x^k$. The preceding sum must be extended to all the roots of the equation $\psi(x) = 0$; it is a rational and symmetric function of these roots, and therefore a rational function of the coefficients of the two polynomials $f(x)$ and $\phi(x)$. The calculation of this sum can be facilitated by noticing that $\Sigma \pi(x_i)/\psi'(x_i)$ is equal to the sum of the residues of the rational function $\pi(x)/\psi(x)$ relative to the N poles in the finite plane $x_1, x_2, \cdots, x_N$. By a general theorem that sum is also equal to the residue at the point at infinity with its sign changed (§ 52). It will be possible, then, to obtain the coefficient of δa_k by a simple division.

It is easy to prove that this coefficient is zero if the integral $v(x, y)$ is of the first kind. We have by supposition $q \leqq p - 1$; the degree of $\pi(x)$ is $q + \mu + k$, and we have

$$q + \mu + k \leqq \mu + k + p - 1.$$

Let us find the degree of $\psi(x)$. If there is no cancellation between the terms of highest degree in $R(x) \phi^2(x)$ and in $f^2(x)$, we have

$$2\lambda \leqq N, \qquad 2p + 1 + 2\mu \leqq N,$$

whence

$$\lambda + \mu + p + 1 \leqq N,$$

and, a fortiori,

$$k + \mu + p + 1 \leqq N.$$

If there were a cancellation between these two terms, we should have

$$\lambda = \mu + p + 1;$$

but since the term $a_k x^{\lambda + k}$ has no term with which to cancel out, we should have $\lambda + k \leqq N$, from which the same inequality as before results. It follows that we always have

$$q + \mu + k \leqq N - 2.$$

The residue of the rational function $\pi(x)/\psi(x)$ with respect to the point at infinity is therefore zero, for the development will begin with a term in $1/x^2$ or of higher degree. It will be seen similarly that the coefficient of δb_h in δI, b_h being one of the variable coefficients of the polynomial $\phi(x)$, is zero if the polynomial $Q(x)$ is of degree $p - 1$ or lower degree. This result is completely in accord with the general theorem.

Let us take, for example, $\phi(x) = 1$, and let us put

$$f(x) = \sqrt{A_0}\, x^{p+1} + a_p x^p + a_{p-1} x^{p-1} + \cdots + a_1 x + a_0,$$

where $a_0, a_1, \cdots, a_p$ are $p + 1$ variable coefficients. The two curves

$$y^2 = R(x), \qquad y = f(x)$$

cut each other in $2p + 1$ variable points, and the sum of the values of the integral $v(x, y)$, taken from an initial point to these $2p + 1$ points of intersection, is an *algebraic-logarithmic* function of the coefficients $a_0, a_1, \cdots, a_p$. Now we can dispose of these $p + 1$ coefficients in such a way that $p + 1$ of the points of intersection are any previously assigned points of the curve $y^2 = R(x)$, and the coördinates of the p remaining points will be algebraic functions of the coördinates of the $p + 1$ given points.

The sum of the $p + 1$ integrals

$$v(x_1, y_1) + v(x_2, y_2) + \cdots + v(x_{p+1}, y_{p+1}),$$

taken from a common initial point to $p + 1$ arbitrary points, is therefore equal to the sum of p integrals whose limits are algebraic functions of the coördinates

$$(x_1, y_1), \cdots, (x_{p+1}, y_{p+1}),$$

plus certain algebraic-logarithmic expressions. It is clear that by successive reductions the proposition can be extended to the sum of m integrals, where m is any integer greater than p. In particular, the sum of any number of integrals of the first kind can be reduced to the sum of only p integrals. This property, which applies to the most general Abelian integrals of the first kind, constitutes the addition theorem for these integrals.

In the case of elliptic integrals of the first kind, Abel's theorem leads precisely to the addition formula for the function $p(u)$. Let us consider a cubic in the normal form

$$y^2 = 4x^3 - g_2 x - g_3,$$

and let $M_1(x_1, y_1)$, $M_2(x_2, y_2)$, $M_3(x_3, y_3)$ be the points of intersection of that cubic with a straight line D. By the general theorem the sum

$$\int_\infty^{(x_1, y_1)} \frac{dx}{\sqrt{4x^3 - g_2 x - g_3}} + \int_\infty^{(x_2, y_2)} \frac{dx}{\sqrt{4x^3 - g_2 x - g_3}} + \int_\infty^{(x_3, y_3)} \frac{dx}{\sqrt{4x^3 - g_2 x - g_3}}$$

is equal to a period, for the three points M_1, M_2, M_3 are carried off to infinity when the straight line D goes off itself to infinity. Now if we employ the parametric representation $x = p(u)$, $y = p'(u)$ for the cubic, the parameter u is precisely equal to the integral

$$\int_\infty^{(x, y)} \frac{dx}{\sqrt{4x^3 - g_2 x - g_3}},$$

and the preceding formula says that the sum of the arguments u_1, u_2, u_3, which correspond to the three points M_1, M_2, M_3, is equal to a period. We have seen above how that relation is equivalent to the addition formula for the function $p(u)$ (§ 80).

104. Extension of Lagrange's formula. The general theorem on the implicit functions defined by a simultaneous system of equations (I, § 194, 2d ed.; § 188, 1st ed.) extends also to complex variables, provided that we retain the other hypotheses of the theorem. Let us consider, for example, the two simultaneous equations

(44) $P(x, y) = x - a - \alpha f(x, y) = 0, \quad Q(x, y) = y - b - \beta\phi(x, y) = 0,$

where x and y are complex variables, and where $f(x, y)$ and $\phi(x, y)$ are analytic functions of these two variables in the neighborhood of the system of values $x = a$, $y = b$. For $\alpha = 0$, $\beta = 0$ these equations (44) have the system of solutions $x = a$, $y = b$, and the determinant $D(P, Q)/D(x, y)$ reduces to unity. Therefore, by the general theorem, the system of equations (44) has one and only one system of roots approaching a and b respectively when α and β approach zero, and these roots are analytic functions of α and β. Laplace was the first to extend Lagrange's formula (§ 51) to this system of equations.

Let us suppose for definiteness that with the points a and b as centers we describe two circles C and C' in the planes of the variables x and y respectively, with radii r and r' so small that the two functions $f(x, y)$ and $\phi(x, y)$ shall be analytic when the variables x and y remain within or on the boundaries of these two circles C, C'. Let M and M' be the maximum values of $|f(x, y)|$ and of $|\phi(x, y)|$, respectively, in this region. We shall suppose further that the constants α and β satisfy the conditions $M|\alpha| < r$, $M'|\beta| < r'$.

Let us now give to x any value within or on the boundary of the circle C; the equation $Q(x, y) = 0$ is satisfied by a single value of y in the interior of the circle C', for the angle of $y - b - \beta\phi(x, y)$ increases by 2π when y describes the circle C' in the positive sense (§ 49). That root is an analytic function $y_1 = \psi(x)$ of x in the circle C. If we replace y in $P(x, y)$ by that root y_1, the resulting equation $x - a - \alpha f(x, y_1) = 0$ has one and only one root in the interior of C, for the reason given a moment ago.

Let $x = \xi$ be that root, and let η be the corresponding value of y, $\eta = \psi(\xi)$. The object of the generalized Lagrange formula is to develop in powers of α and β every function $F(\xi, \eta)$ which is analytic in the region just defined.

For this purpose let us consider the double integral

$$(45) \qquad I = \int_{(C)} dx \int_{(C')} \frac{F(x, y)\, dy}{P(x, y)\, Q(x, y)}.$$

Since x is a point on the circumference of C, $P(x, y)$ cannot vanish for any value of y within C', for the angle of $x - a - \alpha f(x, y)$ returns necessarily to its initial value when y describes C', x being a fixed point of C. The only pole of the function under the integral sign, considered as a function of the single variable y, is, then, the point $y = y_1$, given by the root of the equation $Q(x, y) = 0$, which corresponds to the value of x on the boundary C, and we have, after a first integration,

$$\int_{(C')} \frac{F(x, y)\, dy}{P(x, y)\, Q(x, y)} = 2i\pi \frac{F(x, y_1)}{P(x, y_1)\left(\dfrac{\partial Q}{\partial y}\right)_1}.$$

The right-hand side, if we suppose y_1 replaced by the analytic function $\psi(x)$ defined above, has in turn a single pole of the first order in the interior of C, — the point $x = \xi$, to which corresponds the value $y_1 = \eta$, — and the corresponding residue is easily shown to be

$$\frac{2i\pi F(\xi, \eta)}{\left[\dfrac{D(P, Q)}{D(x, y)}\right]_{\substack{x=\xi \\ y=\eta}}}.$$

The double integral I has therefore for its value

$$I = -4\pi^2 \frac{F(\xi, \eta)}{\left[\dfrac{D(P, Q)}{D(x, y)}\right]_{\substack{x=\xi \\ y=\eta}}}.$$

On the other hand, we can develop $1/PQ$ in a uniformly convergent series

$$\frac{1}{(x-a-\alpha f)(y-b-\beta\phi)} = \sum \frac{\alpha^m \beta^n f^m \phi^n}{(x-a)^{m+1}(y-b)^{n+1}},$$

which gives us $I = \Sigma J_{mn}\, \alpha^m \beta^n$, where

$$J_{mn} = \int_{(C)} dx \int_{(C')} \frac{F(x,y)[f(x,y)]^m[\phi(x,y)]^n\, dy}{(x-a)^{m+1}(y-b)^{n+1}}.$$

This integral has already been calculated (§ 94), and we have found that it is equal to

$$-\frac{4\pi^2}{m!\,n!}\frac{\partial^{m+n}[F(a,b)f^m(a,b)\phi^n(a,b)]}{\partial a^m\,\partial b^n}.$$

Equating the two values of I, we obtain the desired result, which presents an evident analogy with the formula (50) of § 51 :

$$(46)\quad \frac{F(\xi,\eta)}{\left[\dfrac{D(P,Q)}{D(x,y)}\right]_{\substack{x=\xi\\y=\eta}}} = \sum_m \sum_n \frac{\alpha^m\beta^n}{m!\,n!}\frac{\partial^{m+n}[F(a,b)f^m(a,b)\phi^n(a,b)]}{\partial a^m\,\partial b^n}.$$

We could also obtain a second result analogous to (51), of § 51, by putting

$$F(x,y) = \Phi(x,y)\frac{D(P,Q)}{D(x,y)},$$

but the coefficients in this case are not so simple as in the case of one variable.

EXERCISES

1. Every algebraic curve C_n of degree n and of deficiency p can be carried over by a birational transformation into a curve of degree $p+2$.

(Proceed as in § 82, cutting the given curve by a net of curves C_{n-2}, passing through $n(n-1)/2 - 3$ points of C_n, among which are the $(n-1)(n-2)/2 - p$ double points, and put

$$X = \frac{\phi_2}{\phi_1}, \qquad Y = \frac{\phi_3}{\phi_1},$$

the equation of the net being $\phi_1(x,y) + \lambda\phi_2(x,y) + \mu\phi_3(x,y) = 0$.)

2. Deduce from the preceding exercise that the coördinates of a point of a curve of deficiency 2 can be expressed as rational functions of a parameter t and of the square root of a polynomial $R(t)$ of the fifth or of the sixth degree, prime to its derivative.

(The reader may begin by showing that the curve corresponds point by point to a curve of the fourth degree having a double point.)

3*. Let $y = \alpha_1 x + \alpha_2 x^2 + \cdots$ be the development in power series of an algebraic function, a root of an equation $F(x,y)=0$, where $F(x,y)$ is a polynomial with *integral coefficients* and where the point with coördinates $x=0$, $y=0$ is a simple point of the curve represented by $F(x,y)=0$. All the coefficients $\alpha_1, \alpha_2 \cdots$ are fractions, and it suffices to change x to Kx, K being a suitably chosen integer, in order that all these coefficients become integers.   [EISENSTEIN.]

(It will be noticed that a transformation of the form $x = k^2 x'$, $y = ky'$ suffices to make the coefficient of y' on the left-hand side of the new relation equal to one, all the other coefficients being integers.)

INDEX

[Titles in italic are proper names; numbers in italic are page numbers; and numbers in roman type are paragraph numbers.]